THE COMPLETE
ENCYCLOPEDIA OF
SHELLS

**Informative text with
hundreds of photographs**

R.H. DE BRUYNE

REBO
PUBLISHERS

© 2003 Rebo International b.v., Lisse, The Netherlands

This 2nd edition reprinted 2004

Text: R.H. de Bruyne
Translation: Guy Shipton for First Edition Translations, Cambridge
Photographs: R.H. de Bruyne
Production and editing: TextCase, Groningen, The Netherlands
Cover design: Minkowsky Graphic, Enkhuizen, The Netherlands
Layout: Studio Imago, Amersfoort,The Netherlands
Proofreding: Joshua H. Joseph, Jarmila Peskova Skranakova

ISBN 90 366 1514 3

Contents

Species descriptions

Species descriptions contain the following successive abbreviations:
D: dimension. The average length, width, or height of adult specimens.
S: shape. The general shape of the shell.
O: ornamentation. Any external structures on the shell.
C: color. Coloration and patterning.
H: habitat. Preferred living environment, divided into four categories according to depth.
     d1 = from the littoral to the sublittoral, to a depth of approximately 25m; d2 = 25–200m;
     d3 = 200–500m; d4 = deeper than 500m.
W: world geographical distribution. For the letter coding, see the malacological regions given in
     Chapter 4 and the accompanying map.
R: rarity factor: 1–5. 1 stands for widespread distribution/commonly found; 2 = less common;
     3 = uncommon to relatively rare; 4 = rare; 5 = extremely rare.
NB: Additional remarks.

Foreword

Shells and their inhabitants, the mollusks, have received great attention from humankind for as long as we have existed. Their soft parts served as food for many peoples around the planet (often this remains the case) and they were also used as bait for fishing. The shell itself has played a role as an implement, such as for weighting fishing nets, or as a means of communication to signal to one another as with a horn (*Triton*, *Turbinella*). Shells such as large species of melon, or baler, shell (*Melo*) were used to bale out canoes, to hold water (*Syrinx*) or even as fonts in which to baptize children (*Tridacna*; giant clams). And let us not forget to mention the cowries, used in former times as currency. Yet it was the conches and bivalves that were admired above all the rest for their beautiful colors and shapes. As a result, it was not long before people began to make collections of them.

In the past, dozens of artists, scientists, and collectors made efforts to depict these natural creations in color. This resulted in magnificent works that remain preserved to this very day. A veritable flood of books and other publications on shells really took off following the invention of photography and nowadays volumes of publications on this subject appear every year.

Conus aurantius Hwass, 1792 – golden cone.
(Bonaire, 1978. Collection P.L. van Pel).

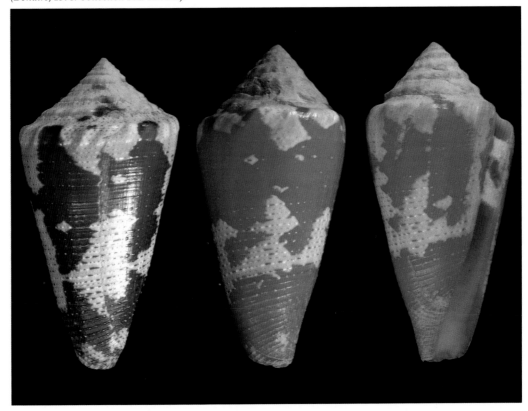

As the writer of this foreword, I should say that I have been a devoted collector of shells for some 43 years. During my career in the Dutch Royal Navy I have sailed the seas of the world and visited many places around the globe. I have also made several journeys on my own initiative, often returning home afterward with an extensive collection of shells. They do say that only the true collector understands completely the fascination produced by a neatly arranged collection that meets with scientific and aesthetic standards. After having given various lectures on this subject, from the many reactions to publications and from all the responses from people who have viewed my collection, I now know better: scarcely a soul can remain unmoved after beholding so much beauty.

In this publication, the editors and the publisher of this illustrated encyclopedia of shells have provided an overview of the enormous variety of shape and color that appears within the world of shells. I am pleased that it was possible to use a considerable amount of material from my own collection to do this. An encyclopedia has been created from this that is not intended only for the bookcases of scientists or collectors but for all admirers of such overwhelming beauty within the natural world.

P.L. van Pel, Egmond aan Zee.

Introduction

Mollusks live in all the seas of the world and even appear on land and in fresh water. Remains from this group of animals, their shells (actually the exoskeletons of these soft-bodied, invertebrate animals), can be found almost everywhere. Shells captivate and fascinate people with their magnificent display of color and wealth of forms. They wash up on all the coasts of the world, where they are easy to collect, or else are fished up out of deeper waters and sold, bartered, or given away. You come across them in buildings from antiquity—they were used as sacred objects and status symbols and in ages past also had value as currency or as a means of exchange.

The phenomenon of shell collecting will endure in the world for as long as there are people like yourselves with an eye for form, color, and detail, and an interest in marine life, whether you might simply be picking up a shell while wandering along a stretch of beach, or during a holiday in the tropics, or whether you are building up a collection in earnest. It is no wonder that the collecting of shells has expanded so greatly over the last few centuries to become one of the most engrossing and informative of hobbies and that shells are collected, exchanged, and traded across the whole world.

Xenophora japonica Kuroda & Habe, 1971 – Japanese carrier shell. A shell collector among mollusks. These animals collect smaller shells or gravel, attaching this material to their own shells. (Philippines; 1989. Collection P.L. van Pel).

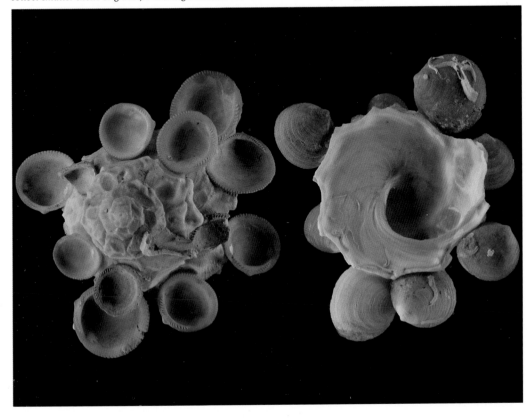

This encyclopedia is intended for all those interested in shells and the organisms that produce them, the mollusks. It contains information for the chance collector and for the more serious collector or nature lover who makes a hobby of collecting shells. This book can also serve as a preparation for more serious, scientific study. It provides a systematic alphabetical overview of the many different families and genera, and identifies and names over one thousand species of conch, bivalve, and other shells on the basis of photographs and descriptions. We hope that the enthusiasm of the writers in compiling this encyclopedia will be transferred equally to its readers and users.

1. Mollusks (Mollusca)

Life on earth is exceptionally rich and varied. It can appear in the shape and on the scale of anything from infinitesimally small bacteria to gigantic animals, such as the blue whale. Over the centuries, students of nature have attempted to describe and investigate all this life on earth. A thorough classification system has been developed for that purpose with which to classify and identify all organisms on earth. Insects, with all possible subgroups and families, constitute far and away the largest group of animals on earth. Everyone knows what an insect is and most people would be unsurprised to hear that there are many hundreds of thousands of insect species living across the globe. However, far fewer people appear aware of what the second largest group of animals on earth is. In terms of the number of species, it is the mollusks (the phylum Mollusca, also known as shellfish) that come a strong second. Although nobody has actually been able to count all the species, it is generally accepted that at least 100,000 species of mollusk live on earth. However, there is quite some confusion about this and higher figures are given of up to 150,000 species (being those documented and those, as yet, undocumented). Thousands of mollusks still await discovery both on land and in the sea, while many tens of thousands more of extinct, fossilized species are present in ancient beds of soil and rock. Mollusks occur in every imaginable type and size. From the giant squid of the deep oceans and the enormous, tropical giant clam *Tridacna gigas*, weighing up to 230 kilograms, to minuscule species, such as the atom snail *Omalogyra atomus* measuring less than half a millimeter. Apart from size, they also display a huge diversity of color and shape. Mollusks, along with the insects, easily constitute the most varied group of animals on earth.

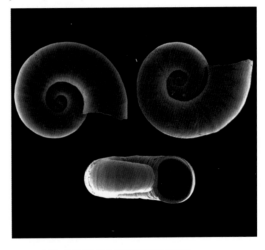

Omalogyra atomus (Philippi, 1841) – atom snail. One of the smallest shells in Europe. Adult specimens reach a maximum size of up to 1mm across but remain smaller than this as a rule. (Image produced by the Scanning Electron Microscope of SEM; photograph J. Goud, Leiden.)

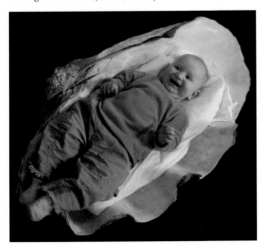

Tridacna gigas (Linnaeus, 1758) – giant clam. The largest species of bivalve on earth can grow to 135cm across and weigh over 230kg. (Collection of the Zoological Museum, Amsterdam.)

WHAT ARE MOLLUSKS?

Mollusks can be recognized by a few common characteristics. In 1795, Cuvier devised the name Mollusca and, as this name suggests (mollis = soft), the mollusk body is delicate and vulnerable with more than 90% of it being composed of water. They are invertebrates, animals that do not possess an internal skeleton to support and protect bodily tissue and organs. Instead, a large sheath of skin—the mantle—surrounds the animal. In addition to protection of delicate body parts, this mantle is also responsible for the formation of a shell. The majority of the internal organs lie in what is referred to as the visceral hump or mass. Between the visceral hump and the mantle there lies a cavity, the mantle cavity, where the respiratory organs are found. This cavity also acts as an outlet for the kidneys, reproductive organs, and anus.

The heart lies on the dorsal side and has two symmetrical auricles. The circulatory system is partially open, the body fluids flow between gaps in the tissue. The mouth is in the anterior of the body in the head. For snails and most of the other groups, this mouth is provided with a calcareous rasping organ: the radula or odontophore. The shape of the "teeth" (denticles) on the radula varies depending on the group concerned. The radula is used to graze on algae from the substrate or to grind up prey into small pieces.

The majority of bivalves living buried in the sea floor do not have any radula but instead possess two siphons, either fused together or separate: a type of respiratory tract through which water with food particles is passed and waste materials are expelled from the body. Respiration itself is achieved with gills. Over the course of millions of years, these gills have evolved into primitive types of lungs for many terrestrial and freshwater species of mollusk.

Locomotion is performed by the foot: a flat, broadly tapered, muscular organ. Undulation is created through the successive contraction and relaxation of a large number of small muscles simultaneously, enabling many snails and some bivalves to move forward slowly but surely. The foot is also used for other purposes apart from locomotion. Most bivalves use the foot when burrowing into the sea floor. In the case of squids, the foot has been transformed into a number of tentacles covered in suckers, which are used when seizing prey.

Mollusks are usually of different sexes but there are also various species in which both sexes are found in one individual (hermaphroditic). The majority of species lay eggs (oviparous), but in some species the embryos develop in the mother (ovoviviparous).

However, the group's most familiar feature is the shell. The shell forms the exterior skeleton of the mollusk. Unlike, for example, crustaceans, which every so often "molt" and thus continually make way for the production of a new, larger exoskeleton, a mollusk's shell grows in tandem with the mollusk. Shells give support to internal organs and provide protection against predators, desiccation and other dangers. Their construction and most important identifying features will be examined in more detail in Chapter 2.

DIFFERENT CLASSES

On the basis of their cohesion and relationship to each other, all organisms on earth are grouped and ordered—classified—according to a particular system. The phylum Mollusca, the phylum of the animal kingdom to which all mollusks belong, is divided into two separate subphyla based on characteristics of the body and shell: Aculifera and Conchifera. Two classes come under Aculifera: Aplacophora (spiny, shell-less mollusks)—sometimes classified in two separate classes as Caudofoveata and Solenogastres—and Polyplacophora (chitons or coat-of-mail shells with eight shell plates, or valves). These are further divided into subclasses: Aplacophora into Chaetodermomorpha and Neomeniomorpha, and Polyplacophora into Neoloricata and Palaeoloricata. The other five classes come under Conchifera, which contains far and away the majority of species including those that are most familiar.

A species of Charonia or triton, creeping forward on its large, muscular foot (underwater photograph: P.L. van Pel).

Table of classes and subclasses.

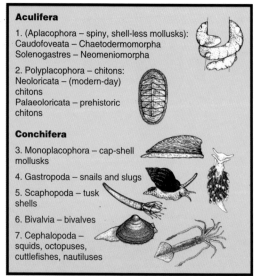

Aculifera

1. (Aplacophora – spiny, shell-less mollusks): Caudofoveata – Chaetodermomorpha Solenogastres – Neomeniomorpha

2. Polyplacophora – chitons: Neoloricata – (modern-day) chitons Palaeoloricata – prehistoric chitons

Conchifera

3. Monoplacophora – cap-shell mollusks

4. Gastropoda – snails and slugs

5. Scaphopoda – tusk shells

6. Bivalvia – bivalves

7. Cephalopoda – squids, octopuses, cuttlefishes, nautiluses

Subphylum Aculifera

HATSCHECK, 1891
"spiny, shell-less mollusks"

Aculifera live only in the sea. The bodies of these animals are flattened ventrally and dorsally. They lack eyes and tentacles. The epithelium cells in the outer layer of the mantle create a protective epidermis (cuticula) that is covered either in calcareous scales or spicules or both. The Chaetodermomorpha (also known as Caudofoveata) and the Neomeniomorpha (also known as Solenogastres) are often brought together within one class, Aplacaphora (spiny, shell-less mollusks), but are sometimes classed separately. Due to their relative rarity, behavior and, in particular, the lack of an exterior shell, these small, wormlike mollusks are unknown to the majority of collectors and malacologists. This encyclopedia does not deal with them further.

Class Polyplacophora

DE BLAINVILLE, 1816
chitons

The animals from the second class within Aculifera, Polyplacophora or chitons, are reasonably well known among collectors. All of the animals in this group possess eight (in rare cases seven) hinged shell plates that run along their bodies like roof tiles (polyplacophora = "bearing many plates"), held together by a muscular girdle of mantle tissue (perinotum). Representatives of this group live exclusively in

chitons on a stone in the sublittoral zone. Chaetopleura angulata (Spengler, 1797) – great latticed chiton. (Algarve, Lagos. 1984. Photograph P.L. van Pel).

the sea. Worldwide, the class contains approximately 800 species, most of which live in the western Pacific Ocean and on the west coast of Central America. Relatively few species appear in European waters. Most of these animals depend on a hard and solid surface. Ventrally, they possess a wide muscled foot with which they attach themselves extremely firmly to stones, empty shells, and hard substrates. However, some species also crawl "happily" on mud or sand. The mouth cavity in the head contains a powerful radula with which food is scraped from rocks (algae in particular). The profile of the body is more or less oval and is flattened ventrally and domed dorsally.

Chitons are found particularly in shallow water (the intertidal zone) under stones and on any other hard substrates. They usually forage for food at dusk or nocturnally. Their food consists mostly of small algae. Some species have adopted a carnivorous diet and these live chiefly at greater depths (up to 4000m). Sizes vary according to species from 4mm to over 30cm in length, the largest chiton, which ranges from Japan to California, being *Crypochiton stelleri* Middendorff, 1847. Many species measure between 10 and 55mm. Chitons are divided into two subclasses: the Neoloricata and the Palaeoloricata. Only fossil remains exist of the latter subclass. Modern-day chitons are divided into three orders, which contain various separate families.

Subphylum Conchifera

GEGENBAUR, 1878
'shell-bearing mollusks'

The subphylum Conchifera contains Monoplacophora, Gastropoda, Scaphopoda, Bivalvia and Cephalopoda. All these either possess a shell (concha) or descend from ancestors that had one. Gastropoda, or snails, constitute the largest class, followed by Bivalvia, the bivalves. Next, in declining order of species numbers, come Cephalopoda (squids), Scaphopoda (tusk shells) and Monoplacophora (neopilinids or cap-shelled mollusks), covered by just one shell plate.

Class Monoplacophora

ODHNER, 1940
neopilinids or cap-shell mollusks

With only a few dozen species among them, these form an extremely small group. They are deep-sea dwellers, which means that both body and shell display some very individual characteristics. The flat shell covers the whole animal like a cap. Although fossil types of Monoplacophora were already known from rock strata, the oldest finds dating from the beginning of the Cambrian period, they appeared to have become extinct after the Devonian. That was until contemporary, living animals were unexpectedly found by the Danish "Galathea" expedition at a depth of over 3500m off the west coast of Central America. During subsequent expeditions, such as in 1958 and 1967 in the Red Sea, the Pacific Ocean, the Atlantic Ocean, and around Antarctica, Monoplacophora were also occasionally fished up as "living fossils" at depths of between 2500 and 6500m. For collectors, the opportunities for acquiring specimens are limited in the extreme.

Class Gastropoda

CUVIER, 1795
snails

Snails constitute the largest mollusk group on earth with more than 50,000 species. Their habitat can be marine, freshwater, estuarine, or terrestrial. Although there are all manner of shell-less species of snail—including the slugs—by far the majority of their representatives have a more or less spiral coiled shell in one piece: the conch or snail shell. The body of a snail is composed of a muscular foot, a head with eyes and tentacles and, in most cases, a twisted visceral hump that is always retained within the shell. The mouth in the head contains a rasping tongue used to crush and grind food. Most species of snail are herbivorous. Some species feed on live prey or carrion. Snails are usually classified into three large groupings according to the type and position of their respiratory organs. In Prosobranchia, the original posterior location of the mantle cavity and visceral hump, containing within it all the organs, has come to be located in the anterior by means of clockwise torsion (twisting). Consequently, respiration is performed by means of gills located in front of the heart. Torsion has also crossed the nerve cords, which explains why Prosobranchia are often also summarized under the heading Streptoneura (twisted nerves). In the second group, Opisthobranchia, the gills lie behind the heart. In most opisthobranch species the shell is either extremely small or entirely lacking (particularly in the case of the shell-less slugs).

In the third group, Pulmonata, or lung snails, the gills have disappeared and the mantle cavity, saturated with blood vessels, acts as a pulmonary sac. The latter group dwells almost entirely on land or in fresh water. The two other groups live principally in the sea. The presence or absence of an operculum, a "trapdoor lid" carried on the back of the foot in prosobranch snails with which the snail can seal off the shell aperture, is important to their classification.

Diagram of Gastropoda and Bivalvia anatomy.
A: anus; D: intestine; H: heart; IS: inhalant siphon;
K: gills; LE: liver; M: stomach; MO: mouth opening;
O: operculum, or sealing disk; SL: adductor muscle;
ST: hinge teeth; T: apex; TA: tentacles (feelers); U: umbo
(or beak, in bivalves); US: exhalant siphon; V: foot.

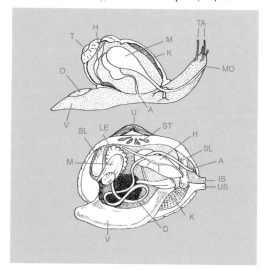

Class Bivalvia

LINNAEUS, 1758
bivalves

With over 20,000 species, the bivalves form the second largest group of mollusks on earth. They live exclusively in water, be it marine, estuarine, or fresh water. These animals have a shell divided into two halves or shell valves. These are usually mirror images of each other and are held together by a hinge plate with interlocking teeth and an elastic ligament. The mollusk can usually shield itself completely from the outside world by closing its valves. In some species—especially borers (piddocks) and shipworms—there are, apart from the two valves that encase the body, one or more additional "accessory shell plates." The shell valves are opened and closed by means of muscles known as adductors. The majority of species have two adductor muscles, located on the anterior and posterior, respectively. The anterior adductor is usually smaller. It can be entirely absent causing the remaining posterior adductor to move more toward the center (*Lima, Ostrea, Pecten*, etc.). In borers from the family Pholadidae, the anterior adductor is located on the exterior of the hinge. The points at which the adductors are attached are visible on the inside of the valves in the form of glistening, often comma-shaped, "muscle scars."

The body of a bivalve has no head. The mouth lies at the anterior of the shell, surrounded by ctenidia (respiratory gills modified to assist in feeding) and labial palps. The mouth opening does not contain a radula. Food is usually obtained through water filtration. The body is surrounded by two mantle lobes attached close to the underside of the shell by delicate muscles. Enclosed by the mantle lobes is a mantle cavity where the gills are located that serve both for respiration and for the collection of food. In many cases, the respiratory tubes or siphons also emerge in the mantle cavity; the two ducts may or may not be fused together, and can be extremely long, particularly in the case of species that bury themselves deeply. One siphon takes in water containing oxygen and food particles, the other expels water and waste material.

By far the majority of species possess a large, strong foot. This enables them to move short distances or burrow into the sea floor and move rapidly upward or downward within the burrow (*Ensis*). In such an instance, the foot swells and fixes itself like an anchor in the substrate. A small number of groups also possess a locomotory foot (*Glycymeris, Nucula, Tellina, Venus*).

Most species live permanently buried in the substrate. Several groups live in cavities and crevices or in self-bored holes in wood or rock (*Petricola, Pholas*). Some groups (*Arca, Mytilus, Pecten, Pinna*) live secured to a hard surface by byssus threads secreted by a gland in the foot. These threads harden in the water. The animals can free themselves either by detaching each thread individually (*Mytilus*) or by breaking off the hardened byssus in its entirety (*Pinctada*). A number of bivalves can "cement" themselves to a surface with one of their valves (*Ostrea*). There are also species that can virtually swim (*Ensis, Solemya, Solen*) by forcibly squeezing out jets of water held between the valves in the mantle cavity through clefts at the rear edge of the shell. *Lima* and *Pecten* flap their valves open and shut like a bellows and can guide their movements by channeling the flow of water in a particular direction.

Most species are different sexes. However, hermaphroditism also occurs, as well as species that are protandrously hermaphroditic, changing sex throughout their lives (oysters). Fertilization of the eggs takes place in open water or in the mantle cavity of the mother (incubation).

Some species of bivalve, such as scallops, are able to swim and have several eyes on their mantle lobes. (Aequipecten opercularis (Linnaeus, 1758) – queen scallop. Photograph, P.L. van Pel).

Class Scaphopoda

BRONN, 1862
tusk shells

Scaphopoda (tusk shells) live exclusively in the sea. Relatively speaking, they represent a very small group of mollusks with 300–400 species. The shell has the shape of a miniature elephant's tusk and can vary in size from <25–150mm. Tusk shells live buried in the sea floor, in a slanting position, with only their narrow tip exposed above the surface of the sediment. Respiration occurs through the mantle surface. Gills are not present. Oxygenated water flows in and out through the shell aperture protruding above the sediment surface. However, the animals do possess a radula. Virtually all species live in deep to extremely deep water. Nonetheless, a few species from the genus Dentalium also appear in the sublittoral or littoral zones. Their food consists of foraminifers (unicellular organisms with a hard calcified shell) and other microorganisms.

Class Cephalopoda

CUVIER, 1798

squids, octopuses, cuttlefishes, and nautiluses

Cephalopoda are the most highly developed of the mollusks, numbering 1000–1200 species. The body can be divided into a head and a mantle-covered trunk. The head contains two well-developed eyes that, in a number of species, display similarities with those of mammals. The head also contains a mouth opening with both a pair of powerful jaws and a radula. The mouth is surrounded by eight or ten tentacles covered in suckers (eight in octopuses, ten in most other cephalopods), which are used principally to catch prey. The internal organs are highly developed. The mantle contains the digestive organs and the ink sac, which is used to eject a cloud of ink into the water in the event of danger. Squids can move quickly when swimming by squeezing a quantity of water through a "funnel" lodged within part of the mantle and then shooting away in the opposite direction. A number of species have an internal shell (cuttlefishes) or a corneous "pen" (squids) within the posterior of the mantle.

There are also cephalopods with external shells (nautiluses), as well as shell-less species. Cephalopods are active carnivores. Squid species in the deep ocean can reach sizes of twenty meters or more.

2. Enormous variety of form

The layer of nacre (mother-of-pearl) in some species is extremely thick and lustrous. It is renowned in bivalves like the black-lipped pearl oyster Pinctada margaritifera (Linnaeus, 1758), which produces beautiful pearls (top left). However, this nacreous layer can also be revealed in the shells of other mollusks through acid-bath treatment and is used to manufacture jewelry, buttons, and other objects. Top right: treated top shells (family Trochidae), below: a semi-treated abalone (Haliotidae).

A CALCAREOUS BASIS

The most familiar characteristic of mollusks is the shell, which supports the internal organs and provides protection against predators, desiccation, and other dangers. More than 90% of the shell is made of calcium carbonate and is usually built up of three layers. The innermost layer, the nacre, is composed of mother-of-pearl and the intensity of the luster varies depending on the composition of its extremely thin, lamellate crystals (parallel to the surface). The middle and thickest layer is made up of tiny prismatic crystals perpendicular to the shell surface. The third, outer layer, called the periostracum or epidermis, is not calcareous but made of conchiolin, a corneous material that has similarities with the chitin found in insect carapaces. The periostracum constitutes only a very small part of the shell and is seen in many shells as an exceptionally thin, sometimes hairy in appearance and irregular in growth, yellowish brown, green, or black membrane that is often soon abraded. Since calcium maintains its form for an extremely long time, strata from former seabeds often contain great numbers of fossil shells millions of years old. Although their chemical structure is altered (the soft, albuminous and corneous parts are the first to decay and the calcium structures are subsequently replaced by other maerials, ion by ion), fossil shells look almost the same thousands or millions of years later as the recent species that live in our oceans and wash up on our shores. At most, it is the colors that will have altered. Consequently, it can be difficult to distinguish fossil shells from recent ones.

Shells with and without the periostracum: Melongena patula (Broderip & Sowerby, 1829) – Pacific crown conch (snail from the family Melongenidae) and Samarangia quadrangularis (A. Adams & Reeve, 1850) – samarangia clam (bivalve from the family Veneridae).

Fossil shells originating from a former seabed can wash up on beaches. Left: a recent specimen of Flexopecten flexuosa (Poli, 1795) – arched scallop; Algarve, Portugal. Right: fossil, extremely faded specimen, washed ashore at Cadzand-Bad, Zeeland, The Netherlands. Originating from the Pleistocene epoch.

SHELL STRUCTURE

The different classes of mollusk are classified on the basis of both anatomical features and the external features of the animal and shell. A brief explanation of shell structures follows below.

Chiton shell plates

Chitons possess eight separate shell plates. Two wings protrude anteriorly on either side of the plates (apophyses), which under normal circumstances grip below the shell plate in front. The edges of the plates where they attach to the girdle differ in shape according to species or group, often being toothed or indented. The head and posterior plates are rounded and differ from the middle plates. The surface of the plates may be ribbed, pitted, or granulose, or display grooves or nodules. Numerous tightly bundled spicules, scales, hairs, or clumps of bristles may feature on the girdle surrounding the plates.

The gastropod shell (conches; snail shells)

Most representatives from the class Gastropoda possess a spirally wound single shell, the conch. However, there are various exceptions. For example, species exist with cap or cup-shaped shells, with cylindrical shells, and with all manner of round, oval, or coffee-bean-shaped shells. In addition to this, there are also various slugs, which, through evolution, have either lost their shells, possess a shell so reduced in size that the animals cannot withdraw into it, or else contain the shell internally. Snails appear in marine, estuarine, and freshwater habitats and also live on land. Both the shell-bearing species and the slugs can be brilliantly colored and display the most fantastical shapes and forms imaginable, particularly those species found in the sea.

A standard spirally wound snail shell can be compared to an ever-widening hollow tube being rolled up around a vertical axis. A convolution or whorl is created each time the tube completes a full revolution. The boundary between the whorls is called the suture. The first complete whorl is called the apex, with the last being called the body whorl. The correct way of viewing a snail shell is with the apex pointing upward and the aperture to the front. In almost all cases, the aperture will open to the right; thus the conch will have been formed in a clockwise rotation. However, marine, freshwater, and terrestrial species can be found that naturally grow counterclockwise. In rare instances, a species naturally growing clockwise will grow "wrongly" in a counterclockwise direction. "Four-leafed clovers" such as these are complete aberrations and have even been assigned magical properties in some cultures.

In many gastropod or conch shells, the base of the aperture ends in a groove, the siphonal canal. It is through this that the living snail extends its siphons outside when creeping forward. The exterior of the aperture, the outer lip, can be folded outward or much thickened. In many species, former aperture lips can still be seen in the thickened ridges on previous whorls. These are known as varices. The interior of the aperture, the inner lip, is usually smooth and can sometimes be extended over a part of the last whorl in the form of a callused layer. Indentations, nodules, or folds are sometimes visible within the aperture. In some species a small hole, the umbilicus, can be seen to the left of the aperture. However, the umbilicus may be absent or largely covered. The umbilicus is, in fact, the open extremity of the axis, or columella, around which the whorls rotate. Snail shell ornamentation can vary markedly. Both horizontal (spiral) and vertical (axial) ribbing can occur, or a combination of the two (lattice ornament). Horizontal, concentric, or

The various components of a shell. AS: anal siphon or anal canal; BI: inner lip; BU: outer lip; C: columella; Cr: crenulated edge; Ct: columellar folds (also teeth/folds within outer lip); Kn: nodules or beads; M: aperture; MB: pallial sinus; ML: pallial line; NA: umbilicus; PR: protoconch; Ps: pitted ornament; Rs: axial ribs (vertical/radial ribs); S: siphonal canal; SB: hinge ligament; Sc: oblique ornament; SI: muscle scar; Ss: (for the Gastropod shell (left)) spiral ribs; (for the Bivalve shell (right)) concentric ribs; ST: hinge teeth; St: spines; U: umbo (or beak); W: whorl.

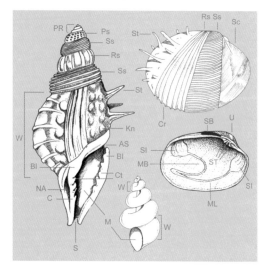

spiral ribbing means ribs that run parallel to the suture; vertical, radial, or axial ribs, or folds, run from the apex to the base of the whorl. Apart from ribs, the shell surface can also be pitted or covered in grooves, scales, and other patterning. The external appearance of snail shells can vary enormously, particularly among marine species. The shells of terrestrial and freshwater snails are often far less thick, sometimes even paper-thin.

Bivalve shells

The shells of bivalves (class Bivalvia, formerly also known as Pelycopoda) are composed of two valves joined together. Their form varies greatly, from rounded and convex to oviform, oval, sphenoid (wedge-shaped), beaked, and scabbard- or sheath-like.

The shell's anterior and posterior often show clear differences: anteriorly rounded and posteriorly more tapered or truncated. The valves are usually bilaterally symmetrical (equivalved). However, there are also species with gaping or asymmetrical valves where one valve grips over the edge of the other, or where the two valves are asymmetrically deeply curved (inequivalved). In the latter case, this often coincides with the way the animals live (lying on one side, such as Pectinidae, or growing on one side fixed to the substrate, such as Chamidae, Ostreidae, Spondylidae). The posterior of Semelidae and Tellinidae valves may bend to one side.

The exterior of the valves can be smooth or display a whole range of distinctive ornamentation, from growth rings alternating in thickness to (radial) ribs radiating from the umbo (or "beak," equivalent to the apex in gastropod shells), or (concentric) ribs following the lines of growth. The surface can be covered in scales, nodules, or spines. Many bivalves are uniformly chalky white or cream-colored, while others display quite striking patterning and coloration. The shell is often covered with a brownish-yellow, scaly or smooth epidermis (periostracum). The inner surface of the shell valves is usually white, but can also be flecked with color or covered in mother-of-pearl (nacreous).

Gleaming marks, often shaped like commas, can be seen where the adductor muscles once connected to the shell. These are called muscle scars. Also visible is the mantle, or pallial line. This runs along the bottom of the shell, roughly parallel to its edge (this also relates to the imprint of small muscles that, in the living animal, were attached to the edge of the mantle). In bivalves, able to retract their siphons into their shell valves, the pallial line often has a deep inward curvature at the point where the siphons are withdrawn within the valves (the pallial sinus).

The ligament, the hinge that joins both shell valves, has two layers: an outer and an inner layer that exert different forces when closing the shell valves; pulling from the outside and pushing from the inside. The innermost part, internally located within the hinge, often takes the form of a triangular pad, the resilium, made of resiline, a material with extraordinary elastic properties. When the shell is closed, the resilium is under pressure. As soon as the adductor muscles relax, the resilium pushes the shell valves apart without exertion. The resilium may be present in a cleft or pit (resilifer), or be found in a spoon-shaped, rounded protuberance next to the hinge, the chondrophore. Ligament structures appear in various guises. Under normal circumstances the ligament is composed only of the outer layer and works against the adductor muscles. Sometimes, the ligament is made up of several layers, with or without resilium. The ligament may also be diminished. In borer mussels from the family Pholadidae, the anterior adductor muscle is located on the exterior of the hinge, where it performs the function of the resilium.

The oldest parts of the shell valves, the umbones (plural of umbo), are located dorsally, usually not far from the centerline. Umbones may point slightly forward (prosogyrate) or backward (opisthogyrate). Sometimes, they are so far apart that this creates a wide ligamental area between them, as in Arca, for example. In most cases, they are positioned right next to each other, thus dividing the ligamental area into zones to the front of and behind the umbones, known respectively as the lunule and escutcheon. Often, the lunule and escutcheon also differ from the rest of the shell surface, exhibiting grooves and/or other markings. The ligament can extend out from between the umbones to either side of them (amphidetic), or be present simply at the point of the escutcheon (opisthodetic).

The dorsal margin of both shell valves usually widens internally into a hinge plate, marked with interlocking teeth (a locking device). Many variations occur in hinge and hinge teeth structure.

Tusk shells

Scaphopoda shells have the appearance of elephant tusks. They usually take the form of slightly curved, gently tapering hollow tubes. There is an opening at either end. The extremities are usually smooth but can also be grooved toward the posterior end or possess a slit. As growth progresses, part of the shell sometimes becomes sealed off. The exterior is usually smooth but may also bear concentric rings or longitudinal ribs. It is a small group and, in the main, most collectors will come across the relatively few species that live in shallow waters.

Cephalopoda: squids, octopuses, cuttlefishes, and nautiluses

Most cephalopod species have no external shell. However, various species, including the cuttlefishes, or Sepiidae, possess internally a dorsal carapace, the cuttlebone, that can be seen only

changes to the quantity of fluid make rising and descending possible.

Calliodentalium crocinum (Dall, 1907). A relatively slender, well-curved tusk shell from deeper waters (Japonic and Indo-Pacific region). Measures up to 85mm; collection P.L. van Pel.

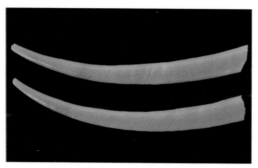

Chambered nautilus Nautilus pompilius Linnaeus, 1758. Cross-section of the shell. The buoyancy chambers can be clearly seen (Australia 1993; collection P.L. van Pel).

after the animal has died. This cuttlebone has the appearance of an oval or somewhat torpedo-shaped calcareous plate, on one side built up of soft, brittle layers of calcium, while the other side is hard. A yellowish-brown membrane girdles the plate, terminating in a sharp point (rostrum) in some species. Cuttlebones will stay afloat due to their light weight and the gas contained between the porous layers, and can sometimes be found washed ashore in hundreds. They are also commonly placed in birdcages, serving as a rich source of calcium for the birds. Other cephalopod species, including the highly developed squids, have an internal carapace or "pen" without calcareous layers in the shape of a corneous bird's feather. However, there are also cephalopod groups that have a true, external shell. In structure, this is comparable to a snail shell. In the past, many thousands of shell-bearing cephalopod species lived in the world's oceans. The remains of these can be found all around the globe as fossils in rock strata (ammonites, belemnites). Comparatively speaking, the number of species still living today is very small. Familiar representatives are Nautilus and Spirula. The interior of the spirally wound shell is thickly nacreous. The whorls are divided into chambers by partitions. The entire shell acts as a hydrostatic organ for these active swimmers. In addition to the outermost chamber in which the animal lives, the shell contains buoyancy chambers in the older whorls, which allow the animal vertical movement. The chambers are filled with gas and fluid and are connected by a single tube called a siphuncle. As with the swim bladder in fish,

Every so often, specimens from some species of gastropod are discovered with counterclockwise whorls, while they are normally clockwise in orientation. In Europe, this has been seen in, for example, Nucella lapillus (Linnaeus, 1758) – dog winkle, and Buccinum undatum Linnaeus, 1758 – common northern whelk (Collection Zoological Museum, Amsterdam).

3. The use of shells

ZOOLOGICAL FUNCTION

Most mollusks are able to withdraw wholly or at least partially within their shells. Obviously, the most important function of the shell for the mollusk itself is to provide support for its internal organs and to protect it against external forces. The shell offers protection against attack by predators and also against desiccation. Its structure and the various components of its exterior design, such as nodules, spines, thorns, ribs, etc., increase the defensive effect. In some cases these projections also serve other functions— acting as stabilizers, for example. This can be seen in bivalves that live in locations with a strong current. The shell helps to prevent dehydration in mollusks that live on land and in the intertidal zone. Littoral species retain a stock of water in the shell in order to bridge the time of

A variety of functions. Top: some snails, such as the thorn latirus, Opeatostoma pseudodon (Burrow, 1815), have at the base of the outer lip a long, strong, thorny projection that is used to lever open bivalve prey (Taiwan, 1992; collection P.L. van Pel). Bottom left: the Atlantic carrier, Xenophora conchyliophora (Born, 1780), on occasion also uses objects other than stones and shells to strengthen its own shell (Aruba, 1980; collection I.E.M. Peeters). Below right: animals from other zoological groups also make use of shells, such as this hermit crab employing the shell of a West Indian top shell, Cittarium pica (Linnaeus, 1758), as protection for its own soft body. (St. Maarten, 1969. Collection I.E.M. Peeters, presently in the collection of the Zoological Museum, Amsterdam.)

low water. Terrestrial species, on the other hand, use the moisture retained in the shell as coolant against high air temperatures. Various snails, such as *Acanthina* and *Busycon*, use their shells as tools. The siphonal canal or other protruding parts are used to lever open prey (mostly bivalves). Some borer mussels use their shells when boring. The twisting movements they make in limestone, wood, or peat grind out whole burrows in which they make their homes. Others, such as *Aporrhais*, *Lima*, and *Pecten*, use their shells when walking or swimming. Some cephalopods use their shell as a hydrostatic organ, enabling them to rise or descent in a similar way to fish with a swim bladder (see previous chapter).

USE BY MAN

Jewelry and tools made from shells have been found in caves inhabited by humans in prehistoric times. Large heaps of oyster shells and other remains are evidence of their use as food. From these and other finds, we can conclude that shells have been used for a variety of purposes for as long as man has been on earth. Nowadays, we continue to use the soft parts of these animals in great quantities as food or bait. The majority of mollusks, are edible, certainly, even if only a few species have actually come to be marketed for consumption on a grand scale, such as mussels and oysters from the families Mytilidae and Ostreidae. However, even the shells themselves have an enormous number of applications due to their diversity of color and shape.

Religion and culture

Shells are used as a status symbol in some cultures. A famous example of this is the golden cowrie, *Cypraea aurantius* (Gmelin, 1798), which, in the Fiji islands, could be worn only by important people and tribal chiefs. There were sometimes dangers attached to the finding of a specimen: for example, the spirits of the Loyalty Islands condemned such finds if made by a woman and the unfortunate collector would quickly die. It was also a death sentence to be in the possession of other shells coming from the genus *Mikadotrochus*. These shells were intended exclusively for the emperor. Anyone else discovered with them in their possession was beheaded. In Ancient Rome, the wearing of robes dyed the color purple was reserved for the emperor, victorious generals, and dignitaries. The dye was obtained from two sea snails: *Murex brandaris* (Linnaeus, 1758), the purple-dye murex, and *Murex trunculus* (Linnaeus, 1758). The hypobranchial gland of these snails secretes a colorless substance that slowly changes color in sunlight to produce a deep purple. This was known as Tyrian purple. Huge quantities of snails were needed to produce enough dye for one cloak. Some other species of snail also produce purple dye, including the dog winkle *Nucella lapillus* (Linnaeus, 1758).

Some shells are used as sacred objects, serving as implements in rituals, for example. Well-known objects include the Akshamala or Buddhist prayer beads with 108 beads produced from the shell of *Turbinella pyrum* (Linnaeus, 1767), the Indian chank or sacred vase shell. The above and a few other large shells fulfill another sacred purpose: the Sankha or shell trumpet, sometimes referred to as a triton's shell. By blowing on it through a hole or a specially added and often elaborately decorated mouthpiece, people were called to prayer. A similar status was accorded to sacred shells within Hinduism. The god Vishnu is often depicted with a Sankha and the god Krishna is also often depicted with a sacred shell. Legend has it that an evil spirit lived on the seabed in the shell of *T. pyrum* and was defeated by Krishna only after a fearsome battle. As proof of his victory, he brought the shell with him to the surface. From that time onward, the sacred shell was blown before all conflicts and battles. The extremely thick shells of *T. pyrum* occur in the waters around India and Sri Lanka and usually grow in a clockwise orientation. They are collected and turned into jewelry or lamps. Only very rarely are counterclockwise specimens found. These are costly in the extreme, often richly decorated and kept in Hindu temples where they are revered as "the sacred snail of Vishnu."

Scallops also belong among shells connected with religion. In many European countries the species *Pecten maximus* (Linnaeus, 1758) and *Pecten jacobaeus* (Linnaeus, 1758) are associated with St. James the Apostle of Compostela, in Galicia, northwestern Spain. The story goes that, after much wandering in Jerusalem, St. James was imprisoned by Herod Agrippa I, who had him beheaded. Angels are said to have brought his mortal remains back by ship to Galicia, where the apostle had once preached the Gospel. The ship carrying his mortal remains is supposed to have washed ashore spontaneously on the right stretch of coast, completely covered in scallop shells. For many centuries afterward, images of St. James, as well as depictions of the devout on pilgrimages to Santiago de Compostela (the city named after him), were adorned with one or several scallop shells. On their arrival in Santiago, each pilgrim would receive a certificate signed by the bishop and a scallop shell blessed at the site, both as a precious amulet and as proof of the completed pilgrimage.

Scallop shapes are still used a great deal in architecture to decorate houses or on façades, postage stamps, municipal coats of arms, etc. Scallops were used as far back as the Romans, who often used shells to ornament tombs. Even

The sacred snail of Vishnu. Rare, counterclockwise specimens of the Indian chank, Turbinella pyrum (Linnaeus, 1767), are considered highly sacred within Hinduism. The photograph shows a "normal" clockwise specimen, as well as an extremely rare counterclockwise one (Collection of the Zoological Museum, Amsterdam).

Confused scallops. In 1758, Linnaeus dubbed the strictly Mediterranean St. James' scallop with the name Pecten jacobaeus (right), rather than the Atlantic great scallop. Conversely, he called the species prevalent in Galicia (northern Spain) Pecten maximus (left). As has also been concluded from burial finds, the scallop actually used by pilgrims should in fact be the latter species, and this is the one still used today in Santiago de Compostela.

the logo of a famous oil company is based on the scallop. A footnote to this is that the founder of the company concerned, Marcus Samuel, originally began as a trader in antiques, curiosities, and exotic shells.

Trade and currency

Some sort of shell currency is thought to have existed in China as early as 5000 BC. In the seventeenth century, at the time of the East India Company, shells were used as a form of barter and currency in Asia, the Indian Ocean, Malaysia, and Central Africa, particularly different species of cowrie. Strung together in ropes, the shells made a convenient means of exchange. From about 1600 onward, large numbers of the species *Cypraea moneta* (Linnaeus, 1758), the money cowrie, were collected in the Maldives (or Cowrie Islands). These shells were sent by boat to what is present-day Sri Lanka and to Bengal in India. Buyers bought quantities of these and shipped them on to Africa via the Persian Gulf. The merchants of the East India Company subsequently used the shells to help finance trade there, especially the slave trade. However, in the waters around Ambon in the Moluccas, quick-witted Dutchmen soon began catching another species of cowrie, *Cypraea annulus* (Linnaeus, 1758), the gold-ringer cowrie, which was extremely similar in appearance and introduced that cowrie to the market instead. The Native Americans on the west coast of North America used tusk shells as a form of barter and currency. Embedded in ceremonial robes and headdresses, these shells added to the status of the bearer. "Tusk money" served as real money for many hundreds of years. The Native Americans on the east coast also had shell currency. In this case it was "wampum belts" that were held to be exceptionally valuable. These were belts of beads made from the shell of *Mercenaria mercenaria* (Linnaeus, 1758), the northern quahog. Belts containing a great deal of purple in them – only a small part of the shell – were the most highly prized of all. Here, too, it was Dutch colonists who quickly started to copy wampums and trade them in. Later, the English took this over. Nowadays, only in Papua, New Guinea and on the Solomon Islands are shells still used as currency. In both cases, this involves money belts of beads and objects made from shell material.

Jewelry and other uses

In addition to being used for food, as sacred objects, as a means of exchange, and as a source of dyestuff, shells serve all other imaginable purposes worldwide. The shell's shape has been an inspiration for artists throughout the centuries. Besides very famous illustrations, such as the (counterclockwise) marbled cone snail *Conus marmoreus* by Rembrandt (1640) and Boticelli's 'The Birth of Venus' (ca. 1485), there are countless other examples where shells have played an important or lesser role in art. In some cases a shell is not clearly discernible (as in 'The Snail' by Matisse, 1953). Of course, apart from serving as a source of inspiration, the shells themselves were used for all sorts of purposes. The use of the world's largest bivalve, *Tridacna gigas* (Linnaeus, 1758), the giant clam, as a font in which to baptize babies is well-celebrated, and in several European churches these shells remain in use as such or as holy-water basins. A famous example is the splendidly contrived giant clams in the parish church of Saint Sulpice in Paris. Several other shells have been put to particular uses because of their distinctive shape. For example, large species of melon shell (*Melo*) are used by natives of Polynesia to bale out canoes and to carry water, while scallops and abalones serve as eating or drinking vessels or as ashtrays. The broad augur shell *Terebra maculata* is known to have been used for drilling. Especially in tropical coastal regions the uses to which shells can be put are numerous. Cowries and other species are used to decorate head dresses, chains, bracelets, ankle chains, masks, and shields. The cowrie can even serve as a "cache-sexe." Shell parts are also used. Mother-of-pearl is employed in all imaginable jewelry settings and inlaid in expensive pieces of furniture and objects. Only a few decades ago, most shirt buttons were still made of mother-of-pearl.

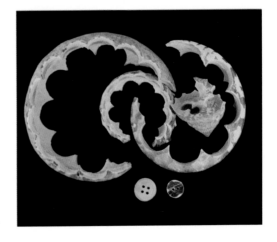

Mother-of-pearl creations. In the past, great quantities of buttons were made in particular from large thick-shelled conches such as Trochus niloticus Linnaeus, 1767, the commercial trochus. Nowadays, this branch of manufacturing has all but disappeared and buttons are mostly made from plastic. (Collection of the Zoological Museum, Amsterdam.)

Nowadays, apart from use as food and for shell trading, shells are mostly collected for the tourist industry. Anyone entering a typical tourist shop in a seaside resort will soon stumble across all kinds of shell art and shell kitsch imaginable. Naturally, there is no point in arguing about taste. However, in some cases the inventiveness and imagination of their creators can give rise to no small degree of amazement.

Shell ornaments. All sorts of figurines can be made using shells from the beach and a tube of glue.

Various useful objects and fancy goods employing shells.

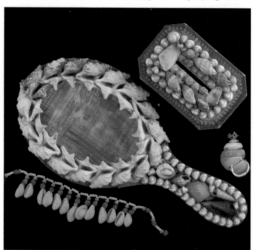

4. Where do mollusks live?

Land snails, in particular, have an extremely restricted habitat. For example, many species occur only on one island, in one valley, or on one mountain summit (endemic occurrence). Species such as these are often under serious threat from human encroachment on the landscape, as well as from shell collecting. The Manus Island tree snail, Papuina (Papustyla) pulcherrima (Rensch, 1931) is subject to both these threats and, as a result, is high on the American list of endangered zoological species.

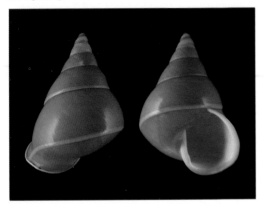

Large saltwater mussels (superfamily Unionioidea) are under threat across the whole world. In the past, the threat came from the over-fishing of pearl-forming species. Nowadays, other hazards such as pollution, acidification, and drought caused by man affect their habitat and threaten their existence. For example, of nearly 300 American species, over a quarter are seriously endangered. Various species are declining in Europe too. An example is the swan mussel in the Netherlands, where it is now rare to find Anodonta cygnea (Linnaeus, 1758) any larger than 15cm. These mussels are dredged in bulk mechanically from drainage ditches, leaving the large, adult specimens behind in the mesh scoop, only to be dumped on the side to die.

WORLDWIDE DISTRIBUTION

Mollusks can be found everywhere in the world. You will come across them in almost all saltwater environments (except in water that is simply too saline, such as the Dead Sea): lakes, rivers, streams, ditches, drainage channels, springs, and every other aquatic biotope. Areas with limestone often contain a huge diversity of species. Larger, often brilliantly colored land snails are particularly prevalent in tropical rainforests. Somewhat smaller species often live in the relatively moist leaf litter found in temperate mixed woodland and pine forests. In addition, land snails appear in all sorts of biotopes, such as heath land, coastal dunes, and even in the desert. Since many terrestrial and freshwater species occur only in an extremely restricted area, damage to the habitat and (in some cases) the overenthusiastic activities of mollusk spotters and collectors can sometimes have negative consequences.

OCCURRENCE AT SEA

This encyclopedia deals with marine mollusks: the shell-bearing species that live at sea. In the nineteenth century, S.P. Woodward classified these species on the basis of where they lived according to "malacological provinces." This classification system is still used to show the areas in which certain species live. Each entry described in this encyclopedia gives the coded abbreviation for the regional occurrence of a species.

Malacological provinces (from north to south)

ARC	Arctic region
ALE	Aleutian region
KEL	Celtic region
LUS	Lusitanian region
VIR	Virginian or Carolinian region
CAL	Californian region
JAP	Japonic region
PAN	Panamic region
CAR	Caribbean region
WAFR	West African region
PER	Peruvian region
INDP	Indo-Pacific region
PAT	Patagonian/Argentine region
MAG	Magellanic region
ZAFR	South African region
AUS	Australian region

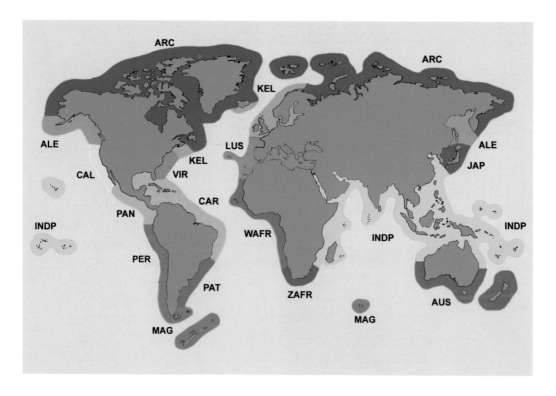

Explanatory notes to the malacological regions

The regional classifications used include the following areas:

1. Arctic region (circumpolar zone): Arctic Ocean, northern Alaska and Canada, Greenland, northern Siberia.

2. Aleutian region (northern part of Pacific Ocean, from Siberia, via the Bering Sea, to southern Alaska (Alexander archipelago) and onward, via British Columbia, to Washington state.

3. Celtic region (also known as the **Boreal region**): Baltic Sea, North Sea, coasts of Great Britain and Ireland, English Channel coast of France, Brittany, also southern Iceland and part of eastern Canada and the northeastern United States. A further subdivision is sometimes made: 3a. subarctic part of the North Atlantic-Boreal—northern Norway, Iceland, southern Greenland, Hudson Bay, Labrador, Newfoundland, east coast of United States to Cape Cod.

4. Lusitanian region (also known as the **Mediterranean region**): Mediterranean Sea and adjoining part of Atlantic Ocean (Bay of Biscay; Canary Islands up to, but not including, Mauritania and Cape Verde Islands).

5. Virginian region (also known as the **Carolinian/Transatlantic region**): Eastern and southeastern United States (Cape Cod to Florida).

6. Californian region: west coast of the United States (from Point Conception, Washington to Baja California).

7. Japonic region: east coast of Korea, Sea of Japan, and Japanese islands.

8. Panamic region: Baja California, western part of Mexico, western Central America to Ecuador.

9: **Caribbean region**: Gulf of Mexico, southern Florida, West Indies, Bermuda, Antilles, Caribbean Sea, Venezuela, and northeastern Brazil to Salvador.

10: **West African region** (also known as the **Senegalese** or **Afro-Atlantic region**): Cape Verde Islands to Walvisbaai.

11: **Peruvian region** (west coast of South America from Punta Negra to Capo Taitao (in southern Chile).

12: **Indo-Pacific region**: east coast of Africa from Durban, Red Sea, Persian Gulf, Arabian Sea, Bay of Bengal, East and South China Sea, Yellow Sea, tropical part of Pacific Ocean from Kyushu south-eastward to Easter Island, and Hawaii. The largest malacological province or region. (This encyclopedia summarizes the entire zone with the term Indo-Pacific.)

13: **Patagonian region** (also known as the **Argentine region**): east coast of South America from Salvador to Golfo de San Jorge.

14: **Magellanic region** (also known as the **Sub-Antarctic region**): southern Chile, Tierra del Fuego, Falkland Islands, Prince Edward Island, Crozet Island, Kerguelen Islands.

15: **South African region**: southwestern and southeastern Africa: Namibia to Durban.

16: **Australian region**: Australian northern coast (tropical), western and eastern coasts (subtropical), southern coast (cool temperate). Various subregions. Sometimes classified separately, 16a: Neozelanic region: coasts of New Zealand's North and South Islands, Stewart Island and Chatham Islands (cool temperate), Antipodes Islands and Macquarie Island (sub-Antarctic).

It should be mentioned that the following regional classifications are sometimes made as well: an Antarctic region containing the South Shetland Islands, South Orkney Islands, South Georgia, South Sandwich Islands, and a Northern Pacific Boreal, or subarctic region containing the Sea of Okhotsk, Kamchatka, Hokkaido, Bering Sea, Alaska, Aleutian Islands, southern coast of Alaska.

Depth zones

Maritime mollusks can be distinguished according to the depth of water in which they occur. Depth zone denominations (d1–d4) are given for each entry in this encyclopedia.

Eulittoral, littoral (intertidal zone), and upper part of sublittoral (d1)

0–25m. This includes the intertidal zone, from the highest high-water mark to the lowest low-water mark, and the zone immediately below this. In the tropics this contains the upper part of coral reefs. It also accounts for rocky coasts and sandy and muddy areas where the strongest currents occur with consecutive wet and dry periods (high and low water). In practice, this is the zone from which people are able to collect the most shells, either with or without the use of simple collecting apparatus (scuba-diving equipment, drags).

Lower part of the sublittoral, deeper water, benthic zone (d2)

25–200m. From the edge of the intertidal zone up to the edge of the continental shelf. Under the influence of sunlight still able to penetrate the water, green, brown and red kelp can grow up to a depth of approximately 60m (*Laminaria* zone). At between 30 and 80m deeper (or deeper still for corals where the temperature barrier is approximately 20°C), organisms occur such as coralline algae (coralline zone), hydroid polyps, and bryozoa.

Archibenthic or bathyal zone, very deep water (d3)

200–500m. Starting from the edge of the continental shelf. The 500m limit is artificial. This is the limit for sunlight (approximately 400m) and also the zone in which mollusks occur that are only rarely fished or dredged up. In fact, the limit of the bathyal zone is 200–4000m. Often the zone contains steep inclines and there is a sharp reduction in light and plant growth disappears.

Abyssal zone, the deep sea (d4)

From 500m to the deep sea. (Deep sea = 4000–6000m, including ridges and crests.) No light penetrates the abyssal zone. It is characterized by high water pressure, low temperatures, and high levels of carbon dioxide.

Zones d1 and d2 contain particularly those mollusks that can attach themselves to the substrate (rocky coasts). Additionally, they contain species that burrow into the sediment (sandy, silted, and muddy substrates). Herbivores or carnivores live in the deeper waters of d2, depending on the seabed type. Carnivores occur particularly in zones with coralline algae. Smaller and less brightly colored species typically occur in zone d3. These are principally carnivorous or species that live off suspended and sinking food particles (detritus). In the main, the food of the deep-sea organisms occurring in zone d4 consists of dead, organic elements (deposit or detritus feeders) or organisms living in the ooze sediment of the ocean floor.

Additional remarks

The zone underneath the abyssal zone, at depths below 6000m, is sometimes separately classified as the "hadal zone." These are the deep ocean trenches: deep, elongated recesses in the ocean floor. Famous trenches include the Marianas Trench at a depth of 11,000m and the Java and Puerto Rico Trenches at 7500m.

Hydrothermal vents emerge at the rift zones of the earth's crust in the abyssal zone. These are "chimneys" many meters high, out of which hot water flows at up to 350°C. This is mixed with hydrogen sulfide, mineral salts, and nitrogen compounds and bubbles up in the form of clouds of smoke (known as "black smokers"). The metallic compounds in the smokers are deposited around the chimneys as black metallic sulfides. A separate ecosystem exists around these vents containing heat-seeking—thermophile—bacteria that derive energy from the sulfurous compounds present. Hundreds of species live on this, including tubeworms, crabs, fish, and also bivalves and snails.

5. Classification and nomenclature

In the past, persons of learning described all the component parts of nature, each in their own way. Yet, try as they might, they could not avoid making groupings and cataloging (classifying). Organisms that looked like each other were categorized together in the same group: trees with trees; birds with birds. Among the birds, waterfowl were categorized separately from birds of prey; among the birds of prey, owls looked more like each other than like other birds of prey, and so forth. Snails and bivalve shellfish were placed under "shellfish" because of their most obvious, commonly shared characteristic, their hard exoskeleton—the shell (Testacea, Ostracoderma). Animals without shells, such as squids and slugs, were assigned to a different group, that of the "mollusks" (Mollusca). Around 1800, Cuvier discovered during an anatomical investigation that the two groups showed no differences in terms of their internal structure. Since then, these "shell-bearing" and "shell-less" animals have been assigned to the same division of the animal kingdom: the phylum of mollusks (Mollusca). Both the Latin "mollis" and the Greek "malakos" mean soft. Consequently, the area of biology that concerns itself with the study of Mollusca is referred to as "malacology." In the past, reference used to be made to conchyliology or conchology (Latin: "concha"; Greek: "conchylion" = shell valve). These days, these terms continue to be used only for areas of malacology that exclusively study the shell, without any analysis of the internal structure, behavior, or other characteristics of the animals.

Catalogs have been made throughout the ages. Even many centuries ago, attempts were made to group shells together according to their external appearance. As a result, the idea soon took hold to illustrate all of these different types.

NOMENCLATURE

Naturalists consider the Swedish scholar Carl Linnaeus to be the founding father of taxonomy. He was the first to conceive of a system of classification and nomenclature—naming—that could be used for every organism in the world. This "Systema Natura," published in 1758, is simple, effective, and still in use today. Instead of "common" names, such as top shell, scallop, etc., which can vary markedly from country to country and from language to language, the same unique scientific name is now used everywhere in the world to describe any one particular type of organism. In principle, a scientific species name always consists of two Latin or Latinized words (binomial nomenclature). For example, the tiger cowrie is known as *Cypraea tigris*. The first word, always capitalized, is the genus name (generic name, like a surname). The second word, not capitalized, is the individual species name: the "epitheton specificum." In other words, each generic name consists of a genus name and an epitheton specificum, together forming a binomial name. Species closely related to one another are grouped together in the same genus and, consequently, have the same genus name. The relationship between species within a single genus will always be stronger than that between species from different genera.

Progressive classification

Linnaeus saw the entire living world as one entity composed of many progressive stages, as if descending the steps of a pyramid. Right at the summit is the "kingdom," the term that contains everything that lies below it. This is progressively subdivided into subkingdom, phylum (chief division, in our case Mollusca), subphylum, class (for example, Gastropoda and Bivalvia), subclass, order, suborder, superfamily, family (in our example, the cowrie family or Cypraeidae), subfamily and genus (plural "genera"). All species have unique (specific) species names within their genera. Gradations can also be included within genera. Species that are assigned to one genus on the basis of common properties are sometimes further grouped into subgenera within that genus. In such cases, the name of the subgenus is placed between brackets after the genus name. For example, *Chlamys (Chlamys) islandica* and *Chlamys (Mimachlamys) varia*. One of the separated subgenera always keeps the same name as the genus to which it belongs: *Chlamys (Chlamys) islandica* is referred to as *Chlamys s.s.* (Latin: sensu stricto = in the strict sense) as opposed to *Chlamys (Mimachlamys) varia* s.l. (sensu lato = in the wider sense).

Authorship

In scientific publications and identification reports, the name of the author is mentioned after the species or subspecies name, being the name of the person who first described the species concerned in a publication and provided it with a name. If a name is written as *Buccinum undatum* Linnaeus, it shows that it was Linnaeus who first published on the whelk and named it. If the author's name is bracketed, it shows that the newly published species was initially assigned to another genus. For example, Linnaeus published on a species that he called *Cardium edule*, which we, today, place in the genus *Cerastoderma*. The correct notation is now *Cerastoderma edule* (Linnaeus). The date on which the species was named is important. Often, the description of a species will have been published many times over the centuries by different authors because an author did not realize that another author had discovered and published on that particular species previously.

In the years that followed the publication of Linnaeus' Systema Naturae, a plethora of beautiful catalogs appeared, often containing hand-colored plates, in which the various "conchylia" were illustrated and described in detail. Unfortunately, the use of binomial nomenclature was far from universally accepted. As a result, many works containing readily identifiable species were rejected subsequently. Thus, the names used are deemed invalid. (Martini, F.H.W., & J.H. Chemnitz, Neues systematisches Conchylien Cabinet. 11 Vol. Nuremberg 1769–1795.)

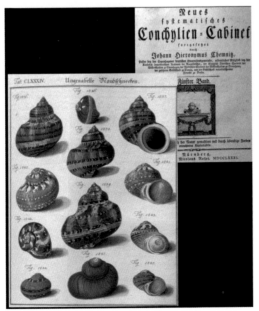

Confusion is prevented by further including, after the author's name, the year of publication in which the binomial name concerned was introduced, which then makes it possible to discern which name has the longest legitimacy. Only the oldest name is valid. A valid generic description must comply with the standards laid down in the International Code of Zoological Nomenclature, known by the acronym ICZN.

Species are sometimes published as a separate species, but later assigned as a subspecies of a species. The year is also very important in these instances: the oldest, binomial name applies to the species first published and the name of the subspecies is transformed into a tripartite (trinomial subspecies) name. For example, in 1791, Gmelin published on the species *Patella ulyssiponensis* and, in 1844, Bean published on the species *Patella athletica*. Many scientists now consider *athletica* a subspecies of *ulyssiponensis* and, consequently, reference is made to: *Patella ulyssiponensis athletica* Bean, 1844. The author's name is not bracketed because it was Bean who published on the species being in the genus *Patella*.

Synonyms

Only the oldest name is valid if the description of a single species has been published several times by several people. Taxonomists consider all later names to·be "synonyms" and thus invalid. Clearly, this use of the term synonym is not the same as that used in normal parlance, given that this would mean "an equivalent word with the same or nearly the same meaning," whereas in this case only one name is ever the "correct" one. Some species that vary particularly in structure or color can sometimes have a great many synonyms.

Systematics and taxonomy

Systematics is the study of the relationships between organisms. Species that, at first sight, may look alike, can turn out to differ from each other markedly on closer examination. For example, the false angel wing *Petricola pholadiformis* looks very much like a "true" borer mussel in terms of its shell structure and lifestyle, but scientists assign it to an entirely different superfamily and thus an entirely different place in the system. Systematics and taxonomy are components in scientific studies that are not (merely) concerned with superficial similarities but with evolutionary patterns: kinship and the emergence of (sub-) species. All aspects of the animal are examined in the greatest possible detail in order to discover these things. Although morphological studies of the shell are becoming ever more refined (morph = relating to form and structure), assisted, for example, by electron microscopes, this constitutes only one part of it. More new data is constantly coming to light thanks to anatomical studies of the reproductive organs, the vascular and renal system, and other internal organs, as well as through DNA analysis of proteins and splitting enzymes using electrophoresis. These data result in new perspectives and amendments to taxonomic classifications. Consequently, parts of a taxonomic classification can sometimes change and, (partly) because of this, species can suddenly be classified in quite different genera, families, and divisions even higher up the taxonomic tree.

The concept of a species

The term "species" is usually defined in biology as a group of organisms sharing similar characteristics that are able to interbreed successfully, and can be distinguished from organisms in comparable groups. An example often cited is that of the mule, a cross between horse and donkey, which is unable to produce any fertile offspring and is thus not designated as a separate species. However, anyone venturing more deeply into the taxonomy of mollusks will soon discover dozens of dubious cases. Often, it appears to be a question of deciding whether two candidates should be accepted as separate species or not (yet). The fact that the concept of a species has not been well defined is not due to human failure but stems from the fact that evolution is an ongoing process. After all, even at this very moment new species are emerging. However important the concept of a species may be in determining relationships, it is certainly not a term by which to define something forever.

The following definition could be applied to a subspecies: divisions of a species that are developing by evolution into separate species or that have been doing so for some time. Variation determined by geographical inheritance plays a role in the development of subspecies. If features appearing in specimens of one species in a particular environment (A) are different from features appearing in specimens from another environment (B), with "mixed forms" displaying both sets of features in a small border zone between A and B, this excludes A and B from being classed as separate species. This is because the animals from A and from B are still able to interbreed and produce fertile offspring despite their different features. In this case, where inherited properties are concerned, A and B are referred to as separate subspecies. A subspecies can be seen as a "species under development."

Types

In scientific jargon, words arise such as "holotype" and "paratype." The term "type" has similarities to a point of calibration on a set of weighing scales or a clock face. The author submits one specimen that is considered as "typical of the species": the "holotype." This is published and illustrated. The other specimens viewed are called "paratypes". It should be obvious that this material regarding type is of the utmost importance. After all, the basis for the entire species rests on it. Types should be kept with the utmost care, preferably in a museum. Further nomenclature exists in addition to the type nomenclature already mentioned. However, it would be taking things too far for this encyclopedia to go into detail about type analysis and all the terms and problems associated with it.

A system according to rank

Just as for all groups of organisms on earth, there is also an "order of rank" for mollusks when cataloging the classes and other taxonomic divisions below this. Taxonomic ranking is based on the Linnaean system and follows the line, in principle, of evolutionary history. Primitive groups/species, such as the class of chitons, are placed at the top of the taxon (or taxonomic division). Highly developed groups in terms of evolution are placed at the bottom of the taxon. A certain degree of taxonomic ranking also occurs within the classes and other taxonomic divisions. Particularly in the case of lower taxa (families, subfamilies, genera, subgenera), this ranking is in continual flux and new perspectives on it appear regularly.

In this encyclopedia of shells, a conscious decision has been made to classify entries partly according to taxonomy and partly alphabetically. The arrangement of the families (always ending in "-idae"), and the species discussed within them, has been done alphabetically. Classification according to subfamilies, subgenera, and subspecies has not been included. However, the order given to the superfamilies (division names ending in "-oidea") and higher taxa has been done taxonomically. A conscious decision has been made to aim for a conservative layout. In relation to the scientific nomenclature of species, it has been decided not to include all recent name changes but, instead, to attempt to produce a practical encyclopedia with recognizable names. The end of the encyclopedia contains an overview of taxonomic ranking according to current standards.

6. Shell collecting

In the past, for a variety of reasons, both professionals and amateurs made collections of shells. To this day, they often still form the basic material for museum and other scientific collections. Without having recourse to a carefully assembled comparative collection, it is virtually impossible to build up a thorough knowledge of species within the context of the study of mollusks. As evidence, retained specimens sometimes constitute the only reliable source of verification that a particular species does, or did, indeed occur in a particular area. Even so, the majority of private collections were created, in particular, with an aesthetic point of view in mind. After all, neatly arranged in their display cabinets or showcases, the different species exhibited are a timeless source of joy and information.

Collecting

An attractive shell collection is to be cherished. It is now typical for collectors to want to possess the most beautiful and flawless collectors' objects possible. The reigning notion is that animals collected alive are the most beautiful of all. In practice, this typically means mint-condition conches, preferably with operculum and periostracum still intact and doublets: bivalves with both valves still connected. However, the collecting of live animals from their habitat, simply because of their shells, is not advisable. In any case, a collection of empty, washed-up, or self-collected shells can be just as enjoyable a possession. There are exceptions to this, of course. For example, it makes little sense to throw still living mollusks that have been washed up onto the beach back into the sea. In most cases, these will have been marked down for death anyway, and live collection is sometimes necessary for scientific research.

The ever-increasing demand for rare species provides a living, in many parts of the world, for fishermen and their families. On the other hand, increasing commercialization is resulting in the irreversible plunder of nature. In most cases, it is not so much their capture that leads to the extinction of species, but the destruction of their habitats. At the present time, a ban on collections is in force in a number of areas. Many terrestrial and freshwater mollusks, in particular, are now on the emergency lists. A collection ban applies to most species. Decline at the hands of shell collectors is a less significant danger to maritime mollusks. However, species that are fished commercially can become seriously depleted, sometimes to a level at which any proper recovery of the population is no longer possible. Therefore, the collecting of empty shells, washed or appearing ashore, is still the only proper method for many collectors. Most mollusks live a relatively short time. After death, their soft parts decay or are consumed by other organisms. Subsequently, tides or currents can move the shells nearer the coast or even wash them up onto a beach, where they can be collected.

If live collection is involved, any harmful impact should, of course, be kept to the bare minimum. Never collect more than the quantity needed and kill the animals as quickly as possible. In estuaries and other fragile ecosystems, always keep in mind the other flora and fauna that live there. If rocks, or other objects, are moved or dislodged from their resting positions, they should be returned to how they were before as quickly as possible. If this is not done, it means an unnecessary death for all kinds of organisms, large and small, that live on and under the rocks. Furthermore, one should be aware that many coastal areas are of the utmost importance to birds and other animals. Be constantly vigilant that you do not disturb foraging animals (seeking food), and make sure you damage the flora and seaweed growth as little as possible: all types of different organisms depend on it.

Summary: please observe the following rules when collecting:
– after inspection, put rocks and other material that has been moved back in their original positions;
– collect the smallest number of animals possible and leave eggs, mating, and egg-laying animals alone. If possible, do not collect immature specimens;
– collect only the most urgently needed living material. Always let damaged and juvenile animals go free;
– if you can manage with empty shells and are content with photographs of living animals, substitute a camera for your collection bag as often as you can;
– search only in sand and between loose rocks and coral, but leave living coral alone.

Empty shells can usually be collected effortlessly. Given that a great many species live in shallow water, you can achieve extremely good results just with a pair of goggles and a snorkel.

Edible species are fished commercially in many places. This can sometimes have disastrous consequences, especially for large, longer-lived species. At various places in the Caribbean, the catching of Tricornis gigas (Linnaeus, 1758), the pink conch, has now been stopped. A strict import ban applies even to the empty shells. (Pile of shells on Bonaire, photograph P.L. van Pel.)

Buying and exchanging

Shells are offered for sale all over the world. Almost all seaside tourist shops sell shells and/or objects made from them. There are also specialized shell retailers. Most of these can now be found and contacted via the Internet. They will usually send you species inventories and price lists on request. Many such traders sell by mail order. You will often come across traders, too, at collectors' fairs. The price of special shells can vary considerably. Traders are quick to ask substantial sums for sought-after specimens, but many "more ordinary" species can be obtained for relatively little money. Quality grades are often given to the shells on offer, such as "gem," or "perfect," "fine," "good," or "fair," or "poor." If you collect your own shells, you can,

of course, try to exchange an item for something else. Both nationally and internationally, there exist a variety of associations for kindred spirits (see Addresses section at the end of the encyclopedia).

Preparation

Where you have empty shells without mollusk remains, all you need do is clean them and remove any growths. Try not to damage the periostracum (epidermis) and, if possible, place your shells in drinking water for a little while to counteract the corrosive effect of the sea salt. Afterward, they can be dried (preferably not in the sun as it bleaches the colors) and stored. Animals still alive are killed in boiling water. Most bivalves then automatically open their shell valves. Otherwise, you can cut through the adductor muscles with a fine knife. You should allow doublets with hinge ligaments intact to dry closed up with a piece of twine or elastic band. The dead, fleshy parts can be removed from snail shells and conches by sticking a bent pin into the body and removing the remains with a twisting motion. Any remains can be dissolved with domestic bleach. However, this can damage the shell's periostracum and mother-of-pearl, as well as the operculum and the hinge ligament in bivalves. The operculum is usually kept carefully with the conch. Many collectors will fill a shell with cotton wool and glue back the operculum, correctly replaced in its aperture. Small and delicate species are best left in an alcohol bath (70%) for 48 hours, whereupon they dry up in the shell. You can also allow the soft tissue to rot away by steeping it in water. Soft tissue can be preserved in a solution of 60 to 80% alcohol or 5% formalin. However, the latter fluid is poisonous and irritates the lining of the nose and throat.

Storage and records

Store shells in a manner that prevents them from becoming damaged and makes them easy to find again. Most collections are stored in filing cabinets or displayed in glass showcases (often a combination of both). Keep careful record of the data with every find. This increases the (scientific) value of a collection considerably. Important data includes the date, the location of the find and who found it, as well as weather conditions, such as wind direction. As far as possible, try to note down particulars— for example, whether the species was found alive or dead and whether it relates to a native find (discovered in the place where the animal lived) or whether, for example, it was found carried on some floating object. It is useful to be able to mention this if you should want to sell or exchange the item, not least because some traders are not so scrupulous about the proper place of origin. It is best to write such information on a label or card that is placed with the shell in its box, sleeve, or tube. Your shells can be stored in plastic or cardboard boxes, for example. Smaller species are often put in test tubes, the smallest of all in transparent gelatin capsules that can be bought from a pharmacist. A serious collection is usually accompanied by proper records. In addition to labeling, many collectors also store data in logbooks, a card retrieval system, or in a computer database. Many practical ways are now available for printing out find location labels using a normal printer.

Through the eyes of the collector. The dream of every collector: a splendid collection as your own private museum.

7. Concerning this encyclopedia

Many hundreds of distinct mollusk families live in the seas of the world. This encyclopedia provides descriptions of the most important families of the shell-bearing species of mollusk. It also gives a summary of any subfamilies and the most important genera that come within these families. Various examples of species are discussed and illustrated in each family. In particular, commonly occurring shells have been included, as well as various species that are known among collectors for their form or rarity.

Order

An encyclopedia needs to be ordered appropriately. If a strictly alphabetical format were adhered to, the taxonomic interrelationships would be lost in all of the species related to each other, which would make comparison and naming extremely hard to achieve. For that reason, it has been decided to employ a combined alphabetical and taxonomic system. The upper taxonomic divisions have been given in strict taxonomic order (classes, subclasses, orders, suborders, and also superfamilies {division names ending in "-oidea"}). Conversely, the arrangement of all the families belonging under the superfamilies (ending in "-idae") is alphabetical, as is that of any species discussed and illustrated in these families.

Names

At the request of the publisher, an English vernacular name has been given for each species included in the encyclopedia, in addition to the scientific name, the name of the author who published on the species, and the year in which this occurred. In the case of some species, where an English name was lacking, this name has been based on the scientific name, the appearance of the species, and, sometimes, its behavior.

Species descriptions

Species descriptions contain the following successive abbreviations:
D: dimension. The average length, width, or height of adult specimens.
S: shape. The general shape of the shell.
O: ornamentation. Any external structures on the shell.
C: color. Coloration and patterning.
H: habitat. Preferred living environment, divided into four categories according to depth.
d1 = from the littoral to the sublittoral, to a depth of approximately 25m; d2 = 25–200m; d3 = 200–500m; d4 = deeper than 500m.
W: world geographical distribution. For the letter coding, see the malacological regions given in Chapter 4 and the accompanying map.
R: rarity factor: 1–5. 1 stands for widespread distribution/commonly found; 2 = less common; 3 = uncommon to relatively rare; 4 = rare; 5 = extremely rare.
NB: additional remarks.

Selection

This encyclopedia could scarcely deal with all the 100,000 species of mollusk present on earth. In order to create a work of reference that is nonetheless practical, with recognizable species and familiar names, a conscious decision has been taken in the case of several generic groups for the use of conservative, scientific nomenclature. When you compare a shell you have found, or otherwise acquired, against the photographs and descriptions, it will certainly be possible to put a name to it. The families of other species can often be ascertained by comparing them with the structure and general family descriptions. Afterward, you could pursue this further through additional literary research and/or through contacts with museums, associations, and shell societies.

8. Class Polyplacophora

DE BLAINVILLE, 1816
chitons or coat-of-mail shells

Worldwide, the class of chitons contains some 800 species and is subdivided into one order and four suborders. Consequently, it is one of the smallest mollusk classes on earth. Most species live in the tropics, although several species do occur in colder maritime regions, such as the North Sea. Chitons have eight separate shell plates, hinged one on top of the other. The contour of the body is roughly oval, flattened ventrally and domed dorsally. It has eight, dorsal shell plates, overlapping each other like roof tiles, held in place by a muscled girdle of mantle tissue. (See also Chapter 2 and the Glossary of Terms.)
The families dealt with (family=taxonomic divisions ending in "-idae") and the genera/species belonging under them have been arranged alphabetically according to suborder. Dimensions relate to the animal including the mantle girdle.

ORDER NEOLORICATA

BERGENHAYN, 1955

SUBORDER LEPIDOPLEURINA

THIELE, 1910
Various, less well-known families of chiton come under the suborder Lepidopleurina. With the exception of species from the family Leptochitonidae, most of the other species occur in either fairly deep or deep water, such as the species from the family Hanleyidae Bergenhayn, 1955. Various families live on sunken driftwood or shipwrecks, such as Ferreiraellidae Dell'-Angelo & Palazzi, 1991 and Nierstrasziellidae Sirenko, 1992. The latter family contains only one species: *Nierstrasziella lineata* (Nierstrasz, 1905). Hardly any species from the latter families appear in any private collections.

Leptochitonidae

DALL, 1889
sow bug chitons

Family containing both extremely small and larger species. Elongated oval. Girdle edge of shell plates not toothed or indented. Found in both shallow waters and in the deep sea. Genera include: *Hanleyella, Lepidopleurus, Leptochiton, Oldroydia*.

SUBORDER CHORIPLACINA

STAROBOGATOV & SIRENKO, 1975

Choriplacidae

ASHBY, 1928
This family exclusively contains the Australian species *Choriplax grayi* (A. Adams & Angas, 1864).

SUBORDER ISCHNOCHITONINA

BERGENHAYN, 1930

Acanthochitonidae

PILSBRY, 1893
bristly chitons (and others)

Measuring from a few millimeters to over 350mm. Often with diminished plates, covered on either side by the highly developed, leathery girdle. Bristles sometimes found on the girdle. Especially found in temperate maritime zones. Subdivided into the subfamilies Acanthochitoninae Pilsbry, 1893. Several genera, including: *Acanthochitona, Craspedochiton, Cryptochiton, Cryptoconchus, Notoplax*.

Acanthochitona crinita

(PENNANT, 1777)
little bristly chiton

D: 20mm. S: grainy, relatively wide girdle with 8–9 small bristly tufts on either side. 1st plate with 4–5 indentations, 8th with 2 or more, oth-

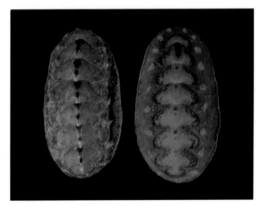

ers only 1. O: plates have teardrop-shaped, fairly broadly separated granulose markings. C: variable: yellowish-green with orange to brown flecks or stripes. Plates often greenish within. H: d1; under rocks in the littoral and sublittoral. W: KEL, LUS. R: 2. NB: *A. fascicularis* [great bristly chiton] grows larger, up to 60mm, and has a rounder, more delicate granulose structure.

Cryptochiton stelleri

(VON MIDDENDORFF, 1847)
giant chiton

D: up to 350mm. S: shell plates entirely encapsulated, plates without tegmentum, white. O: leathery girdle covered in groups of spicules. C: grayish-brown girdle. H: d1; sublittoral, rocky coasts. W: ALE, JAP. R: 3. NB: the largest chiton.

Chitonidae

RAFINESQUE, 1815
scaly chitons (and others)

Medium to large. Clearly defined plates with grooved girdle edges. Girdle leathery or with scales, bristles, and spicules. Worldwide. 3 subfamilies: Acanthopleurinae Dall, 1889; Chitoninae Rafinesque, 1815; Toniciinae Pilsbry, 1893. Various genera, including: *Acanthopleura, Chiton, Enoplochiton, Liolophura, Onithochiton, Radsia, Rhyssoplax, Squamopleura, Tonicia.*

Acanthopleura gemmata

(DE BLAINVILLE, 1825)
coarsely bristled scaled chiton

D: 150mm. S: oval with extremely wide girdle. Shell plates rounded with central mucro (short, stiff, sharp point). O: flat, indistinct, granulose structure, plates often partly calcified. Girdle with extremely long and coarse, moderately pointed spines. C: grayish-brown to greenish-brown. Girdle dark brown, spines lighter toward yellow. H: d1; littoral and sublittoral, under rocks. W: INDP, JAP. R: 2.

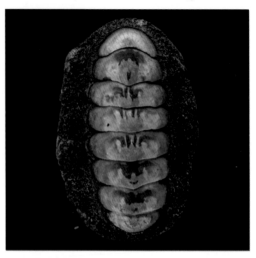

Chiton olivaceus

SPENGLER, 1797
olive-scaled chiton

D: 25mm, sometimes up to 40mm. S: extremely variable, animals occur with high and low shell plates. Plates show a clear ridge (carina) with smooth sides. O: tegmentum on plates with 4–6 wide, radial ribs on the lateral parts. Overlapping parts smooth with 15–20 longitudinal grooves on either side. Fairly wide, scaly, spiny

girdle. C: olive green or with marbled marks in all possible colors. Girdle often has lighter stripes and otherwise is the color of the shell plates. H: d1; under rocks to depth of approx. 25m. W: LUS and southern Portugal. R: 2.

Chiton sulcatus

WOOD, 1815
sulcate chiton

D: 80mm. S: oval with thick shell plates. O: surface of plates heavily ribbed linearly and diagonally, ribs closer together toward the center. Girdle coarsely granulose. C: uniformly black. H: d1; under rocks in littoral and sublittoral. G: PAN; Galapagos Islands. R: 4.

Onithochiton hirasei

PILSBRY, 1901
red-girdled chiton

D: 50mm. S: slender species with wide girdle. First plate roughly triangular. Fairly wide, leathery girdle with very delicate spicules. O: shell-plate surface almost smooth with fine growth lines. C: variable color and patterning, often spotted or with a lighter stripe of color in the center. Girdle pink to red (especially after it has been dried). H: d1; littoral and sublittoral under rocks. W: JAP. R: 2.

Cryptoplacidae

H. & A. ADAMS, 1858
girdled chitons

Medium-sized species. Often with a wide and thick, leathery girdle. Small shell plates, sometimes almost rudimentary, that may be wholly separated from each other. In some cases, the girdle covers the shell plates entirely. The animals are often slender and relatively nimble. Few genera: *Choneplax, Cryptoplax.*

Cryptoplax larvaeformis

(BURROW, 1815)
slender girdled chiton

D: 100mm. S: extremely slender with elongated shell plates, partly covered by the girdle, either nearly or entirely separated from each other. O: indistinct, narrow, transverse ribs fanning out on the shell plates. Girdle has delicate spicules. C: light brown with dark-colored stripes, often with dark rings around the last three shell plates as well. H: d1; sublittoral under large slabs of dead coral and boulders. W: AUS, INDP, JAP. R: 1.

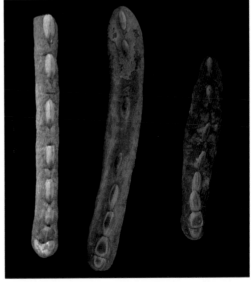

Ischnochitonidae

DALL, 1889
latticed chitons

Oval to elongated. Usually 10–40mm, sometimes larger. Plates slightly arched or buckled in the middle. Very defined structures in some genera. By far the majority of species live on a hard substrate at depths of 0–200m in almost all maritime zones. They are divided into several subfamilies: Callistoplacinae Pilsbry, 1893; Callochitoninae Plate, 1901; Chaetopleurinae Plate, 1899; Ischnochitoninae Dall, 1889; Lepidochitoninae Iredale, 1914; Schizoplacinae Bergenhayn, 1955.

Many different genera, including: *Callistochiton, Callistoplax, Callochiton, Calloplax, Ceratozona, Chaetopleura, Dinoplax, Eudoxochiton, Ischnochiton, Ischnoplax, Juvenichiton, Lepidochitona, Lepidozona, Nuttallina, Nuttallochiton, Particulazona, Schizoplax, Stenochiton, Stenoplax, Subterenochiton, Tonicella, Tonicina.*

Chaetopleura angulata

(SPENGLER, 1797)
great latticed chiton

D: 55mm. S: oval with rounded angular shell plates. O: defined, radial, and diagonal ribs. C: yellowish-brown to dark brown, ribs usually lighter in color. H: d1–2; sublittoral and deeper to 40m. W: LUS, PAT. R: 1. NB: in Europe, only (imported) along the Atlantic coasts of Spain and Portugal, especially the Algarve, Portugal.

Lepidochitona cinerea

(LINNAEUS, 1767)
ash-gray chiton

D: 25mm. S: elongated oval, fairly flat. Elongated plates with 1–2 notches on the underside. O: the shell surface is fairly coarse-grained. Girdle with fine spicules especially at the edges. C: grayish-green to red, sometimes spotted. Often lighter in the middle, girdle often the same color. H: d1; under rocks in the littoral, especially found in mud flats. W: ARC, KEL, LUS. R: 2.

Stenoplax alata

(SOWERBY, 1841)
elevated chiton

D: 75mm. S: narrow, elongated oval with a wide girdle. Flat shell plates, not buckled. Relatively large first plate with projecting mucro. O: shell plates with narrow, granulose radial grooves. Girdle has delicate spicules and grain structure. C: yellowish-brown or with extremely fine, radial stripes. H: d1; littoral and sublittoral under rocks. W: INDP, JAP. R: 1.

Tonicella rubra

(LINNAEUS, 1767)
northern red chiton

D: 15mm. S: oval with narrow girdle. Low shell plates with truncated ridge. O: smooth with sometimes deep growth lines. C: beige to pink, often with reddish-brown marks. H: d1–2; usually 0–40m. On rocks and coralline seabed. W: ARC, KEL. R: 2.

Mopaliidae

DALL, 1889
hairy chitons

Oval up to approximately 130mm. Plates bear few physical markings, divided into central and side segments. Plates with incised girdle edge. Variable girdle width and rows of spicules. Worldwide distribution. 2 subfamilies: Katharininae Jacovleva, 1952 and Mopaliidae Dall, 1889. Various genera, including: *Amicula, Fremblya, Katharina, Mopalia, Placiphorina, Plaxiphora, Plaxiphorella.*

Katharina tunicata

(WOOD, 1815)
black katy chiton

D: 60mm. S: elongated, shell plates narrow and rounded, partly covered by the extremely wide, leathery girdle. O: principally growth lines. Shell plates often calcified. C: girdle of living animal black or dark brown. Shell plates chalky white or gray. H: d1; sublittoral. W: ALE, ARC, CAL. R: 1.

Schizochitonidae

DALL, 1889
ribbed chitons

Oval, up to approximately 90mm. The plates bear level ribs containing photosensitive organs. Girdle pilose or with bristles. A few genera: *Lorica, Loricella, Schizochiton.*

9. Class Monoplacophora

ODHNER, 1940

cap-shelled mollusks, neopilinids

For a long time, it was assumed that the fossil class of Monoplacophora, a group that occurred in the Cambrian, Ordovician, and Silurian geological periods, had been extinct since the Devonian period. However, in 1952, during the Danish "Galathea" expedition off the western coast of Central America, recent, living specimens were dredged up from a depth of over 3500m. In 1958 and 1967, further finds were made of this "living fossil" at depths of between 2500 and 6500m in the Red Sea, the middle of the Pacific Ocean, the southern Atlantic Ocean, and around the Antarctic. Descriptions have been published on between 15 and 20 recent species, measuring up to no more than 35mm in size. They are all deep-sea inhabitants with one flat shell that covers the entire animal.

ORDER MONOPLACOPHORIDA

WENZ IN KNIGHT, 1952

TRYBLIDIOIDEA

PILSBRY IN ZITTEL-EASTMAN, 1899
Opinion is divided about the precise taxonomy for these species and their groups. Five families are often distinguished: Laevipilinidae Moskalev, Starobogatov & Filatova, 1983; Monoplacophoridae Moskalev, Starobogatov & Filatova, 1983; Neopilinidae Knight & Yochelson, 1958; Tryblidiidae Pilsbry, 1899; Vemidae Moskalev, Starobogatov & Filatova, 1983. Several genera: *Laevipilina, Micropilina, Monoplacophorus, Neopilina, Rokopella, Vema*.

Neopilinidae

KNIGHT & YOCHELSON, 1958

Rokopella brummeri

GOUD & GITTENBERGER, 1993
D: 1.4mm. S: cap-shaped shell with slightly overhanging apex. O: extremely fine radial grooves, emanating in part from the apex. C: yellowish-white periostracum, nacreous interior without clear muscular scarring. H: d4; only known in the Atlantic Ocean at a depth of 2162m. W: ARC, KEL. R: 5+. NB: exceptionally rare, included as an example of the class concerned. This and other species of Monoplacophora are never found in private collections; they can be found in the scientific collections of research institutes and museums.

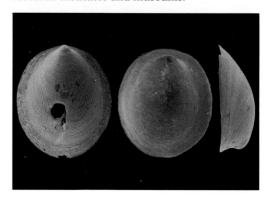

10. Class Gastropoda

CUVIER, 1795
snails and slugs

The largest class of mollusks with representatives on land and in virtually all aquatic environments imaginable. Principally asymmetric animals with a head, foot, mantle, and visceral hump. Usually with a simple, univalve shell. There are a few exceptions, such as the genus Julia that is comprised of bivalve snails. The shell usually takes the form of a spirally wound, hollow tube, but can also be cap-shaped, conical, egg-shaped (oviform) or else can be entirely or partially missing (slugs). Virtually every species has a radula in its mouth opening. These animals breathe using gills or a mantle cavity transformed into a lung. The mantle cavity and visceral hump containing all the organs are located anteriorly in most sea snails. Moreover, the gills are located in front of the heart. This group is often summarized under the name Prosobranchia (anteriorly gilled snails).

In more recent literature, the class of Gastropods is divided into two main groups: the subclass Eogastropoda Ponder & Lindberg, 1996 and the subclass Orthogastropoda Ponder & Lindberg, 1996.

SUBCLASS EOGASTROPODA

PONDER & LINDBERG, 1996
ancient snails

Eogastropoda contains one order, Patellogastropoda Ponder & Lindberg, 1986 Troschel, 1866. This is considered the most ancient line of gastropods, branching from one single evolutionary line. The species concerned, which now also includes their extinct fossil ancestors, were once classified under Archaeogastropoda. The group is subdivided into three suborders: Lepetopsina McLean, 1990, Nacellina Lindberg, 1988, and Patellina Von Ihering, 1876, containing four subfamilies: Acmaeoidea Carpenter, 1857; Lepetopsoidea McLean, 1990; Nacelloidea Thiele, 1891; Patelloidea Rafinesque, 1815.

Regarding the divisions and species that follow, the superfamilies (divisions ending in "-oidea") have been put in taxonomic order, while the families contained within them (divisions ending in "-idae"), and all of the species described within these families, have been arranged alphabetically.

PATELLOIDEA

RAFINESQUE, 1815
Cap-shaped shells with an outward pointing, often abraded, apex. Smooth, with concentric growth rings or radial ribs. Interior often colored, with horseshoe-shaped muscle scar. Radula differs from that of the other Archaeogastropoda. Shell rim without a canal for an anal outlet. No operculum.

Patellidae

RAFINESQUE, 1815
true limpets (shallow water)

Very familiar, cap-shaped species that occur, almost without exception, in the mid- to upper section of the intertidal zone, suckered fast to rocks. Food, consisting of algae, is scraped from rocks with a rasping organ in the mouth (radula). The animals graze, particularly at night, around their set resting places worn away in the rocks. Many hundreds of species on all rocky coasts, usually measuring a few centimeters. Best-known genera: *Cymbula, Patella, Scutellastra*.

Cymbula oculus

VON BORN, 1778
South African eye limpet

D: 100mm. S: oval, star-shaped shell. O: several quite robust ribs protruding beyond the average circumference of the shell and various narrower ribs. C: exterior matt brownish-yellow. Interior has a wide, brownish-black edge. Often a bluish-white edge surrounding the yellowish-brown scars: the whole creating the impression of an eye. H: d1; littoral and sublittoral. W: ZAFR. R:2.

Patella caerulea

LINNAEUS, 1758
rayed Mediterranean limpet

D: 50mm. S: wide, fairly flat shell. O: diverse tightly grouped, fairly low, ribs. C: exterior reddish-brown, often with lighter bands of color radiating from the apex. Interior radiates an iridescent, lilac-blue with grayish-white muscle scarring. H: d1; littoral and sublittoral. W: LUS, WAFR; Canary Islands. R: 1.

Patella ferruginea

GMELIN, 1791
ribbed Mediterranean limpet

D: 70mm. S: thick, fairly flat shell. Edges crenated by rib pattern. O: very coarse, sometimes rather crimped ribs. C: exterior matt light brown. Interior shiny white with a white muscle scar. H: d1; littoral and sublittoral. W: LUS, WAFR; Canary Islands. R: 1. NB: edible.

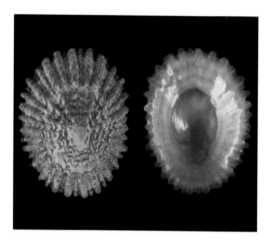

Patella intermedia

MURRAY IN KNAPP, 1857
colored limpet

D: up to 45mm. S: oval shell. Usually flattened off, the apex somewhat depressed. O: blunt or sharp, radiating ribs. Finer riblets in-between. C: yellowish-white to grayish-green. Interior with orange-yellow muscle scar, usually surrounded by black-brown stripes of color radiating to the rim interspersed with bright yellow or orange stripes. H: d1; littoral and sublittoral of rocky coasts, often on steeper, vertical rock faces. W: KEL, LUS. R: 1.

Patella pellucida

LINNAEUS, 1758
blue-rayed limpet

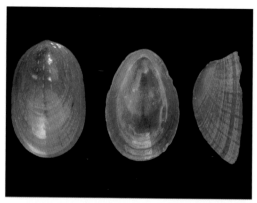

D: 18mm. S: thin to fairly robust shell. Apex very truncated and located quite close to the posterior edge. O: surface has concentric markings. C: horn-colored with intermittent, pale blue to bright green lines radiating from the apex. H: d1; along rocky coasts in the sublittoral and to depth of approx. 30m. Lives attached to brown seaweed (*Laminara* spec.). W:

KEL, LUS. R: 3. NB: in addition to the typical oval type with delicate shells, there is also a larger type with thicker shells, *laevis*. Animals that live in hollows in the seaweed's stem typically develop into this type.

Patella ulyssiponensis

GMELIN, 1791
china limpet

D: up to 55mm. S: oval, fairly flat shell. O: coarse, radial ribs, interspersed with finer riblets. Rough exterior, partly because of small scales often found where the ribs and growth rings intersect. C: chalky white to yellowish-gray. Muscle scar within is bright orange-yellow. H: d1; littoral of rocky coasts. W: KEL, LUS. R: 1.

Patella vulgata

LINNAEUS, 1758
common European limpet

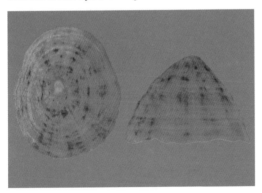

D: 60mm. S: cap-shaped shell with a pointed apex. Length-height ratio varies. The shell perimeter adapts to the shape of the substrate. O: thick, radial ribs run from the apex, interspersed with finer riblets. C: exterior gray to yellowish-green with dark stripes. Matt yellowish-

green interior with a shiny, horseshoe-shaped muscle scar. H: d1; the animals live suckered fast to a hard substrate from the littoral to the sublittoral. W: KEL, LUS. R: 1. NB: the best-known European limpet.

Scutellastra cochlear

(VON BORN, 1778)
spoon limpet

D: 60mm. S: relatively thick shell. Outline roughly spoon or pear-shaped. O: coarse ribs. C: exterior grayish-white to brown. Interior: orange-yellow in the center with a dark muscle scar. H: d1; littoral and sublittoral. W: ZAFR. R: 3.

Scutellastra longicosta

(LAMARCK, 1819)
long-ribbed limpet

D: 80mm. S: spiral ribs run from the apex to project far beyond the average circumference of the shell. O: finer riblets between the primary ribs. C: exterior brown, chalky. Interior has a porcelaneous lining edged in black. H: d1; rocky coasts. W: ZAFR. R: 2.

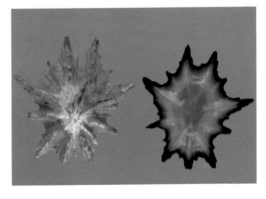

Scutellastra mexicana

(BRODERIP & SOWERBY, 1829)
giant Mexican limpet

D: up to 350mm, usually smaller. S: extremely large and thick shell. O: approximately ten wider ribs between which run more delicate ribs. C: grayish-white to chalky white, apex often abraded. Shiny, pale pink to white interior. H: d1; along rocky coasts in the sublittoral. W: PAN. R: 2. NB: the largest *Patella*. Sought after by collectors.

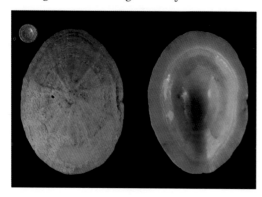

NACELLOIDEA

THIELE, 1891
Shells are often thin, sometimes translucent. Oviform in outline, tapering slightly toward the anterior. Apex close to the anterior edge. One family with few species.

Nacellidae

THIELE, 1891
metallic limpets, ribbed limpets

The family contains two genera. The genus *Cellana* (ribbed limpets) occurs in the Indo-Pacific zone. These species have strong and often clearly ribbed shells. The genus *Nacella* (metallic limpets) occurs in the Antarctic zone and in particular contains species that have thin shells with shiny metallic (iridescent) interiors.

Cellana radians

(GMELIN, 1791)
common New Zealand limpet

D: 45mm. S: almost circular shell. Apex lies off-center, often abraded. O: fairly leveled ribs, equidistant from each other. C: grayish-white, with somewhat darker ribs. Gleaming nacreous-white interior, gray muscle scar. H: d1;

rocks in littoral and sublittoral. W: AUS; New Zealand. R: 1.

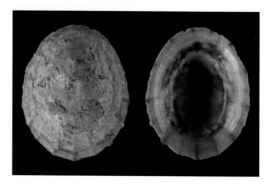

Nacella concinna

(STREBEL, 1908)
south polar limpet

D: 50mm. S: oval, fairly flat shell. O: fairly level ribbing. C: grayish-brown with brown rays of color. Shiny rusty-brown or chocolate brown interior. H: d1; intertidal zone to depth of 100m. W: MAG. R: 2.

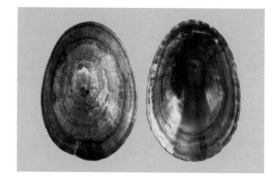

ACMAEOIDEA

CARPENTER, 1857
In terms of shell features, these look like representatives of Patelloidea. Interior porcelaneous, often colored. Behavior like that of Patellidae, but exists at greater depths. Occurs worldwide.

Acmaeidae

CARPENTER, 1857
true limpets (tide pools)

Most shells rather flattened, plate or cap-shaped. Species can be smooth as well as delicately or coarsely ribbed. Interior rim usually has a defined color unlike the rest of the interior, which, as with many Patellidae, has a white porcelaneous glaze. 2 subfamilies: Acmaeinae Carpenter, 1857 and Pectinodontinae Pilsbry, 1891. A few genera: *Acmaea* en *Pectinodonta*.

Acmaea saccharina

(LINNAEUS, 1758)
sugar limpet

D: 35mm. S: fairly flat profile, jagged outline. O: 7–9 wide radial ribs with subtler riblets in between. C: chalky, grayish-white with irregular patches or ribs contrasting in color. Interior white, rim and muscle scar dark brown. H: d1; rocky coasts. W: INDP. R: 1.

Lepetidae

J.E. GRAY, 1850
true limpets (deep-water)

Small, usually almost colorless, saucer or cap-shaped limpets with thin shells. Smooth or lightly ribbed surface. Animals without eyes. Particularly in the Arctic and in deeper water. 2 subfamilies: Lepetinae J.E. Gray, 1842 and Propilidiinae Thiele, 1892. Several genera, including: *Iothia, Lepeta, Propilidium*.

Lepeta caeca

(O.F. MÜLLER, 1776)
northern deep-water limpet

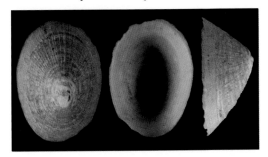

D: up to 16mm. S: oval, apex slightly indented. O: extremely subtle radial riblets. C: milky-white to cream. White interior. H: d2–3; in deeper water on hard substrates. W: ARC, KEL, LUS. In the southern part of these zones in deep, cold water. R: 3.

Lottiidae

J.E. GRAY, 1840
lid limpets

Unlike the preceding groups the micro-sculpture of these species is composed not of foliaceous shell structures, but of prismatic, checkered, plate-like structures (lamellae). As in Acmaeidae, the shell interior has a porcelaneous glaze instead of an iridescent one. Subdivided into three subfamilies: Lottiinae J.E. Gray, 1840; Patelloidinae Chapman & Gabriel, 1923 and Phodopetalinae Lindberg, 1981. Together these include a variety of genera, such as: *Collisella, Discurria, Erginus, Lottia, Notoacmea, Patelloida, Potamacmaea, Rhodopetala, Scurria, Tectura*.

Lottia gigantea

(SOWERBY, 1834)
giant owl limpet

D: 80mm. S: large, flat, oval shell with apex fairly close to one side. O: flattened radial ribs. C: patchily patterned exterior, often covered in concretions. Interior white to pale blue, oval scar and dark brown shell rim. H: d1. W: CAL. R: 4.

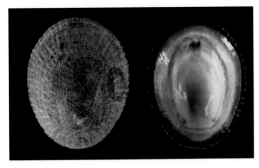

Scurria mesoleuca

(MENKE, 1851)
half-white limpet

D: 80mm. S: oval, thin shell. Fairly flattened profile. O: fairly narrow, radiating ribs. C: grayish-brown, the ribs radiate intermittently to form patches of white. Glazed pale blue or white interior, brownish-blue rim. Muscle scar gray or brown. H: d1; littoral of rocky coasts. W: PAN. R: 4.

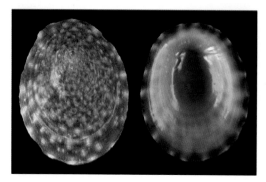

Scurria zebrina

(LESSON, 1831)
zebra limpet

D: 50mm. S: oval, fairly low profile, often with a rather flattened apex. O: approximately 12 wide, robust ribs. C: exterior grayish-brown, often covered in concretions. Interior pale white glaze, often with a brown scar. H: d1; littoral of rocky coasts. W: PER; Chile. R: 4.

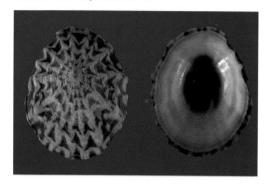

Tectura testudinalis

(O.F. MÜLLER, 1776)
tortoise-shell limpet

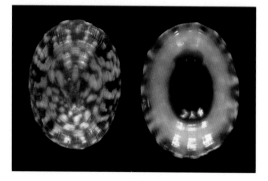

D: up to 20mm. S: oval shell. Apex between the shell's center point and rim. O: very delicate, radial ribs. Appear smooth to the eye. C: grayish-blue with distinct red and dark brown markings in jagged lines and checkered patches. Inner edge also displays brown markings. Dark chocolate brown muscle scar. White, porcelaneous interior surrounding this. H: d1; littoral and sublittoral of rocky coasts, especially on rocks where there are no true limpets. W: ARC, KEL; circumpolar. R: 2.

Tectura virginea

(O.F. MÜLLER, 1776)
pink limpet

D: 10mm. S: small, fairly flattened profile with a relatively truncated apex. O: smooth surface without radial ribs, only growth rings. C: yellowish-white to pale pink. Brownish-pink striping radiating from the apex. H: d2; the animals live along rocky coasts on rocks and on encrusted red kelp. Their food comprises algae and detritus. W: KEL, LUS. R: 3.

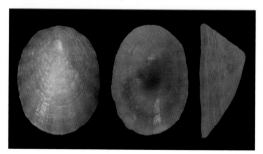

Other limpet species without apical holes or rim notches

In addition to the shallow-water true limpets, tide-pool true limpets, and other limpets discussed above, without holes in the apex or notches in the shell rim, that mostly live in the littoral or occur in relatively shallow water, there are also other groups with a similar shell structure. For example, as well as some fossil families, the suborder Lepetopsina McLean, 1990, also contains the family Neolepetopsidae McLean, 1990, with species that are known only at depths of some thousands of meters in the sulfurous surroundings of hydrothermal vents. The opportunities for collectors to acquire such specimens are limited. Groups of limpet-like shells not easily obtained by collectors also occur in the next subclass, Orthogastropoda. In almost all cases, these relate to the smallest, rather colorless and fragile, limpet-like species, which display distinct adaptations peculiar to their lifestyles. For example, most of the species from the family Cocculinidae Dall, 1882, live on sunken wood at great depths. Many other groups are known about only or largely in the deep sea and in areas with hydrothermal spring activity close to the Galapagos Rift, the East Pacific Ridge, the northern coast of California, and the coast of Florida at depths of between 2500 and 3500m or more. In particular, this concerns species from the families: Addisoniidae Dall, 1882; Bathyphytophilidae Moskalev, 1978; Bathysciadiidae Moskalev, 1978; Bathysciadiidae Dautzenberg & H. Fischer, 1900; Choristellidae Bouchet & Warén, 1979; Cocculinellidae Moskalev, 1971; Cyathermiidae McLean, 1990; Lepetellidae Dall, 1882; Neomphalidae McLean, 1981; Osteopeltidae Marshall, 1987; Peltospiridae McLean, 1989; Pseudococculinidae Hickman, 1983; Pyropeltidae McLean & Haszprunar, 1987.

SUBCLASS ORTHOGASTROPODA

PONDER & LINDBERG, 1996

According to recent opinion, only the limpet species dealt with previously come under the subclass Eogastropoda. All other snails, including various other groups with cap-shaped or limpet-like shells, come under the subclass Orthogastropoda, which is further divided into superorders, orders, suborders, and infraorders.

PLEUROTOMARIOIDEA

SWAINSON, 1840

Probably the oldest group of snails in the history of their lineage. Known as far back as the Cambrian, approximately 600 million years ago. These shells can be conical with several whorls. The aperture's outer lip contains an incision, or slit, that remains visible on the whorls as a groove. Alternatively, these shells exhibit a row of holes that gradually close as the shell grows.

Pleurotomariidae

SWAINSON, 1840
slit shells

Conical in shape and quite large (up to 200mm). The snail carries a corneous operculum. An incision known as the "slit" occurs toward the top of the outer lip. A group of "living fossils" that once was thought to have become extinct. It was only in 1856 that they were fished up alive for the first time from deep water in the Caribbean. There are only a few living species, all of them in deep water (between 200 and 3000m), in the western Atlantic Ocean, the

Caribbean, around South Africa, the Fiji Islands, New Zealand, and Australia. They are known in particular for being valuable and much prized collectors' objects. Only a few (modern-day) genera, including: *Entemnotrochus*, *Mikadotrochus*, *Perotrochus*.

Perotrochus hirasei

(PILSBRY, 1903)
the emperor's slit shell, Hirase's slit shell

D: 100mm. S: thick, conical shell with 8–10 whorls. Slit below the middle of the final whorl. O: undulating, granulose spiral ribs. C: orange-red streaked pattern. Aperture and area around the umbilicus has a greenish-white nacreous luster. H: d3; in deep water. W: JAP. R: 4. NB: the least rare of the slit shells.

Perotrochus westralis

(WHITEHEAD, 1987)
pale slit shell

D: 65mm. S: conical, fairly thin shell, with 8-9 whorls. Slit in the middle of the final whorl. O: has very indistinct, level spiral lines and growth lines. C: pale grayish-white with indistinct yellowish-orange patches. H: d3; in deep water. W: AUS. R: 4.

Scissurellidae

J.E. GRAY, 1847
scissurelles, dwarf slit shells

Only a few millimeters in size, these conical shells have 3–4 whorls. Thin shells. Usually with axial and spiral ornamentation. White, sometimes with a thin lining of nacre inside. With umbilicus. The outer lip has a slit that closes from behind (and sometimes from the front as well) and is visible on the whorls as a groove. Hornlike (corneous) operculum. Worldwide distribution, including cold waters, from the intertidal zone to the abyssal zone. Divided into several subfamilies, including Scissurellinae J.E. Gray, 1847, and the Sutilizoninae McLean, 1989. Various genera, including: *Anatoma, Incisura, Scissurella, Sinezona, Sutilizona, Temnocinclis, Woodwardia.*

Anatoma aetherica

(MELVILL & STANDEN, 1903)
Arabian dwarf slit shell

D: 1.3mm. S: exceptionally thin shell. Slit in the middle of the final whorl. O: delicate checkered patterning of axial ribs and spirals. Faintly scaled at intersections. C: white. H: d3; in deep water. W: INDP; Arabian Sea. R: 4. NB: photo right, the related *Scissurella rota* Yaron, 1983 (same occurrence).

HALIOTIOIDEA

RAFINESQUE, 1815

Haliotidae

RAFINESQUE, 1815
abalones (ear-shells, ormers)

An unmistakable family. Robust shells with 2–3 whorls, the last of which grows into a very large "ear." Contains a row of round indents, or holes, which remain open only on the most recent part of the shell. No operculum. In all species, the interior displays a distinctive mother-of-pearl lining (nacre), from silvery white to greenish-red. The animals live firmly suckered to rocks from the sublittoral to depths of many tens of meters. Approximately 100 species worldwide. Considered a delicacy. Mother-of-pearl much used in jewelry. Only one genus: *Haliotis.*

Haliotis asinina

LINNAEUS, 1758
donkey's-ear abalone

D: 80–100mm. S: elongated, relatively thin shell with 6–7 quite large, oval holes. O: concentric growth lines and fairly widely spaced, intermittent, flattened ribs. C: matt olive green with light and dark patches and stripes. Greenish-white nacreous interior, sometimes with shades of pink and yellowish-green. H: d1; sublittoral. W: INDP. R: 1.

Haliotis australis

GMELIN, 1791
austral abalone

D: 80mm. S: oval, relatively thin shell with 6–7 open holes. O: undulating ribs ranging from indistinct to clear, particularly visible in the interior nacre. C: beige to greenish-brown. Interior

nacre silvery white. H: d1; sublittoral. W: AUS; New Zealand. R: 2. NB: the Maoris call this species and *H. iris* "Paua" (ear).

Haliotis corrugata

WOOD, 1828
pink abalone

D: 150–200mm. S: large, round, thick shell with quite large, round puckered openings. 3–4 holes that are open. O: curved, robust, irregularly beaded ribs. C: dark green to reddish-brown. Nacreous interior, greenish-red and silver. H: d1; sublittoral. W: CAL. R: 1.

D: 250mm. S: oblique oval shell with short, slightly flattened apex. 5–7 slightly raised, open holes. O: robust, round, slightly raised ribs. C: dark brown to greenish-brown. Thick interior nacre, bluish-green. H: d1; sublittoral. W: CAL. R: 1.

Haliotis gigantea

GMELIN, 1791
Japanese giant abalone

D: 200mm. S: large, angular shell. Holes quite protuberant, with 4–5 of these actually open. O: fairly robust, concentric growth lines and quite widely spaced, flattened ribs. C: gray-green with light and dark, red and green patches and stripes. Interior nacre in shades of white, pink and yellowish-green. H: d1; sublittoral. W: JAP. R: 2.

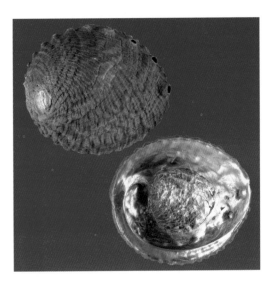

Haliotis fulgens

PHILIPPI, 1845
green abalone

Haliotis iris

GMELIN, 1791
rainbow abalone

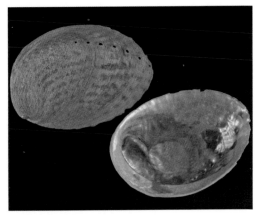

D: 170mm. S: large, rounded oval, fairly thick shell. Openings virtually circular, 6–7 open. O: clearly undulating, spiral ridges, especially on lower edge. C: greenish-brown, very dark green nacre inside. H: d1; sublittoral. W: AUS; New Zealand. R: 2.

Haliotis mariae

WOOD, 1828
Arabian abalone

D: 100mm. S: rounded, oval, fairly thick shell with slightly raised holes, 6 or 7 of which are actually open. O: several wide, flattened spiral ribs and irregularly undulating, nodulosenodulose axial ribs. C: pink, beige to brown, in irregular patches. Interior silver-green nacre. H: d1; sublittoral. W: INDP; Oman. R: 4. NB: edible.

Haliotis midae

LINNAEUS, 1758
Midas abalone

D: 180mm. S: rounded oval, thick, rather flattened shell. Up to 9 round, elevated holes. O: ornamented with wavy, raised ribs that give the shell a crumpled appearance. C: exterior muted, pale pink. Interior has thick green to silver-blue nacre. H: d1; sublittoral. W: ZAFR. R: 3.

Haliotis rubra

LEACH, 1814
ruber abalone

D: 150mm. S: rounded, oval shell. 5–6 slightly elevated holes. O: ornamented with round, tightly packed, irregularly spiraling riblets. C: muted to dark orange-red. Interior silver-green nacre. H: d1; littoral and sublittoral. W: AUS. R: 3.

Haliotis scalaris

(LEACH, 1814)
staircase abalone

D: 100mm. S: rounded oval shell, rather flattened. 5–6 open, elevated holes. The rest are closed. O: ornamented with 3 curved, thick-

ened spiral ribs that are also clearly visible on the inside. C: red-brown with dark red patches, especially at the edges. Interior very iridescent, bright silver-white nacre. H: d1; sublittoral. W: AUS. R: 3. NB: much sought-after collector's item.

Haliotis tuberculata tuberculata

LINNAEUS, 1758
green ormer

D: 110mm. S: rather flattened, oval shell. Several holes, at least 6–8 of which are open. O: tightly packed, undulating, spiral ridges and grooves, crossed by irregular growth lines. C: exterior red-brown, often with a green upper layer. Interior nacre darkens toward the muscle scar. H: d1; sublittoral. W: KEL, LUS; the English Channel is the northern limit. R: 2. NB: a subspecies from the Mediterranean Sea has thicker ribs and is smaller. Eaten in France and other countries.

LEPETODRILLOIDEA

MCLEAN, 1988
thermal limpets

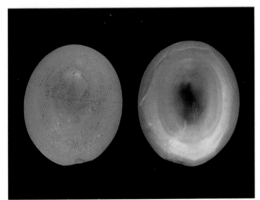

Cap-shaped shells from the deep sea around boiling vents in the eastern Pacific Ocean. Families: Gorgoleptidae McLean, 1988; Lepetodrillidae McLean, 1988. Rarely if ever in private collections. The species shown is *Lepetodrilus ovalis* McLean, 1988, found at a depth of 2633m (East Pacific Rise, 21°(N) (Zoological Museum, Amsterdam).

FISSURELLOIDEA

FLEMING, 1822
Limpet-like. There is a slit or incision in the anterior rim. There is an anal opening either in the apex of the shell or within that area, which can take several forms. The hole is often keyhole-shaped, but can be round, oval, elongated, more constricted, or divided in two by a septum. These shells often have latticed ornamentation. White or colored interior porcelaneous. No operculum. Residents of the littoral and sublittoral. Worldwide distribution, especially in warmer seas.

Fissurellidae

FLEMMING, 1822
keyhole limpets

A large family with several subfamilies and many genera. There are a few basic types. Many species have cap-shaped shells with a round, oval, or triangular hole in the apex. Subfamilies: Diodorinae Wenz, 1938; Fissurellidinae Pilsbry, 1890; Fissurellinae Fleming, 1822. Other species have a more elevated shell, often with an overhanging, usually unperforated apex, although usually with a slit at the edge of the shell (subfamily Emarginulinae J.E. Gray, 1834, with the exception of *Clypidina*). Other species again have an extremely flattened cap shape with only a slight indentation in the shell posterior (subfamily Scutinae Christiaens, 1973). Includes the following genera: *Clypidina, Cremides, Diodora, Emarginella, Emarginula, Fissurella, Fissurellidea, Fissurisepta, Foralepas, Hemitoma, Leurolepas, Lucapina, Macroschisma, Megathura, Montfortula, Nesta, Puncturella, Pupillaea, Rimula, Scutus, Stromboli, Tugali, Zeidora.*

Diodora aspera

(RATHKE, 1833)
rough keyhole limpet

D: up to 60mm. S: oval shell with oval hole about a third off the posterior edge of the shell. O: rough radial ribs and finer concentric markings. C: gray-white, with darker, mauve-colored stripes. H: d1; littoral and sublittoral, often on brown kelp. W: CAL, PAN. R: 1.

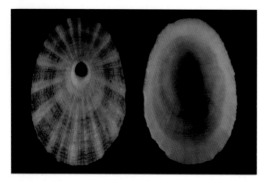

Diodora calyculata

(SOWERBY, 1823)
cup keyhole limpet

D: 20mm. S: oval shell. A septum inside the shell under the keyhole. O: defined, radial ribs. C: reddish-white striping. H: d1; sublittoral, under rocks. W: ZAFR. R: 1.

Diodora graeca

(LINNAEUS, 1758)
Greek keyhole limpet

D: 20mm. S: oval shell. Keyhole-shaped hole. Domed shell base. O: delicate, net-like ornamentation. C: cream to yellowish-white with darker stripes. H: d1; sublittoral under rocks. W: KEL, LUS, WAFR. R: 2.

Diodora italica

(DEFRANCE, 1820)
Italian keyhole limpet

D: 45mm. S: rather flattened, oval shell. Shell rim clearly notched by ribs. O: nodulose-nodulose, net-like lattice ornament. C: variable: simply cream or olive-green, often with rays of color since some ribs have the same coloration. Interior white or greenish sheen. H: d1; littoral and sublittoral, under rocks. W: LUS, WAFR. R: 1.

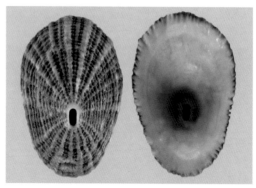

Diodora listeri

(D'ORBIGNY, 1842)
Lister's keyhole limpet

D: 30mm. S: elongated oval shell. Serrated edge, clear keyhole. O: defined, lattice ornament. C: gray-white. Hole sometimes outlined in black. Interior whitish, sometimes with a blue sheen. H: d1; sublittoral under rocks. W: CAR. R: 1.

Emarginula octaviana

COEN, 1939
sugar-kelp emarginula

D: 45mm. S: rather flattened shell. Apex re-treating, curved over backward slightly. Clear slit in shell rim. O: net-like ornament. C: white exterior and interior, translucent. H: d1; littoral and sublittoral, under rocks and on kelp from the genus *Laminaria*. W: KEL, LUS, WAFR. R: 2.

Fissurella barbadensis

(GMELIN, 1791)
Barbados keyhole limpet

D: up to 25mm. S: oval shell. Hole in shape of figure 8 about a quarter of the total width from the posterior side of the shell. O: fairly coarse, irregularly spaced, radial ribs. C: exterior variable, interior typically emerald green (entirely or with a green edge). H: d1; littoral and sublittoral, on rocks. W: CAR, INDP; southeastern Florida, West Indies. R: 1.

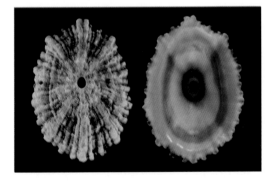

Fissurella maxima

SOWERBY, 1835
grand keyhole limpet

D: 100mm. S: large, heavy shell. Relatively flat-tened. Oval hole in apex. O: flattened ribs and growth rings. C: yellowish-brown with radiating, dark brown stripes created by several similarly colored ribs. Interior white with mauve muscle scar. H: d1; sublittoral. W: PER; Peru, Chile. R: 2.

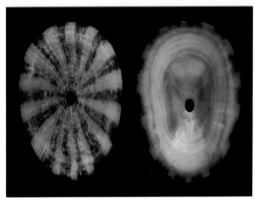

Fissurella nodosa

(VON BORN, 1778)
knobbly keyhole limpet

D: 30mm. S: irregularly shaped shell. Relatively narrow, keyhole-shaped hole in apex. O: coarse, wide, nodulose, radial ribs. Interior has distinctive notching at shell rim. C: white to brown. H: d1; under rocks in sublittoral. W: CAR; southeastern Florida, West Indies. R: 1.

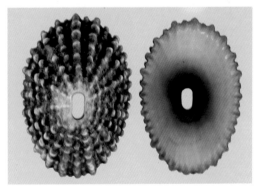

Fissurella nubecula

(LINNAEUS, 1758)
cloudy keyhole limpet

D: 25mm. S: rather flattened, pear-shaped oval shell. O: somewhat flattened ribs, some coarser than others, hardly intersected by concentric ornament, or not at all. C: greenish-gray with purplish-pink, radiating bands of color, some-times interrupted, consisting of patches of cor-responding, similarly colored ribs. H: d1; lower littoral and sublittoral, under rocks. W: KEL,

LUS, WAFR (principally Mediterranean). R: 1.

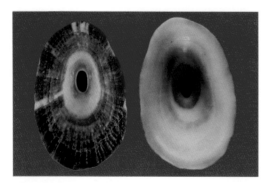

Fissurella rosea

(GMELIN, 1791)
rosy keyhole limpet

D: 20mm. S: almost elliptical shape, hole oval. O: coarse radial ornament. C: chalky white with pinkish-red stripes radiating from the apex. Interior green around the hole, often with a red edge. H: d1; sublittoral on rocks. W: CAR; West Indies. R: 1.

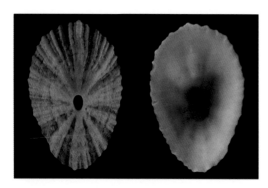

Fissurella virescens

SOWERBY, 1835
green Panama keyhole limpet

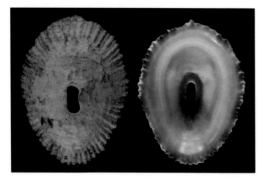

D: 50mm. S: thick shell, oval outline. Sunken keyhole-shaped hole. O: fairly coarse, irregular ribs. C: exterior chalky white, inside bottle green. H: d1; sublittoral on rocks. W: PAN, PER; including around the Galapagos Islands. R: 2.

Megathura crenulata

(SOWERBY, 1825)
great keyhole limpet

D: up to 120mm. S: extremely large shell with a relatively large, oval hole. Delicately crenulated edge. O: delicate, narrow, radial ribs. C: yellowish-brown, interior porcelain-white. H: d1; rocky coasts. W: CAL, CAR. R: 2. NB: among the largest of species with an apex keyhole.

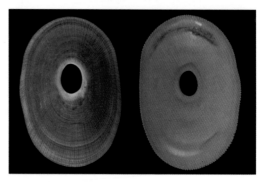

Scutus australis

LAMARCK, 1822
duck shield limpet

D: up to 110mm. S: flat, elongated oval, shield-like shell with a slight curve at the anterior edge. O: concentric striping. C: yellowish-white, interior porcelain-white. H: d1–2; littoral and sublittoral, under rocks and in rocky crevices. W: AUS. R: 2. NB: the animal is quite large, dark, and with a trunk-like extended head.

TROCHOIDEA

RAFINESQUE, 1815
Shells usually pointed and cone-shaped, roughly like a spinning top (seen upside down). Often with an iridescent, nacreous lining in the aperture. The exterior is also often brilliantly colored. The operculum can be corneous or composed of calcium (Turbinidae). The animals live mostly on algae, diatoms, or polyps. Many species live in the intertidal zone, while others live at greater depths. Species from the families Pendromidae, Skeneidae, and Trochclididae have extremely small shells. Worldwide, hundreds of well-known, large and smaller species are represented within the families Trochidae and Turbinidae.

Pendromidae

WARÉN, 1991
Micro-mollusks with extremely small top-shaped shells from deep water. Genus: *Rugulina* Palazzi, 1988.

Skeneidae

CLARK, 1851
dwarf top shells

Micro-mollusks with small shells (a few millimeters in size) that are colorless, top or disk-shaped. Surface often smooth or with extremely fine spiral ornament. No nacre. Aperture round. With operculum. Worldwide from the intertidal to the abyssal zone. Often difficult to identify species in the various genera, which include: *Anekes, Brookula, Cirsonella, Crossea, Dikoleps, Leptogyra, Lissomphalia, Lissotesta, Lodderia, Moelleriopsis, Parviturbo, Pondorbis, Protolira, Putilla, Retigyra, Skenea, Skeneoides, Solutigyra, Xyleptogyra, Xyloskenea.*

Trochaclididae

THIELE, 1928
Micro-mollusks with extremely small shells (1–3mm). Can be distinguished only by the radula.

Trochidae

RAFINESQUE, 1815
top shells

Familiar, large and varied family with many genera and species. Ranging from a few millimeters to over 125mm. Operculum corneous and round with a central nucleus (multi-spiral). Several subfamilies have been identified by such distinctions as the shape of the radula. Representatives of the subfamily Calliostomatinae Thiele, 1924, painted top shells, have a pointed apex and straight sides. The aperture is angular. With or without umbilicus. The inner lip is sometimes thickened, covering the umbilicus. Often delicate or coarser spiral lines. Worldwide range from the littoral to the deep sea. Genera include: *Astele, Calliostoma, Maurea, Otukaia, Photinula, Venustatrochus.* Cataeginae McLean & Quinn, 1987. Caribbean zone in deeper water. Genus Cataegis. Various recent and fossil genera belong to the subfamily Eucyclinae Koken, 1897, including: *Bathybembix, Calliotropus, Cidarina, Convexia, Danila, Euchelus, Ginebris, Herpetopoma, Lischkeia, Mirachelus, Putzeysia, Tallorbis, Turcica.* Worldwide range from the littoral to the abyssal zone. The subfamily Halistylinae Keen, 1958 mostly contains small, cylindrical to cone-shaped shells without an umbilicus. Genera: *Botelloides, Charisma, Fucaria, Halistylus.* Lirulariinae Hickman & McLean, 1990. Genus *Lirularia*. The subfamily Margaritinae Stoliczka, 1868 contains compressed, top-shaped, thin shells up to 20mm in size. Thickly nacreous apertures. Smooth or ornamented with an umbilicus. Especially in northern waters. Genera include: *Gaza, Kaiparathina, Margarites.* The subfamily Solariellinae Powell, 1951 mostly contains smaller top-shaped shells (up to 10mm in size) with rounded whorls and a wide umbilicus. From smooth to distinct ornament. Particularly in deeper, colder waters. Genera include: *Archiminolia, Ethaliopsis, Ilanga, Lamellitrochus, Microgaza, Minolia, Minolops, Solariella, Spectamen, Suavotrochus, Zetela.* The subfamily Stomatellinae J.E. Gray, 1840 (false abalone) contains species with an ear-shaped, expanded shell with mother-of-pearl, which looks like a shell from the Haliotidae family, although without a row of holes. No operculum. Intertidal zone and deeper, on rocks. Genera: *Gena, Pseudostomatella, Stomatella, Stomatia.* The subfamily Tegulinae Kuroda, Habe & Oyama, 1971 contains thick, cone-shaped shells with a convex side profile. Rectangular aperture, level base. Umbilicus often covered by a columellar fold. Inner lip with one or more toothed folds. Genera: *Norrissia, Tegula.* The subfamily Thysanodontinae Marshall, 1988 contains deep-water species: robust, cone-shaped shells with circular whorls and spiral ornamentation. The uppermost whorls are often granulose. Genera: *Carinastele, Herbertina, Thysanodonta.* The subfamily Trochinae Rafinesque, 1815 contains many genera and species, including those best known. Small to large, cone- or top-shaped shells, either with or without an umbilicus. Ornament varies: smooth, or with spirals, nodules, and other decoration. Nacreous interior. Aperture round or rectangular with sharp edges. Toothed inner lip or ending in a nodule. Worldwide range: littoral to sublittoral, on rocks, seaweed, and sea grass. Genera include: *Alcyna, Calthalotia, Cantharidella, Cantha-*

ridus, Chrysostoma, Cittarium, Clanculus, Diloma, Fossarina, Gibbula, Jujubinus, Margarella, Micrelenchus, Monodonta, Nanula, Notogibbula, Phasianotrochus, Priotrochus, Prothalotia, Tectus, Thalotia, Trochus. The subfamily Umboniinae H. & A. Adams, 1854 contains either small, lens-shaped, flattened shells with an umbilicus covered by a white callus (genus *Umbonium*) or else small, extremely pointed shells (genus *Bankivia*).

Astele bullara

GARRARD, 1968
Australian umbilicus top

D: up to 35mm. S: thin shell, whorls in a virtually straight line, often with a very slight keel. Angular aperture. Deep umbilicus. O: delicate spirals that are covered below the sutures in very slight beads. C: cream-colored, apex greenish-yellow, vague, patchy red pattern. H: d1–2. W: AUS. R: 4. NB: the genus *Astele* differs from *Calliostoma* by having an umbilicus.

Bathybembix argenteonitens

(LISCHKE, 1872)
silvery margarite

D: up to 80mm. S: thin shell, with fairly straight sides. O: one nodulose spiral and some flattened spirals on the final whorl. C: beautiful mother-of-pearl on exterior and interior. H: d2–3. W: JAP. R: 3. NB: greatly sought-after by collectors.

Calliostoma annulatum

(LIGHTFOOT, 1786)
ringed top

D: 25mm. S: shell taller than it is wide, nearly straight sides. Angular aperture. O: spiral ornament covered in small, bead-like nodules. C: creamy white, two mauve spirals run around the sutures. H: d1–2. W: CAL. R: 2.

Calliostoma formosensis

E.A. SMITH, 1907
Formosa top

D: up to 60mm. S: large, relatively thin shell. Whorls with slight shoulders. O: spirals covered in tiny, bead-like nodules. Spiral more defined around sutures, forming a keel. C: yellowish-white with patches of orange-red patterning. H: d2–3; deep water. W: INDP; Taiwan. R: 3. NB: sought-after by collectors.

Calliostoma granulatum

(VON BORN, 1778)
European granular top

D: up to 35mm. S: extremely pointed apex, straight-sided whorls. O: regularly interspaced spiral ribs on all whorls covered in small, round beads. Dominant spiral rib around the periphery (body whorl's basal edge). C: yellowish-orange with irregular red-orange patches. H: d1–2. W: KEL, LUS. R: 3. NB: well-known European species.

Calliostoma ligatum

(GOULD, 1849)
western ribbed top

D: up to about 25mm. S: thick shell, rather stepped whorls. O: wide and narrow, irregular spiral ornament. Lamella ornament between the ribs. C: cream to light brown, darker between the ribs or purplish-brown. Sometimes flecked in pink. H: d1–2. W: ALE, CAL. R: 1.

Calliostoma monile

(REEVE, 1863)
Australian necklace or monile top

D: up to 25mm. S: relatively tall shell with straight sides. O: fine spiral ornament with one very wide spiral at base of whorls forming a keel.

C: yellowish-white to orange, wide spiral checkered in alternate white and crimson spots. H: d1–2. W: AUS. R: 4.

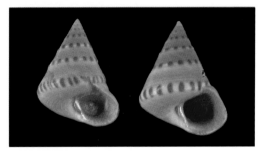

Calliostoma zizyphinum

(LINNAEUS, 1758)
European painted top

D: up to about 30mm. S: about as tall as it is wide. Extremely pointed apex. Up to 12 straight-sided whorls. Rhomboid aperture, no clear umbilicus. O: 5–7 spirals. Sometimes almost smooth with one more defined spiral rib around the periphery. Sometimes slight beading on the first whorls. C: yellowish-white, orange, pink to purple, lowest spiral rib often checkered. Thick nacreous lining in aperture. H: d1; under rocks in the littoral and sublittoral. W: KEL, LUS. R: 1.

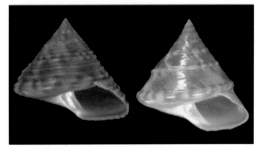

Cantharidus opalus

(MARTYN, 1784)
opal jewel top

D: up to 45mm. S: conical, pointed shell with straight sides. Angular aperture. O: smooth with slight growth lines. C: pale gray with reddish-brown zigzag stripes. Greenish-blue nacre in aperture. H: d2; on seaweed. W: AUS; New Zealand. R: 2.

Cittarium pica

(LINNAEUS, 1758)
West Indian top

D: 70mm. S: extremely thick and heavy, conical shell with rather bulging whorls. Deep umbilicus. O: extremely flat spirals. C: grayish-white with purplish-black patches and axial stripes. Operculum round and corneous. H: d1; sublittoral under large rocks and on reefs. W: CAR. R: 1. NB: eaten in the Caribbean, especially in soup.

Clanculus corallinus

(GMELIN, 1791
red clanculus

D: up to about 10mm. S: robust, rounded, conical shell. Bud- or plate-like teeth in inner lip, also folded teeth at the base of, and elsewhere in, the aperture. Umbilicus cleft-like. O: regularly interspaced spiral ribs, clearly covered in round nodules. C: dark red to chocolate brown with irregular paler patches. Callus, aperture lip, and columellar teeth gleam white. H: d1–2; under rocks along rocky coasts. W: LUS. R: 1.

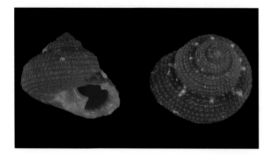

Clanculus pharaonius

(LINNAEUS, 1758)
mantle clanculus

D: up to 20mm. S: robust, rounded, conical shell. Bud- or plate-like teeth in inner lip, also folded teeth at the base of, and elsewhere in, the aperture. Umbilicus cleft-like. O: regularly interspaced spiral ribs, covered in bead-like nodules. C: dark rose red. Some spirals checkered alternately with black and white papilla. Callus, aperture lip, and columellar teeth gleam white. H: d1. W: INDP. R: 1. NB: photo right, the species *Clanculus puniceus* (Philippi, 1846) – purplish clanculus. It closely resembles *C. pharaonius* but has 4 spirals with 2–3 red papilla alternating with one black one.

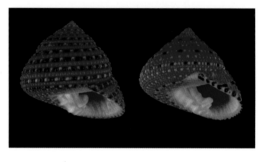

Clanculus stigmatarius

A. ADAMS, 1853
lovely clanculus

D: up to about 25mm. S: small, conical shell. Aperture has many teeth-shaped folds. O: ornamented with alternating wide and narrower spiral ribs covered in round nodules. C: chocolate brown to orange, every fourth spiral bears both pale and dark pink nodules. Callus, aperture, and columellar teeth gleam white. H: d1; on rocks in the littoral. W: INDP. R: 2.

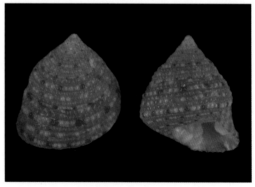

Clanculus undatus

(LAMARCK, 1816)
wavy Australian monodont

D: up to about 35mm. S: large, rather squat, depressed shell. Broad umbilicus. Various tooth-shaped folds in aperture. O: regularly inter-spaced spiral ribs, covered in fairly rough, round nodules. C: (pale) chocolate brown with irregular dark/black nodules. Callus, aperture, and columellar teeth in silver-white nacre. H: d1. W: AUS. R: 3.

Gaza superba

(DALL, 1881)
superb gaza

D: 40mm. S: extremely thin shell. Rounded whorls, deep sutures. Protoconch often broken. Broad umbilicus partly covered by callus. O: smooth with fine growth lines. C: shiny golden green, aperture rim and interior silvery nacre. H: d3–4; deepwater species. W: CAR. R: 4. NB: rare, extremely sought-after collector's item.

Gibbula cineraria

(LINNAEUS, 1758)
gray top

D: 15mm. S: both tall and squat shells. Robust, conical. 5–7 reasonably rounded whorls. Squat apex, angular aperture, round operculum. Deep

umbilicus. O: vague, irregular, spiral grooves crossed by growth lines. C: pale gray with pur-plish-brown patches and stripes. Nacreous aperture. H: d1. W: KEL, LUS. R: 1.

Gibbula fanulum

(GMELIN, 1791)
notched top

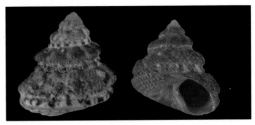

D: 19mm. S: relatively tall shell. Whorls with rounded shoulders. O: fine spiral lines with nodules above the whorls. A broadly scored groove runs under the suture. C: creamy white to pink, patterned with dots, lines and patches. Sometimes in one uniform color. H: d1; in sea grass from the genus *Posidonia*. W: LUS; Por-tugal and Mediterranean Sea. R: 2. NB: sought-after European species.

Gibbula magus

(LINNAEUS, 1758)
nodulose top

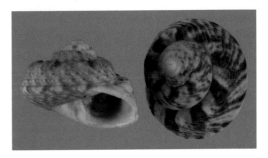

D: 35mm. S: robust shell. Wider than it is tall, 6–7 quite rounded whorls, straightening out at the apex. O: from indistinct spirals to more defined ones. Vague nodules on the shoulder. Pointed apex, rectangular aperture, umbilicus deep and round. C: yellowish-white, pale pink to light brown with reddish-purple streaked pattern. H: d1–2; littoral and sublittoral of rocky coasts. W: KEL, LUS. R: 1.

Gibbula pennanti

(PHILIPPI, 1846)
streaked top

D: 18mm. S: robust, conical shell with moderately full whorls. Squat apex. Umbilicus indistinct or missing. Angular aperture. O: subtle, spiral ridges. C: pale yellow or greenish yellow, with purple or red patches and lines often running diagonally. Outer layer often eroded, revealing the thick nacreous lining. H: d1; littoral of rocky coasts. W: KEL. R: 1. NB: extremely common in Brittany, France. A round umbilicus can be seen clearly in the closely similar *Gibbula umbilicalis* (the umbilical gibbula).

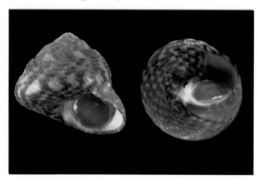

Jujubinus exasperatus

(PENNANT, 1777)
grooved jujubine

D: 9mm. S: robust, conical shell. 6–7 straight-sided whorls. Pointed apex, rectangular aperture with a slight nodule on the columellar side. No umbilicus. O: 4–5 nodulose, spiral ribs, the undermost is widest. Ribs without nodules at the base below the final whorl. C: yellow-orange to purple with dark patches. Apex and groove usually darker. H: d1; sublittoral along rocky coasts. W: KEL, LUS. R: 1.

Lischkeia alwinae

(LISCHKE, 1871)
Alwina's margarite

D: up to about 40mm. S: quite a robust shell composed of mother-of-pearl. Narrow umbilicus, cleft-like. O: granulose spirals and larger, pointed nodules on the whorls. C: creamy white with nacreous aperture. H: d2. W: JAP. R: 3.

Maurea punctulatum

(MARTYN, 1784)
punctate maurea

D: 40mm. S: robust, conical shell with rounded whorls. Oval aperture, cleft-like umbilicus, virtually closed. O: regularly interspaced spiral ribs, covered in round, pustular nodules. C: amber to russet, the nodules on the ribs alternately dark and light. Aperture has gray-white nacre. H: d1; rocky coasts. W: AUS; New Zealand. R: 2.

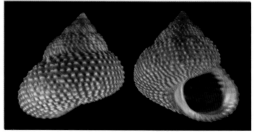

Maurea tigris

(GMELIN, 1791)
tiger maurea

D: up to about 50mm. S: concave shell apex, broad shell base with rounded keel. Rounded whorls, angular aperture. O: fine spiral ornament. C: distinctive brownish-yellow streaks of color. H: d1–2; on rocks, between sea grass. W: AUS; New Zealand. R: 3.

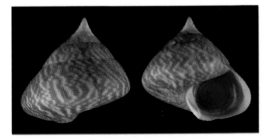

Phasianotrochus eximius

(PERRY, 1811)
green jewel top

D: 40mm. S: extremely pointed shell with straight-sided whorls and an angular aperture. O: shallow but clear spirals. C: greenish-brown or dark brown. Aperture rim and spirals often somewhat lighter. Interior greenish or silver-gray nacre. H: d1; littoral and sublittoral, on seaweed (kelp). W: AUS. R: 1.

Tegula regina

STEARNS, 1892
queen tegula

D: 50mm. S: robust shell with 6–7 straight-sided whorls. Defined keel just overhanging the suture. O: irregular, wavy, axial ribs. Underside has scaly ribs. C: gray-brown with a bright golden stripe around the umbilicus. Silver nacre in aperture. H: d1–2. W: CAL. R: 3.

Trochus niloticus

LINNAEUS, 1767
commercial trochus

D: 140mm. S: very thick and heavy shell with fairly straight-sided whorls and a pointed apex. O: virtually smooth or with nodulose spirals. C: purplish-pink with red-brown, oblique stripes and irregular patches of color. H: d1; sublittoral to a depth of about 20m. Particularly on coral reefs. W: INDP. R: 1. NB: the shell is used in the button-making industry.

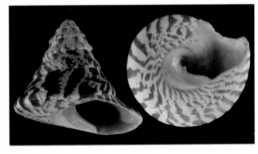

Umbonium giganteum

(LESSON, 1831)
giant button top

D: up to 35mm. S: robust, somewhat flattened shell. Underside covered in a thick, irregular callus. O: indistinct spirals around the periphery. C: variable, often gray-blue with a mottled pattern around the periphery. Underside often slightly pink or yellow. H: d1. W: INDP, JAP. R: 1.

Umbonium moniliferum

(LAMARCK, 1822)
grooved button top

D: 15mm. S: squat, convex shell. Underside covered in thick, irregular callus. O: top of shell with fairly clear spiral grooves. C: either uniformly cream to greenish-yellow, or with irregular pattern of dark brown stripes, dashes, and patches. Callus on underside often uniform cream or pink. H: d1. W: JAP. R: 1.

Umbonium vestiarium

(LINNAEUS, 1758)
common button top

D: 15mm. S: squat, convex shell. O: unlike *U. moniliferum* completely smooth without grooves. C: as for *U. moniliferum*. H: d1. W: INDP. R: 1. NB: much used for decorative purposes (boxes, picture frames).

Turbinidae

RAFINESQUE, 1815
turban shells, and others

Robust, top or cone-shaped, sometimes with extremely thick shells. Smooth or with spiral ornament and sometimes with spines or nodules. Pearly interior. Calcareous operculum grown in a spiral, smooth on the exterior, sometimes colored ("cats-eyes") or ornamented. Angariinae have a corneous operculum. Several subfamilies. The most well-known of these are categorized as follows: shells from the subfamily Angariinae Thiele, 1921 have a rough surface with spines and a corneous operculum. The subfamily Colloniinae Cossmann, 1916 mostly contains micro-mollusks. Columella with a solid layer of calcium. The subfamily Gabrieloninae Hickman & McLean, 1990 contains micro-mollusks, in appearance like moon shells (Naticidae) but with a groove in the aperture into which the operculum fits. The operculum is calcareous with clear ornamentation in the subfamily Liotiinae H. & A. Adams, 1854. The subfamily Moelleriinae Hickman & McLean, 1990 contains micro-mollusks from northern maritime regions with a corneous operculum. The subfamily Prisogasterinae Hickman & McLean, 1990 contains only one genus: *Prisogaster* (Peru). The subfamily Phasianellinae Swainson, 1840 (pheasant shells) contains pointed, conical shells. Smooth or with spirals and with variable coloration. Interior white without nacre. The subfamily Tricoliinae Woodring, 1928 contains small shells, no more than 10mm in size. Pointed, conical shells, smooth or with fine spiral lines (striae), often brightly colored. The subfamily Turbininae Rafinesque, 1815 contains robust, cone or top-shaped shells, usually with rounded whorls. Operculum with a central calcareous nucleus. All together, the family contains dozens of genera, including: *Angaria, Astraea, Astralium, Bolma, Cantrainea, Collonista, Cookia, Cyclostrema, Eugabrielona, Eulithidium, Gabrielona, Guildfordia, Homalopoma, Liotia, Lithopoma, Macrarene, Moelleria, Opella, Phanerolepida, Phasianella, Prisogaster, Tricolia, Turbo*.

Angaria delphinus

(LINNAEUS, 1758)
common delphinula

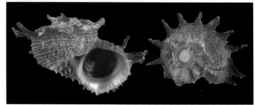

D: 70mm. S: rather squat, thick shell with angular whorls. O: strongly nodulose spirals, developing into spines on whorl shoulders and around the aperture. C: dark brown, red to pale pink. Thick nacreous interior. H: d1; sublittoral on hard substrate. W: INDP. R: 1.

Angaria sphaerula

(KIENER, 1838)
Kiener's delphinula

D: 50mm. S: thick shells. Rather flattened whorls. O: stronger ribs, especially above the body whorl and thick, stunted, spoon-shaped spines. C: red, pink, or orange with thick pearly interior. H: d1–2; specimens with the strongest spines are fished from calmer waters. W: INDP; western part. R: 3.

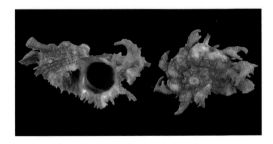

Angaria vicdani

KOSUGE, 1980
Victor Dan's delphinula

D: 50mm. S: very flat-topped spire. Large, broad body whorl. O: very strong spirals below the body whorl, often with spines. C: golden yellow, pink, orange, or red and all shades in between. H: d2–3; usually fished from deeper waters. W: INDP, the Philippines. R: 4. NB: extremely sought-after by collectors.

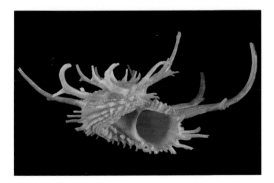

Astraea heliotropium

(MARTYN, 1784)
sunburst star turban

D: 90mm. S: robust, squat shell with a wide, oval aperture and deep umbilicus. O: surface covered in delicate spirals formed by scaly nodules. Wide, triangular, stunted spines below the middle of the whorls. C: yellow-white or silver-gray. Often covered in concretions. H: d3–4; deep water. W: AUS; New Zealand. R: 4.

Astralium rotularia

LAMARCK, 1822
rotary star shell

D: 40mm. S: robust, thickset shell with fairly straight-sided whorls. No umbilicus. O: distinctive ornament with a keel around the periphery of folded, undulating blunt spines. Underside has scaly spirals. C: chalky white to cream. Gray-white nacre in aperture. H: d1; sublittoral of rocky coasts. W: AUS. R: 1.

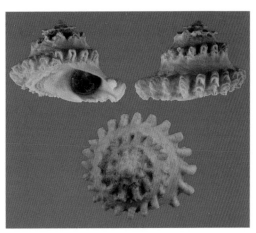

Astralium stellare

(GMELIN, 1791)
blue-mouthed star shell

D: 40mm. S: extremely thick, solid shell with straight-sided whorls and a flattened underside. No true umbilicus, only a vague groove. O: calcareous structure with coarse nodules. Underside has fine, scaly spirals. C: chalky white, sometimes cream. Operculum turquoise to pale blue. Columellar rim is blue. H: d2. W: AUS, INDP. R: 3. NB: one of the few species of shell with blue in its coloration.

Bolma rugosa

(LINNAEUS, 1767)
European turban

D: 40mm. S: squat, conical shell with rounded angular whorls. O: straight-sided spirals covered in scales and nodules. Often rounded ribs on the upper side of whorls. Strong, sometimes sharp shoulder nodules and protuberances. Columellar side has a smooth callus. C: gray-brown to claret colored. Operculum orange-red as is the callus. Aperture with gray-white nacre. H: d1; sublittoral and up to a depth of approx. 50m. W: LUS; Portugal, Mediterranean Sea. R:

2. NB: in the past, orange opercula were highly prized by jewelers. Large quantities of opercula have been found in amphorae in Roman shipwrecks.

Guildfordia aculeata

KOSUGE, 1979
aculeate star turban

D: 40mm. S: deeply flattened, circular shell with an angular aperture. No clear umbilicus. O: spirals of closely aligned bead-like nodules. 8–10 slim, slightly curved, spines around the periphery. C: creamy white to pale yellow. Sometimes pinkish. H: d4; deep water. W: INDP; central areas of the Philippines. R: 3.

Guildfordia yoka

JOUSSEAUME, 1888
yoka star turban

D: 75mm. S: in appearance like the previous species but with considerably longer spines. O: spirals with teardrop-shaped nodules. Underside almost smooth. Spines sometimes as long as the shell. C: amber to pink. H: d4; deep water. W: JAP. R: 2. NB: species from the genus *Guildfordia* are also called "spider shells" because of (usually) having 8 "legs."

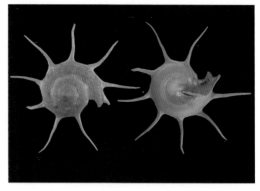

Tricolia pullus

(LINNAEUS, 1758)
European pheasant

D: 9mm. S: moderately robust, conical shell with convex whorls that are widest below the middle of the shell. No clear umbilicus. Thick, calcareous operculum, round to pear-shaped. O: shell surface is smooth. C: extremely varied, brightly colored. Shiny white or pink with rose-red to purple-brown zigzags or streaks. H: d1; sublittoral and deeper, on red kelp, to a depth of approx. 35m. W: KEL, LUS. R: 1.

Turbo chrysostomus

LINNAEUS, 1758
gold-mouth turban

D: 60mm. S: thick shell with rather angular whorls. The aperture is oval, slightly extended at the base. Strongly crenulated outer lip. O: coarse spirals often covered in small scales and, sometimes, nodules. Often a wider, nodulose spiral around the shoulder. Coarser ribs below the middle of the shell than above. C: gray- to yellow-brown, often with dark brown flecks. H: d1; sublittoral along rocky coasts and on reefs. W: INDP. R: 1.

Turbo cinereus

VON BORN, 1778
smooth moon turban

D: 35mm. S: thick shell. Flattened, compressed apex. The aperture is round, stretched at an angle along the base. Large umbilicus. O: smooth spirals, slightly coarser underneath. The shell feels polished. C: gray-green with yellow-white and gray-white mottled spirals. Silver-white aperture. Thick operculum. H: d1; littoral and sublittoral of rocky coasts. W: INDP. R: 1.

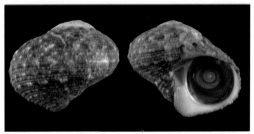

Turbo gruneri

PHILIPPI, 1846
Gruner's turban

D: 40mm. S: thick shell with stepped whorls. No clear operculum. O: strong spirals, especially on the mid- to lower sections. Finer beaded spirals between the whorls. C: amber to orange with dark brown flecks. Silver-gray nacre on aperture rim. H: d2; in deeper water to a depth of approx. 150m. W: AUS. R: 2–3.

Turbo jonathani

DEKKER, MOOLENBEEK & DANCE, 1992
Omani turban

D: 35mm. S: thick shell as tall as it is wide. Fairly deep suture between the whorls. No operculum. O: low spirals, the clearest below the middle of the whorls. Operculum has a low, pustular structure. C: shiny light to dark brown, sometimes orange or green, with irregular, paler patches and mottled spirals. Shiny, nacreous interior. H: d1; sublittoral and deeper, under large rocks. W: INDP; endemic in Oman. R: 4.

d1; sublittoral along rocky coasts and on reefs. W: INDP; the Philippines. R: 2.

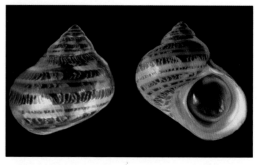

Turbo sarmaticus

LINNAEUS, 1758
South African turban

D: 70mm. S: extremely thick shell with a low spire and a relatively large aperture. Columella, inner lip and lower edge of the aperture are widely expanded and thickened. O: 3–4 broad spirals, covered in squat, coarse nodules. Operculum covered in pustular structures. C: russet, nodules often paler. H: d1; sublittoral along rocky coasts. W: ZAFR. R: 2. NB: the animals are much eaten. The shells are often sold in a polished format revealing the mother-of-pearl lining.

Turbo marmoratus

LINNAEUS, 1758
great green turban

D: 200mm. S: exceptionally thick, heavy shell. Angular whorls with flattened shoulders. Strong fold around base. O: 3 broad, nodulose spirals. Only faint spirals or smooth in between. C: green-brown, thick, pearly aperture. Operculum extremely thick and heavy. H: d1; sublittoral on beds of stony debris. W: INDP. R: 2. NB: largest species in the family. The shell is used in the mother-of-pearl industry.

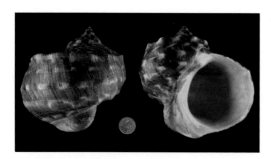

Turbo petholatus

LINNAEUS, 1758
tapestry turban

D: 80mm. S: robust, smooth shell with fairly straight-edged whorls. The aperture is almost circular. No operculum. O: smooth, gleaming. Surface has a polished appearance. C: variable, amber, orange to red, with broad and narrower dark-colored stripes. Gray-white lines cross the stripes which look like tapestry stitching. Aperture usually has a yellowish-green glimmer. H:

Turbo torquatus

GMELIN, 1791
scaled turban

D: 110mm. S: thick shell with low spire and an angular aperture. Clear operculum. A deep suture between the whorls. O: various spirals varying in definition, nodulose around the flattened shoulders. A keel-shaped spiral at the center of the body whorl. Strongly scaled growth lines run vertically down the shell. C: gray-brown, sometimes with dark patches or greenish-brown vertical stripes. Aperture milky white. Operculum white with a deeply depressed spiral structure at its center. H: d1; littoral and sublittoral of rocky coasts. W: AUS. R: 2. NB: photo shows *Turbo torquatus whitleyi* Iredale, 1949—Whitley's turban.

SEGUENZIOIDEA

VERRILL, 1884
Deep-sea species. Principally separated from Trochoidea on the grounds of anatomical differences.

Seguenziidae

VERRILL, 1884
Micro-mollusks. Tiny conical or top-shaped shells. Spiral ornament or radial riblets. Mother-of-pearl. Umbilicus either open or closed. Columella usually with a tooth. Worldwide range, especially in the abyssal zone.

SUPERORDER NERITAEMORPHI

KOKEN, 1896

ORDER NERITOPSINA

COX & KNIGHT, 1960
Neritoidea, the only superfamily to be classified within this order, has representatives on land (Helicinidae and Hydrocenidae) as well as in the sea. Some groups have a reduced shell and look like slugs.

NERITOIDEA

LAMARCK, 1809
Shells without mother-of-pearl. Animals with only one pair of gills (not in the terrestrial species). This group is extremely ancient, dating back as far as the Mesozoic. Various transitional stages can be observed between marine species, freshwater species, and land snails.

Neritidae

LAMARCK, 1809
nerites

Bulbous, semicircular shells with few whorls. The final whorl is extremely large. The spire is usually very truncated. The exterior can be smooth or display subtle to strong spiral ornament. The aperture is a semicircle with a flat, columellar plate at its edge (parietal wall) that is often toothed. The outer lip is usually thickened, often with clear dentate folds within. The operculum is calcareous, reinforced in many cases, and has a characteristic projection (apophysis). This grips behind the edge of the shell when the aperture is closed. Since the shell can be completely sealed off, the animals are able to store water and withstand periods out of water. Many species live in the intertidal zone. Hundreds of species worldwide, mostly with representatives in saltwater (genus *Nerita*, especially in tropical regions). However, species also live in brackish or fresh water (genera *Neritina*, *Theodoxus*). Some species (genus *Neritodryas*) leave water temporarily and graze on the stems of riverside plants. There are 4 subfamilies:
Neritinae Lamarck, 1809; Neritininae Bandel, 2001; Smaragdiinae H.B. Baker, 1923; Theodoxinae Bandel, 2001.
Altogether, these include the genera: *Clithon, Clypeolum, Neripteron, Nerita, Neritina, Neritodryas, Puperita, Septaria, Smaragdia, Theodoxus, Vitta, Vittina.*

Clithon corona

(LINNAEUS, 1758)
crown nerite

D: 10mm. S: oval shell with distinctive needle-like projection just below the shoulder. O: subtle, wavy, slightly raised, axial ribs. The callus is relatively small with very indistinct teeth. No teeth in the outer lip. C: gray-brown to black, aperture and callus gray-white to pale yellow. H: d1; river mouths, on weed. W: INDP; Indian Ocean. R: 1. NB: species sought-after by collectors.

Clypeolum latissimum

(BRODERIP, 1833)
widest nerite

D: 30mm. S: fairly thin shell with a wide aperture that grows into a large ear shape that extends far further than the apex. Parietal shield smooth, at most displaying extremely fine granulation. No teeth in the outer lip. O: smooth, only growth lines. C: yellow-green or brown with mottled, zigzag, or other markings. H: d1; littoral and sublittoral of river mouths. W: CAL, PAN. R: 2.

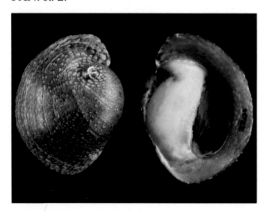

Neripteron violacea

(GMELIN, 1791)
orange-mouthed nerite

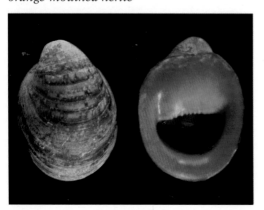

D: 25mm. S: robust, oval shell, with a somewhat protuberant spire and a thickened aperture rim. Smooth parietal shield with a few subtle teeth at the edge. O: only coarse growth lines. C: exterior matt gray-brown to black, often somewhat calcified. Aperture surrounded by orange-yellow callus. H: d1; sublittoral, mangroves. W: INDP. R: 1.

Nerita exuvia

LINNAEUS, 1758
snakeskin nerite

D: 30mm. S: thick shell with flattened spire and a crenulated outer lip. Parietal shield has subtle nodules and sometimes even subtler teeth. O: distinct spirals with deep grooves in between. C: brown-black ribs alternating with light brown to yellow-white mottled dashes. H: d1; littoral, particularly in mangroves. W: INDP. R: 1.

Nerita longii

RÉCLUZ, 1842
Arabian nerite

D: 30mm. S: thick shell with a slight spire. Fine nodules on parietal wall with 3–4 square-edged parietal teeth. Outer lip has several subtle folds and 1–2 larger teeth at top of aperture. O: slightly raised spirals with narrow grooves in between. C: greenish-yellow, gray-brown to russet, often with dots and dashes. Parietal shield and aperture milky white with a dark outer edge. H: d1; littoral of rocky coasts. W: INDP; Arabian Sea, Red Sea. R: 1.

Nerita peloronta

LINNAEUS, 1758
bleeding tooth nerite

D: 30mm. S: thick shell, spire whorls slightly raised. O: smooth or with spirals. C: yellowish-white, pink, or black in all patterns imaginable, including zigzag stripes and colored bands. 1, 2, or 3 orange-red colored teeth in the middle of the parietal shield. H: d1; littoral of rocky coasts. W: CAR. R: 1.

Nerita plicata

LINNAEUS, 1758
plicate nerite

D: 30mm. S: thick, squat shell with a slightly pointed apex. Parietal shield and inner side of outer lip have defined teeth. O: prominent spirals. C: yellow-white to pale pink with dark bands of often alternating color on the ribs. Sometimes in dashes. Operculum black, pustular. H: d1; littoral, on rocks. W: INDP, ZAFR. R: 1.

Nerita signata

LAMARCK, 1822
reticulate nerite

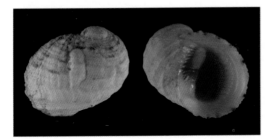

D: 18mm. S: thick shell with slightly raised spire. Columellar callus with narrow furrows. Folds also inside outer lip. O: rather low, irregular spirals, often crossed by growth lines and subtle axial ribs, creating a lattice ornament. C: cream to gray-white with gray-brown, sometimes russet ribs, often mottled and paler. H: d1; littoral and sublittoral on reefs. W: INDP. R: 1.

Nerita squamulata

LE GUILLOU, 1841
Pacific scaled nerite

D: 20mm. S: robust shell with slightly raised spire. O: irregular, thick, slightly scaled spirals with narrow grooves in between. Parietal shield slightly nodulose with 3–4 small teeth. Inner lip also with teeth. Operculum coarsely pustular. C: variable, often brown-gray with orange stripes. H: d1; littoral of rocky coasts. W: INDP, JAP. R: 1.

Nerita textilis

GMELIN, 1791
textile nerite

D: 40mm. S: thick, heavy shell with a flattened spire. O: broad spirals covered in oblique nodules. Pustular callus. C: dashes of dark brown or black alternating with white, creating a woven look. H: d1; upper part of littoral on rocky coasts. W: INDP. R: 1.

Nerita versicolor

GMELIN, 1791
Caribbean four-toothed nerite

D: 18mm. S: thick shell with slightly raised spire. Parietal wall with irregular folds and furrows, edged with 3–4 teeth. Folds also within outer lip. O: thick spirals, often slightly nodulose. C: cream, yellow-white, or gray-brown, mottled with dashes of greenish-black and red. H: d1; littoral, rocky coasts, reefs. W: CAR; Florida, Bermuda, West Indies. R: 1.

Smaragdia rangiana

(RÉCLUZ, 1841)
Pacific emerald nerite

D: 8mm. S: oval, or slightly skewed, shell. Edge of parietal wall has indistinct teeth. No dentate folds within outer lip. O: Smooth, sometimes with more defined growth lines. C: emerald green, often with thin, black lines or dashes. H: d1; sublittoral, in forests of weed and meadows of sea grass. W: INDP. R: 1. NB: there are other species strongly resembling this one, like *S. viridis* (Linnaeus, 1758), which lives in the Caribbean and Mediterranean Sea.

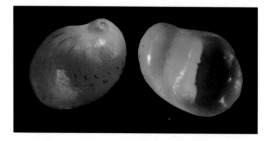

Vitta virginea

(LINNAEUS, 1758)
lagoon nerite

D: 10mm. S: fairly thin shell with a rounded spire. Parietal edge either with or without a few very indistinct teeth. No teeth on inner lip. O: smooth, shiny surface, sometimes with distinct growth lines. C: black, greenish-brown, purple, or orange, with spiral or axial stripes, zebra markings, zigzags, and many other kinds of patterns. H: d1; sublittoral, in lagoons and calm coves, often in sea-grass meadows. W: CAR, VIR. R: 1.

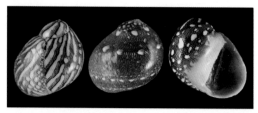

Vittina waigiensis

LESSON, 1831
zigzag nerite

D: 15mm. S: thin, rounded shell with a moderately raised spire. O: toothed columella. Virtually smooth surface. C: exceptionally varied. All possible combinations of yellow, white, red, and black bands with wide to narrow zigzags. H: d1; littoral, mangrove swamps. W: INDP. R: 1.

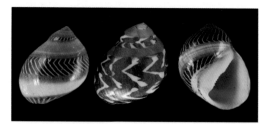

Neritopsidae

J.E. GRAY, 1847
Distorted, ovoid shells, up to 15mm in size. Relatively small whorls. Nodulose spiral ornament. Large, final whorl, circular aperture. Indo-Pacific and Atlantic Oceans. One genus: *Neritopsis*.

Phenacolepadidae

PILSBRY, 1895
latticed limpets

Limpet-like shells, usually with a granulated spiral or latticed ornament. From a few millimeters to approximately 25mm in size. A wealth of species in warmer seas, some genera known only from areas around hydrothermal vents. Genera include: *Cinnalepeta, Olgasolaris, Phenacolepas, Plesiothyreus, Shinkailepas*.

Phenacolepas crenulatus

(BRODERIP, 1834)
scaled latticed limpet

D: 20mm. S: limpet-like shell, the apex between the center and the posterior edge. O: wide and narrower ribs radiate from the apex, crossed by transverse ribs. Scaly ridges at intersections. C: white. H: d1–2; sublittoral and deeper, under rocks lying deep in the substrate. W: AUS, JAP. R: 3.

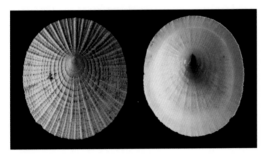

SUPERORDER CAENOGAS-TROPODA

COX, 1960
Nowadays, according to many taxonomists, the superorder Caenogastropoda should be divided into two orders: Architaenioglossa and Sorbeoconcha.

ORDER ARCHITAENIOGLOSSA

HALLER, 1890
Nowadays, the order Architaenioglossa contains only the terrestrial superfamilies Cyclophoroidea and Ampullaroidea, found mostly in tropical freshwaters. All other earlier Mesogastropoda, including Neogastropoda, are presently classified within the order Sorbeoconcha.

CYCLOPHOROIDEA

J.E. GRAY, 1847
Terrestrial. Have an operculum, unlike most land snails. Various families have been identified, ranging across the whole world.

AMPULLARIOIDEA

J.E. GRAY, 1824
Freshwater snails. Mostly in the tropics, including the "apple snails" familiar to many with aquariums. Only one family in Europe, the Viviparidae J.E. Gray, 1847—river snails. These are large, plump, relatively thin shells. Often tawny with dark brown transverse stripes. Corneous operculum. Some species are ovoviviparous (bearing live young): the eggs develop in the uterus, the young leaving the mother's body only in an advanced state of development.

ORDER SORBEOCONCHA

PONDER & LINDBERG, 1997
All of the groups presently classified within the order Sorbeoconcha often suck breathing water into the mantle cavity through a furrow in the edge of the mantle that has developed into a siphon (Latin: sorbeo=suck up). The water passes nerve cells allowing the water to be assessed chemically. (A synonym for the group is Neotaenioglossa).

SUBORDER DISCOPODA

P. FISCHER, 1884
Only the superfamilies Campaniloidea, Cerithioidea, and Loxonematoidea are contained within this suborder.

CERITHIOIDEA

DE FÉRUSSAC, 1822
The superfamily Cerithioidea is one of the largest and most varied within the Caenogastropods. The group has a worldwide range, from entirely marine environments to estuarine and freshwater areas. Species from this group often have a dominant presence in intertidal zones of the tropics and subtropics. Although they exhibit differences in shape and size, many species have a straight-sided and/or high-spired shell, sometimes ornamented with nodulose spirals and radial ribs. The aperture usually ends in a slight bulge or in an extruded, sometimes twisted siphonal canal, varying in size. The operculum is corneous and formed in a spiral.

Batillariidae

THIELE, 1929
horn snails

Recently separated from the family Potamididae. Both groups live in shallow water in brackish, estuarine areas and lagoons in temperate and subtropical regions. Various genera, often with dark colored, spire-shaped shells made up of numerous whorls. Many species are only a few millimeters in size, but there are also species measuring up to 100mm. Radial and spiral ornament, often with blunt nodules. Aperture with a somewhat flared outer lip at the base. Operculum with a central corneous nucleus. A few genera: *Batillaria, Batillariella, Pyrazus, Rhinocoryne, Velacumantus, Zeacumantus*.

Batillaria minima

(GMELIN, 1791)
false Caribbean cerith

D: 5mm. S: robust, pointed shell with slightly bulbous whorls. The aperture is a little widened, the siphonal canal is short and curves to the side sharply. O: broad, axial ribs especially on upper whorls, which very soon become indistinct, however. Additional spiral ornament as well. C: gray-brown, often with a wide chocolate-brown band on the lower half of the whorls. H: d1; littoral, on mudflats. W: CAR. R: 1.

Pyrazus ebeninus

(BRUGUIÈRE, 1792)
ebony swamp cerith

D: 100mm. S: large, thick, pointed shell with angular whorls. The aperture is greatly expanded and surrounded by a thick callus. Slightly curved, gully-shaped siphonal canal. O: A spiral rib below the suture with coarse, angular nodules, otherwise subtler spirals. C: chocolate brown to ebony. H: d1; mudflats and muddy lagoons. W: AUS. R: 1.

Cerithiidae

DE FÉRUSSAC, 1822
ceriths

Spired shells with clear radial and spiral ornament. Variable in color and size, from a few millimeters to over 120mm. Slight inward curve at base of aperture or a clear siphonal canal. The animals typically live on a sandy substrate in shallow water and feed on vegetable matter and detritus. Mostly in tropical maritime areas, a few species along European coasts.

The family is divided into two subfamilies: Bittiinae Cossmann, 1906 and Cerithiinae De Férussac, 1822. The latter mostly contains larger, robust, pointed shells, with or without distinct nodules and spirals. The former contains various small, slender, spire-shaped shells with radial, spiral, lattice, or granulose ornament and often varices. Jointly, the family contains many genera, including: *Bittium, Cassiella, Cerithioclava, Cerithium, Clypeomorus, Colina, Fastigiella, Glyptozaria, Gourmya, Lirobittium, Pseudovertagus, Rhinoclavis, Royella, Semivertagus, Varicopeza, Vertagus*.

Bittium reticulatum

(DA COSTA, 1778)
baby corn cerith

D: 12mm. S: thick, spire-shaped shell with up to 12 slightly bulbous whorls. Pointed apex. The oblong aperture ends at the base in a short siphonal canal. No umbilicus. O: horizontal and vertical ribs cross to create a lattice ornament. Former aperture lips visible here and there (varices). C: light to dark brown. Ribs, varices, and apex often paler. H: d1; littoral and sublittoral of rocky coasts and muddy bays amid weed and sea grass. W: KEL, LUS. R: 1.

Cerithium atratum

(VON BORN, 1778)
Florida cerith

D: 25mm. S: thick shell, sharply pointed. Aperture slightly enlarged. Siphonal canal alone curves slightly to the side. O: coarse, nodulose ribs with subtler ones in between. C: chalky white, grayish-yellow or darker, often with dark red to black-brown dashes, especially on the nodules, but also elsewhere. H: d1; sublittoral, amid seaweed. W: VIR, CAR. R: 1.

Cerithium echinatum

LAMARCK, 1822
spiny cerith

D: 40mm. S: thick shell, short and squat. Aperture slightly enlarged, severely folded at the edges and with a nozzle-shaped anal canal at the top of the aperture. O: defined spirals covered in sharp, almost spine-like nodules. Much subtler nodulose spirals in between. C: amber, sometimes with russet dashes. H: d1; sublittoral. W: INDP. R: 1.

Cerithium nodulosum

BRUGUIÈRE, 1792
giant knobbed cerith

D: 150mm. S: extremely thick shell with angular, step-like whorls. The aperture is enlarged and slanted causing the siphonal canal to be bent at an angle. An anal canal at the top of the aperture. Outer lip has blunt projections. Thick nodule on the columella, as well as a tooth-shaped projection within the top of the aperture. O: rough, nodulose lateral ribs and finer spiral grooves. C: cream to pale yellow, with irregular brown-black and russet patches. H: d1; sublittoral, rocky coasts and reefs. W: INDP. R: 1. NB: one of the largest ceriths.

Cerithium vulgatum

BRUGUIÈRE, 1792
European cerith

D: 70mm. S: robust, spire-shaped shell with a great many whorls and a slightly enlarged aperture with a short siphonal canal. Thin, corneous operculum. O: 2 rows of nodulose spirals on the first whorls. Several smaller spirals below the middle of the body whorl. C: amber with irregular dark brown to russet coloration of spirals and dashes. H: d1; sublittoral of sandy, rocky coasts, on rocks and in forests of weed. W: LUS, WAFR. R: 1. NB: congregate in great numbers, are sometimes eaten.

Cerithium zonatum

(WOOD, 1828)
zoned cerith

D: 30mm. S: robust, pointed shell with an ovate mouth. Short siphonal canal, broad, slightly curved to the side. Small anal canal within top of aperture. O: various pale, nodulose spirals. C: amber with white, dark brown and russet bands of color. H: d1; sublittoral, on sandy substrate. W: INDP. R: 2–3.

Pseudovertagus aluco

(LINNAEUS, 1758)
aluco vertagus

D: 75mm. S: robust, pointed shell with rather flat to more angular whorls between which the suture can barely be seen. Outer lip with thickened callus, siphonal canal sharply to one side or curved, bending more to the rear. Underside of the aperture also curved sideways. O: from virtually nodule-free to heavily nodulose spirals. C: cream with indigo (ink color), irregular dots, stripes, and dashes. Aperture and callus creamy white. H: d1; sublittoral to a depth of approx. 10m. W: INDP. R: 1. NB: below is the subspecies *Pseudovertagus aluco cumingii* Sowerby, 1855.

Pseudovertagus nobilis

(REEVE, 1855)
noble vertagus

D: 120mm. S: thick shell, extremely slender and pointed. Straight-sided whorls with a slight shoulder. Siphonal canal bent away from aperture into a spout. Aperture thickly callused. O: subtly nodulose spirals, occasionally with distinctive grooves. C: cream to yellowish-gray. Often paler flecks on the spirals. White aperture. H: d1–2; deeper water to a depth of approx. 100m. W: INDP. R: 3–4.

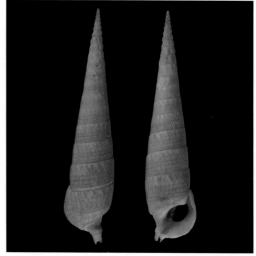

74

Rhinoclavis brettinghami

CERNOHORSKY, 1974
Brettingham's vertagus

D: 50mm. S: robust, thick shell with straight, stepped whorls. Thickened inner and outer lips. Anal canal present within top of aperture. Siphonal canal short and narrow, bent to the side. O: wide axial ribs, almost perpendicular. Fine spirals run around the shell. C: amber with dark brown dashes and stripes. H: d1; littoral and sublittoral. W: AUS. R: 1.

Rhinoclavis fasciata

(BRUGUIÈRE, 1792)
banded vertagus

D: 75mm. S: robust shell with level to almost straight-sided whorls. Angular aperture, thickened with callus over the columella and inner lip. O: nodulose spire whorls, subsequent whorls smooth or slight axial ribs above the suture. C: wide and narrower, brown spiral bands. H: d1; sublittoral to a depth of approx. 20m. W: AUS, INDP. R: 1. NB: a sought-after species due to its coloration.

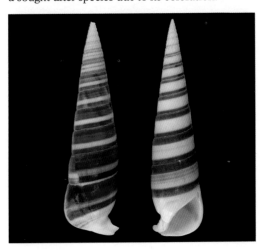

Rhinoclavis vertagus

(LINNAEUS, 1758)
common vertagus

D: 70mm. S: robust shell with level whorls and an oblique aperture with a siphonal canal bent away into a spout. Thickened inner lip with two folds. Thin outer lip. O: wide axial ribs, fainter in the middle. C: milky white or chestnut brown. H: d1; sublittoral. W: INDP. R: 1.

Dialidae

LUDBROOK, 1941
conical ceriths

Micro-mollusks with spire or cone-shaped shells. 5–8mm. Only possess spiral ornament with colored markings. No siphonal canal. Corneous operculum. Indo-Pacific; shallow bays and river mouths. Usually close to coral reefs.

Diala varia

(A. ADAMS, 1861)
semi-striped conical cerith

D: 2mm. S: reasonably thin, pointed shell. Grooved suture. O: spirals only on lower half of body whorl. C: brown, sometimes bands of color. H: d1; sublittoral and deeper water. W: INDP; Arabian Sea. R: 2.

Diastomatidae

COSSMANN, 1894
dwarf ceriths

High-spired, pointed or conical shells. Radial ornament and spirals. Deep sutures between the whorls. Oval aperture, sharper at the top. Corneous operculum with central nucleus. Shallow water in the intertidal zone, on sand and sea grass. East coast of USA, California, Pacific Ocean, and Australia.

Cerithidium diplax

(WATSON, 1886)
broad-ribbed dwarf cerith

D: 4mm. S: thin, pointed shell. Very broad siphonal canal merging into lower edge of the aperture. O: axial ribs and spirals widely separated. Nodules on intersections. C: cream or white. H: d1; littoral and deeper water. W: INDP; Arabian Sea. R: 2.

Diastoma varium

(PFEIFFER, 1840)
variable dwarf cerith

D: 13mm. S: robust, pointed shell. O: nodulose spirals, sometimes with varices. Ornament often less pronounced at base of final whorl. C: cream to gray-brown. Periostracum brownish-

red. H: d1; littoral and sublittoral on seaweed and sea grass. W: CAR, VIR. R: 1.

Litiopidae

J.E. GRAY, 1847
sargassum snails

Relatively pointed, thin to almost transparent shells. No larger than 25mm. Differ from Daliidae in the protoconch ornament. Fine spiral lines. In warm seas on floating algae.

Gibborissoa virgata

(PHILIPPI, 1849)
weak-ribbed sargassum snail

D: 4.5mm. S: thin, pointed shell. Straight columella without tooth-shaped nodule. O: wide, subtle axial ribs and broadly interspaced spirals. C: white with brown dashes. H: d1; sublittoral and slightly deeper water. W: INDP. R: 2.

Melanopsidae

H. & A. ADAMS, 1854
Similar to the freshwater species of Thiaridae. Several genera, including: *Amphimelania, Fagotia, Melanopsis, Microcolpia.*

Modulidae

P. FISCHER, 1884
modulus shells or button snails

Top-shaped shells with a flattened apex. Up to 15mm in size. Nodulose ornament. A few whorls, the last of which is large. Big aperture, columella with a downward pointing tooth. In shallow water, on sea grass and rocks in tropical seas.

Modulus modulus

(LINNAEUS, 1758)
Atlantic modulus or Caribbean button snail

D: 16mm. S: very thick shell with a squat cone shape. The apex ranges from blunt to flattened. Angular whorls. Older whorls hang clearly over the suture. Thickened aperture edge with a nodule on the columella. Inner lip has columellar folds. Clear umbilicus. O: rough nodules and finer spiral grooves. C: cream or with russet-spotted coloration. H: d1; littoral and sublittoral, amid seaweed and sea grass. W: CAR. R: 1.

Planaxidae

J.E. GRAY, 1850
These shells have a passing resemblance to *Littorina*, but, among other things, differ in their slight inward curvature at the base of the aperture. The subfamily Fossarinae Troschel, 1861, has high, top-shaped shells with few whorls, a broad final whorl, and a wide umbilicus. The subfamily Planaxiinae has no umbilicus. In the intertidal zone of warmer seas on hard substrates. A few genera, including: *Angiola, Fissilabia, Fossarus, Planaxis.*

Potamididae

H. & A. ADAMS, 1854
modderspitshorens e.a.

Pointed, conical shells composed of a multitude of whorls. Ornamented with spiral bands and radial ribs. Some species display varices. Apex often eroded. Angular outer lip, bent outward, curving inward for the siphonal canal. Often with a thick periostracum. Corneous operculum with a central nucleus. In muddy mangrove swamps and river mouths with regularly exposed mudflats. Tropical and subtropical regions.

Telescopium telescopium

LINNAEUS, 1758
telescope snail

D: 100mm. S: extremely thick, heavy shell. Pointed, with level whorls that very gradually widen and between which it is almost impossible to find the suture. Skewed, oval aperture. Twisted columella is like a corkscrew in appearance. O: regular spirals and more distinct growth lines. C: dark brown, spirals often somewhat lighter. Aperture dark brown. H: d1; littoral and sublittoral in mangrove swamps and lagoons. W: INDP. R: 1.

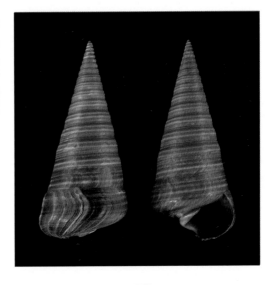

Terebralia sulcata

(VON BORN, 1778)
sulcate swamp cerith

D: 50mm. S: thick, spire-shaped shell. Enlarged aperture, thickly callused outer lip. O: densely nodulose spirals and rounded axial ribs that intersect creating a lattice. C: dark brown to gray-brown. Shiny orange-yellow aperture. H: d1; littoral and sublittoral, on mud banks, in estuaries and swamps. W: INDP. R: 1.

Scaliolidae

JOUSSEAUME, 1912
camouflage ceriths

Micro-mollusks with spired shells. Latticed (genus *Finella*) or smooth and covered with attached grains of sand (genus *Scaliola*). Aperture without siphonal canal. Mostly in shallow water in tropical and subtropical regions.

Scaliola glareosa

A. ADAMS, 1862
Japanese camouflage cerith

D: 4mm. S: slender, fairly thick shell. O: the whorls are smooth but always covered in attached sand granules. C: white. H: d1; sandy and muddy area, sublittoral. W: JAP. R: 1. NB: Scaliolidae are hard to identify.

Siliquariidae

ANTON, 1838
slit worm shells

Unusually shaped shells with a strong resemblance to worm shells (Turritellidae). The first whorls are spirally wound but start to become disentangled from each other later and adopt irregular shapes. The disentangled tube displays a slit or a row of holes along all or part of its length. Intertidal zone in warmer seas.

Tenagodus anguina

(LINNAEUS, 1758)
squamous slit worm shell

D: 50mm. S: irregularly wound tube —the slit is present along its entire length. O: irregular spirals and rough spicules. C: gray-white to milk-white. H: d1–3; sublittoral and deeper, up to approx. 200m. Lives in sponges. W: INDP, JAP. R: 2.

Tenagodus armata

(KURODA, HABE & KOSUGE, 1967)
spiny slit worm shell

D: 40mm. S: irregularly wound tube—the slit is quite narrow. O: has both scales and coarse spicules. C: light to dark brown or violet. H: d1–2; sublittoral and deeper water, attached to rocks on which sponges grow. W: INDP. R: 2.

Thiaridae

TROSCHEL, 1857
freshwater ceriths

As with Melanopsidae, far and away the majority of this family's representatives are found in freshwater or estuarine environments. Various genera, including: *Faunus, Hemisinus, Horea, Melanoides, Plottia, Thiara.*

Faunus ater

(VON BORN, 1778)
black faunus

D: 50mm. S: very pointed shell with slender, level whorls. An anal siphon is at the top of the aperture, the siphonal canal is open. Outer lip flares outward. O: smooth with only subtle spirals. C: dark brown to black. H: d1; tropical fresh water. W: INDP. R: 1.

Melanoides tuberculata

(O.F. MÜLLER, 1774)
red-rimmed melania

D: 8mm. S: thin, pointed shell with slightly bulbous whorls and an oval aperture pointed at the top. O: subtle spirals and vertical grooves, sometimes nodulose. C: variable, usually yellowish-green with red-brown dashes. H: d1; freshwater. W: CAR, INDP. R: 1. NB: familiar

snail in aquariums and used all over the world for that purpose.

Turritellidae

LOVÉN, 1847
turret, screw and worm shells

Distinctively pointed shells with a large number of whorls (10–15) that very gradually increase in size, creating a turret or screw shape. They are divided into two subfamilies. Species from Turritellinae Lovén, 1847 (turret or screw shells) are shaped as described above. Species from the subfamily Vermiculariinae Faustino, 1928 (worm shells) also develop spirally wound shells in the youthful stage of their growth. However, during later growth, the whorls separate completely from each other and grow haphazardly. The tube is complete and closed off with a circular, corneous operculum. Both groups live on plant remains that are fished from the water using nets of mucus known as slime nets. After a mobile immature stage, some Vermiculariinae may attach themselves to a hard substrate. Others will live unattached on sand or mud from the intertidal zone to deep water. Found worldwide in all maritime zones. Several genera, including: *Archimediella, Armatus, Colpospira, Gazameda, Haustator, Maoricolpus, Mesalia, Peyrotia, Protoma, Stephopoma, Tachyrhynchus, Turritella, Turritellopsis, Vermicularia, Zaria, Zeacolpus.*

Archimediella maculata

(REEVE, 1849)
maculated turritella

D: 65mm. S: quite a thin shell with an almost quadrangular aperture. O: has 2, sometimes 3, roughly rounded spiral ribs with some finer ones in between. C: cream to tawny with a pattern of russet stripes and flecks. H: d1–2; sublittoral and slightly deeper water. W: INDP; northern part of the Arabian Sea. R: 2–3.

gray-brown, spirals dark brown to black. Aperture dark brown. H: d1; sublittoral. W: PER. R: 1.

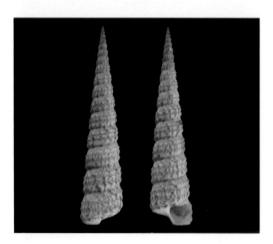

Mesalia opalina

(A. ADAMS & REEVE, 1850)
opal turritella

D: 25mm. S: pointed shell with bulbous whorls. The aperture is oval. O: very fine spiral ornament. A fold next to the inner lip. C: amber with undulating or comma-shaped, russet or chestnut markings. H: d1–2; sublittoral and deeper water. W: WAFR. R: 1.

Turritella communis

RISSO, 1826
common European turritella or screw shell

D: 50mm. S: robust, awl-shaped shell with up to 18 fairly bulbous whorls. The apex is pointed, the aperture virtually circular. Round, corneous operculum. No clear umbilicus. O: 3–10 spiral ribs. C: gray or yellowish-brown with red-brown markings. H: d1–3; on sand to a depth of approx. 200m. W: KEL, LUS. R: 1.

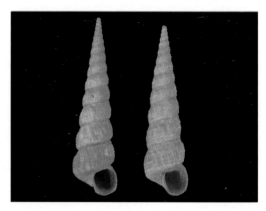

Turritella cingulata

SOWERBY, 1825
banded turritella

D: 70mm. S: robust, relatively wide shell with level whorls. O: fairly coarse and fine spirals. C:

Turritella gonostoma

VALENCIENNES, 1832
angle-mouth turritella

D: 100mm. S: large, robust shell with somewhat stepped, subtly shouldered whorls. O: very fine spiral ornament, usually one slightly more defined, keel-shaped, spiral rib just under the suture. Somewhat more defined spirals also on the base. C: yellowish-gray with irregular russet markings. H: d1; sublittoral. W: PAN. R: 1.

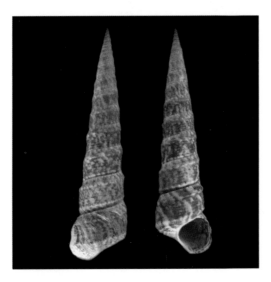

Turritella terebra

(LINNAEUS, 1758)
screw turritella or tower screw shell

D: 180mm. S: thick, slender, pointed shell with up to 25 bulbous whorls. Deep suture, oval aperture. O: around 6 defined spirals on each whorl with many finer ones in between. C: usually a uniform cream, amber, or dark brown. H: d1; sublittoral on sand. W: INDP. R: 2.

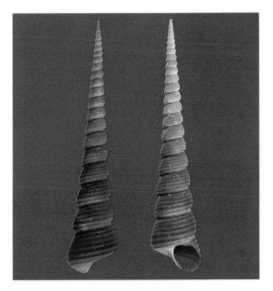

Turritella turbona

MONTEROSATO, 1877
Mediterranean turritella

D: 45mm. S: fairly thin shell with reasonably level whorls. Deep suture, angular oval aperture. O: usually 2–3 somewhat more defined, rounded spirals in the middle of the whorls. The rest of the shell otherwise covered by finer spirals. C: cream to amber with russet markings. H: d1–2; sublittoral and deeper water. W: LUS. R: 3. NB: *Turritella monterosatoi* Kobelt, 1887 closely resembles this species but is considerably larger and rarer.

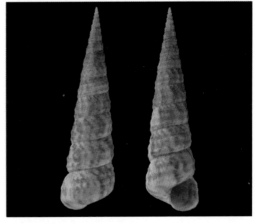

Vermicularia fargoi

OLSSON, 1951
brown worm shell

D: 80mm. S: the oldest part wound roughly like a normal shell, afterward quickly becoming unwound, forming a haphazard tube. O: 2–3 spi-

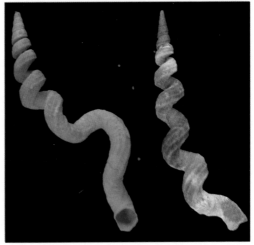

rals along the entire tube, becoming thicker toward the end of the tube. C: apical whorls usually dark brown, becoming progressively lighter. H: d1–2; sublittoral and deeper. W: CAR. R: 1.

Vermicularia spirata

(PHILIPPI, 1836)
West Indian worm shell

D: 10mm. S: whorls for only the first 10mm or so, afterward a haphazardly unwinding tube. O: often slightly nodulose, thicker spirals along the entire tube, becoming fainter toward the aperture. Often a few subtle, narrow spirals as well. C: yellowish-white or light brown, apical whorls usually a little darker. H: d1; sublittoral, often in the proximity of sponges. W: CAR. R: 1.

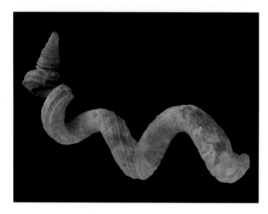

Zaria duplicata

(LINNAEUS, 1758)
Indian purple or duplicate turritella

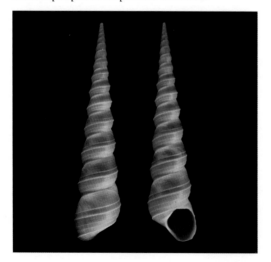

D: 120mm. S: thick, slender shell with very bulbous whorls made somewhat angular by the ornament. Oval aperture. O: below the middle several defined, keel-shaped spirals. Additionally, finer spirals. C: cream, amber, or dark brown. Sometimes violet-brown on the upper half of the whorls. H: d1; sublittoral. W: INDP. R: 2.

CAMPANILOIDEA

DOUVILLÉ, 1904

Campanilidae

DOUVILLÉ, 1904
clapper shells

The only recent representative still living occurs along the coast of Australia. Other species are only known of as fossils. At the beginning of the Tertiary period, some fossil ancestors reached lengths of up to a meter, making them the largest gastropods ever to have lived on earth.

Campanile symbolicum

IREDALE, 1917
bell clapper

D: 200mm. S: exceptionally thick, turret-shaped shells with straight-sided whorls. Slightly concave when seen side on. The base forms a smooth curve, columella curved. Short siphonal canal bending away. O: smooth, usually weather-beaten. C: chalky white. H: d1; to a depth of 10m. W: Australia, southwest coast. R: 3. NB: this species is not only a living fossil in terms of its genealogy but also very much in terms of its appearance.

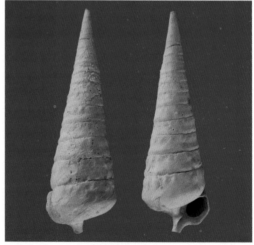

Plesiotrochidae

HOUBRICK, 1990
pyramid shells

Pointed, conical shells that are quite small (5–10mm, and one species that is up to 24mm) with level to convex whorls. Twisted columella and siphonal canal. Coarsely ribbed with varices or else only with spiral ornament. Pilose periostracum. Operculum has eccentric nucleus. Indo-Pacific region, sublittoral amid weed.

Plesiotrochus penetricinctus

(COTTON, 1932)
Australian pyramid shell

D: 10mm. S: thin-shelled, pointed, pyramid or pagoda-shaped. Very short, indistinct siphonal canal. Angular aperture. O: 1 strong and 1 weaker keel-shaped spiral on lower half of the whorls. Other spirals are more delicate. C: amber with russet patches. H: d1; sublittoral. W: AUS, INDP. R: 4. NB: identification of the specimen shown not 100% certain.

SUBORDER MURCHISONIINA

COX & KNIGHT, 1960

LOXONEMATOIDEA

KOKEN, 1889
This superfamily, originally employed only for fossil species, now includes a few modern-day families containing eyeless deepwater snails. Abyssochrysidae Tomlin, 1927 have pointed spire-shaped shells up to 50mm in length with low whorls and radial ribs. They live at depths of up to 1500–1800m along the coast of South Africa and in the Indo-Pacific region. Provannidae Warén & Ponder, 1991 have spire-shaped shells with a broad aperture, as well as radial and spiral ornament. Up to depths of 2700m on the edge of hydrothermal vents (western Pacific Ocean, East Pacific Ridge, Gulf of Mexico).

SUBORDER HYPSOGASTROPODA

PONDER & LINDBERG, 1997
According to recent thought based on genealogy, the suborder Hypsogastropoda ought now to contain virtually all of the younger taxa in Caenogastropoda. This encompasses the infraorder Littorinimorpha, as well as Heterobranchia, Neogastropoda, and Ptenoglossa.

INFRAORDER LITTORINIMORPHA

GOLIKOV & STAROBOGATOV, 1975

LITTORINOIDEA

CHILDREN, 1834
Robust, thick shells. Either rounded, or spirally wound and pointed. Either smooth or with ornament. Ovate aperture, outer lip usually curved outward. Operculum paucispiral or multispiral, corneous. Residents of the upper shore and shallow water. A few genera in deeper water. Some representatives live on land (family Pomatiidae) or in freshwater (genus *Cremnoconchus* from the family Littorinidae).

Littorinidae

CHILDREN, 1834
periwinkles

Top-shaped or pointed, conical shells. Quite robust to thick-shelled. Porcelain appearance or else calcified without nacre. The operculum seals the shell tight, enabling the animal to retain sufficient oxygen-bearing water in dry conditions. These animals feed principally on algae and live in the intertidal zone of mud flats and rocky coasts, on rocks and among seaweed. They are divided into subfamilies, classified as follows: the subfamily Lacuninae J.E. Gray, 1857 (chink shells) chiefly contains cold-water species from northern regions. Thin-shelled, often with a distinctive umbilical groove in or right next to the aperture rim. The subfamily Laevilitorininae Reid, 1989 contains only a few less well-known Antarctic and Australian species. The subfamily Littorininae J.E. Gray, 1840 (true periwinkles) contains the majority of species. Occurrence in both warm and colder maritime environments. Shells usually have the characteristic conical periwinkle shape. Often with spirals. Some species with nodules, spicules, or else smooth.

Shape and color differ markedly even within individual species. All together, they account for various genera, including: *Bembicium, Cenchritis, Lacuna, Laevilittorina, Littoraria, Littorina, Mainwaringia, Melarhaphe, Nodilittorina, Peasiella, Risellopsis, Tectarius.*

Cenchritis muricatus

(LINNAEUS, 1758)
beaded periwinkle

D: 25mm. S: solid, conical shell with a very pointed apex and a small umbilical groove next to the aperture. O: spiral ribs covered in round nodules, widest in the middle of the whorls. C: creamy white to milk-white. H: d1; littoral of rocky coasts. W: CAR. R: 1.

Lacuna vincta

(MONTAGU, 1803)
banded chink shell

D: 10mm. S: thin shell, a distorted triangle in profile. 5–6 fairly convex whorls. Ovate aperture. A distinctive, cleft-like umbilicus next to the aperture. O: smooth. C: yellowish-white with 2–4 dark brown bands. H: d1; littoral of sheltered rocky coasts, on sea grass and brown and red seaweed. W: KEL, LUS. R: 1.

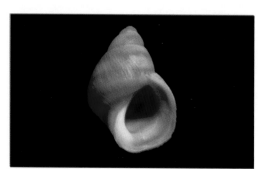

Littorina littorea

(LINNAEUS, 1758)
common periwinkle

D: 40mm. S: thick shell with quite level whorls. Pointed apex, ovate aperture and operculum. No umbilicus. O: level, spiral ribs. C: brownish-gray, often with a number of dark and lighter bands of color. Sometimes a uniform yellow or red. The aperture is white. H: d1; littoral on rocky coasts and found on groins, jetties, etc. W: KEL, LUS, VIR. R: 1. NB: widely eaten.

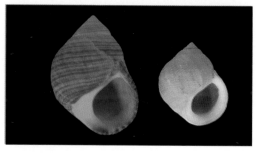

Littorina obtusata

(LINNAEUS, 1758)
flat periwinkle

D: 18mm. S: thick shell, a flattened spire with its whorls quickly increasing in size. Ovate aperture. No umbilicus. O: smooth, only growth lines. C: variable: uniform yellow, brown, olive-green or orange. Otherwise a checkered pattern or bands of color. H: d1; littoral and sublittoral of rocky coasts, on levees and piers, amid species of wrack (*Fucus*). W: KEL (in the USA as far south as New Jersey), LUS. R: 1. NB: *Littorina fabalis* closely resembles this species and has approximately the same range in Europe.

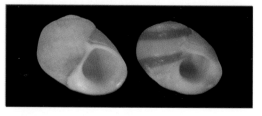

Littorina saxatilis

(OLIVI, 1792)
rough periwinkle

D: 25mm. S: ranges from being thin to (extremely) thick-shelled. Fairly level to convex whorls. Pointed apex, oval aperture, often slightly flared at the base. Sometimes with a broader, round/oval aperture. O: from subtle to very defined, horizontal ribs and grooves. C: exceptionally varied. All imaginable colors and patterns. H: d1; splash zone and littoral of rocky coasts. Also on levees, piers, and groins. W: ARC, KEL, LUS. R: 1. NB: some consider these animals to be a complex of species, others see them as subspecies or varieties (ecomorphs) of a particular species affected by environmental factors.

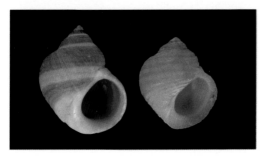

Tectarius coronatus

VALENCIENNES, 1832
coronate prickly winkle

D: 40mm. S: solid, conical shell with a pointed apex. O: spiral ribs adorned with distinct nodules. C: cream to orange-pink. A dark brown band of color around the shoulder. H: d1; littoral of rocky coasts. W: INDP; the Philippines, Celebes. R: 1.

Tectarius pagodus

(LINNAEUS, 1758)
pagoda prickly winkle

D: 50mm. S: large, thick shell. Columellar side of the aperture has a slight nodule, outer lip has teeth. O: irregular, roughly scaled, and nodulose spirals, subtler on the base and a row of defined, truncated to fairly pointed nodules in the center of the whorls. A second row appears on the lower half of the body whorl. C: cream to apricot. H: d1; littoral of rocky coasts. W: INDP. R: 2. NB: the largest representative from Littorinidae.

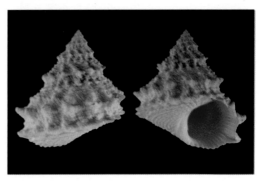

Pickworthiidae

IREDALE, 1917
This family of micro-mollusks contains a few genera with small (0.5–5mm), purely white shells in a variety of shapes. Flattened, conical or spike-shaped with radial, spiral, or latticed ornament, often with nodules at intersections. Thickened aperture rim. Little-known family, including the genera: *Mecoliotia, Microliotia, Pickworthia, Reynellona, Sansonia, Sherbornia*.

Skeneopsidae

IREDALE, 1915
posthorn micro-mollusks

Micro-mollusks measuring up to 2mm. Coiled in a single plane (planospiral) with a wide umbilicus and a circular aperture. Usually without ornament. Atlantic Ocean and Mediterranean Sea on seaweed. Genera: *Retrotortina, Skeneopsis*.

Skeneopsis planorbis

(FABRICIUS, 1780)
planospiral skenea

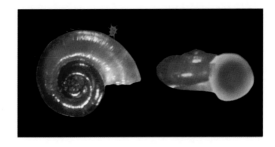

D: 2mm. S: thin, discoid shell with convex whorls coiled on one plane. The apex scarcely rises above the whorls. Extremely wide umbilicus: the whorls barely touch each other. O: smooth, only showing growth lines. C: white, brownish-yellow, red, or chocolate. First whorls often darker. H: d1; sublittoral of rocky coasts on red seaweed. W: KEL, LUS. R: 1.

Zerotulidae

WARÉN & HAIN, 1996

Deep-sea species. Micro-mollusks. From flat-coiled to top-shaped shells. Smooth or with spiral ornament. Includes those in deep water around New Caledonia, New Zealand and Antarctica. Genera include: *Dickdellia, Frovina, Trilirata, Zerotula.*

CINGULOPSOIDEA

FRETTER & PATIL, 1958

Micro-mollusks up to 7mm in size. Top-shaped veering to conical shells. A hook is attached to the operculum and a chitinous organic layer covers the shell interior. These species live mainly on weed and are widely distributed. This includes genera in Europe, Australia and New Zealand, the Indo-Pacific region, and Antarctica. Various families, such as Cingulopsidae Fretter & Patil, 1958 (minute marine snails), including the genera: *Eatonia, Pickenia, Tubbreva*. There are also Eatoniellidae Ponder, 1965 including the genera *Crassitoniella, Eatoniella, Liratoniella, Pupatonia* and Rastodentidae Ponder, 1966 including the genera *Rastodens, Tridentifera.*

RISSOOIDEA

J.E. GRAY, 1947

Very well-known and extensive group of micro-mollusks. Most of its members are only a few millimeters in size. Exceptionally variable in shape, color, and ornament. Various families and a great many genera and species. Prevalent in shallow coastal regions in all maritime environments. Some groups in deeper water.

Adeorbidae

MONTEROSATO, 1884

Micro-mollusks. Resemble Skeneidae, Tornidae, and Orbitestellidae. Compressed shells with a truncated apex. Porcelain-white to transparent. Broad umbilicus. Live in sea grass or shallow water, particularly in tropical and subtropical regions. Several genera, including: *Circulus, Cyclostremiscus, Discopsis, Episcynia, Pleuromalaxis, Solariopsis, Vitrinella, Vitrinorbis.*

Circulus striatus

(PHILIPPI, 1836)
flat circle snail

D: 3mm. S: circular/round shell in a flat spiral. O: a few defined spiral ribs. C: shiny white or cream. H: d1–2; sublittoral to dozens of meters deep. W: KEL, LUS. R: 2.

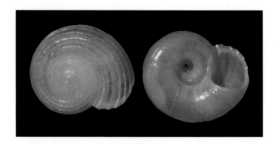

Anabathridae

COAN, 1964

Micro-mollusks. Solid, squat or taller, conical shells. Smooth or ornamented. With or without umbilicus and an organic membrane within. Differ anatomically to the similar Barleeidae and in possessing an operculum made of two layers without a groove on the inside. Round aperture that may or may not be thickened. Mostly intertidal zone and sublittoral of warmer seas, on weed and in between rocks. Genera include: *Amphithalamus, Anabathron, Nodulus, Pisinna.*

Assimineidae

H. & A. ADAMS, 1856
assimineid snails

Conical shells, smooth or with indistinct ornament. Angular or round aperture. Mostly in the tropics or subtropics with a few European species. The animals live in river mouths and in the intertidal zone. Genera include: *Assiminea, Conacmella, Cyclomorpha, Cyclotropis, Omphalotropis, Paludinella, Pseudocyclotus, Quadrasiella, Suterilla.*

Assiminea grayana

FLEMING, 1828
Gray's assiminea

D: 8mm. S: thin shell with level whorls. Pointed apex. Ovate, wide aperture. No umbilicus. O: smooth with only growth lines. C: glossy brown-yellow, often a dark band of color in the center. H: d1; salt marshes and mud flats along the Atlantic coasts and the North Sea. W: KEL. R: 3.

1803) – blunt tube snail. Dimensions: up to 4mm. KEL, LUS. (Bottom) *Parastrophia asturiana* De Folin, 1870 – horn tube snail, 4mm. KEL, LUS.

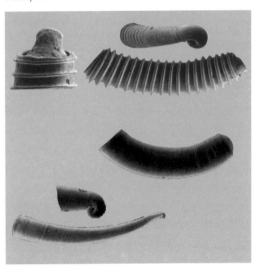

Barleeidae

J.E. GRAY, 1857

Micro-mollusks. Tall, conical shells. Pitted protoconch. Thickened operculum, composed of a single layer, with a transverse ridge within. Worldwide distribution in shallow water on weed. Genera include: *Barleeia, Caelatura, Fictonoba, Lirobarleeia*.

Caecidae

M.E. GRAY, 1850
tube snails

Micro-mollusks. Most aberrant in shape. The first whorls are spirally wound as normal. After further growth, however, the final whorl bends outward, creating the shape of a slightly curved tube. In the subfamily Caecinae M.E. Gray, 1857 the apical whorls are subsequently discarded, and the tube sealed with a partition (septum). The whorls remain present in Ctiloceratinae Iredale & Laseron, 1957. Shallow water in tropical and temperate seas. Some live in the gaps between grains of sand. Genera include: *Caecum, Ctiloceras, Elephantulum, Parastrophia, Pseudoparastrophia*. A compilation photograph has been used to illustrate this distinctive group (taken using a Scanning Electron Microscope).

Genus *Caecum*: tube snails. The photograph above illustrates as follows: (Top) the septum, immature phase and adult phase, respectively, of *Caecum tornatum* Verrill & Bush, 1900 – the Caribbean ringed tube snail. Dimensions: up to 5mm. CAR; sublittoral and limestone caves inland. (Middle) *C. glabrum* (Montagu,

Elachisinidae

PONDER, 1985

Micro-mollusks. Wide, conical shells with a smooth, domed apex. Closely related to Iravadiidae and Vitrinellidae. Occur in the intertidal zone, along (sub-) tropical coasts including those of the Atlantic Ocean, the eastern and western United States, New Zealand, Australia, and the Philippines.

Emblandidae

PONDER, 1985

This family contains only one species, from southeastern Australia: *Emblanda emblematica* (Hedley, 1906).

Epigridae

PONDER, 1985

Micro-mollusks. Exclusively Australian. A small number of species. The shells are elongated spires with a smooth, glossy surface.

Falsicingulidae

SLAVOSHEVSKAYA, 1975

Small, oval/conical, thin shells with straight-sided whorls. Smooth. Includes species in Alaska, the Kuril Islands, and the Aleutians.

Hydrobiidae

TROSCHEL, 1857
river micro-snails

Large, familiar group of small, mostly smooth shells ranging from a few millimeters in size to approximately 10mm. Usually cone or spire-shaped, often with a thin periostracum. Worldwide distribution, especially in freshwater, estuarine water, lagoons, and mangrove swamps. Sometimes also found in maritime environments. In the latter case, found particularly in sandy and muddy locations with algae and sea grass. Some species found in enormous numbers. Divided into several subfamilies, including: Amnicolinae Tryon, 1862; Belgrandiinae De Stefani, 1877; Bithyniinae Troschel, 1857; Cochliopinae Tryon, 1866; Hydrobiinae Troschel, 1857; Lithoglyphinae Troschel, 1857; Littoridininae J.E. Gray, 1857; Moitessieriinae Bourguignat, 1863; Tateinae Thiele, 1925. Many dozens of genera, including: *Alzoniella, Arganiella, Avenionia, Belgrandia, Belgrandiella, Bythinella, Bythiospeum, Clenchiella, Fissuria, Graziana, Hauffenia, Heleobia, Hemistomia, Hydrobia, Iglica, Lithoglyphus, Littoridina, Marstoniopsis, Neohoratia, Peringia, Potamopyrgus, Pseudamnicola, Sadleriana, Ventrosia.*

Just a few European specimens have been included below. In the photograph, from left to right: *Hydrobia ulvae* (Pennant, 1777)—mud-flat snail; *Ventrosia ventrosa* (Montagu, 1803)—swollen mud-flat snail; *Hydrobia neglecta* Muus, 1963—neglected estuarine snail. Dimensions of 8, 6, and 5.5mm, respectively. The first is maritime, living on soft, silty bottoms in the littoral, the other two live mostly in regions with a soft, muddy bottom and in brackish water.

Hydrococcidae

THIELE, 1928
Micro-mollusks. Top to cone-shaped shells, measuring up to 4mm. Small, smooth protoconch. Brackish water, Australia.

Iravadiidae

THIELE, 1928
spiral snails

Pointed, often spire-shaped shells. 4–10mm. Apex often rounded. Smooth surface or with lattice or spiral ornament. Oval aperture, outer lip often thickened. Found in Indo-Pacific coastal areas and in the Mediterranean Sea.

Pseudonoba alphesiboei

(MELVILL, 1912)
great spiral snail

D: 5mm. S: thin, extremely slender shell with a squashed apex. O: regularly interspaced, delicate spirals. C: white. H: d1; littoral and sublittoral. W: INDP; Arabian Sea. R: 2. NB: on the right in the photograph is the closely related species *Lucidinella densilabrum* (Melvill, 1912) that lives in the same distribution zone.

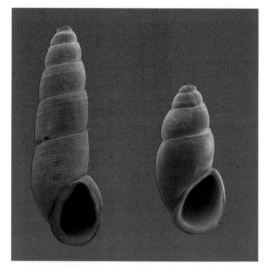

Rissoidae

J.E. GRAY, 1847
floater snails

A very extensive group of micro-mollusks. Mostly 2–6mm. Exceptionally varied in shape, color, and ornament. Especially in coastal areas on weed, under rocks, in sand or mud. Some groups in deeper water. Two subfamilies: Rissoinae J.E. Gray, 1847 and Rissoininae Simpson, 1865. Various genera: *Alvania, Amphirissoa, Attenuata, Benthonella, Boreocingula, Cingula, Crisilla, Frigidoalvania, Galeodina, Linemera, Manzonia, Merelina, Mohrensternia, Obtusella, Onoba, Parashiela,*

Peringiella, Powellisetia, Punctulum, Pusillina, Rissoa, Setia.

Only a few (European) genera have been given below as examples due to the large number of genera and species.

Genus *Alvania*: from left to right, *Alvania cancellata* (Da Costa, 1778)—coarsely nodulose latticed floater snail; *Alvania lactea* (Michaud, 1832)—milky latticed floater snail; *Alvania rykelii* Hoenselaar & Goud, 1998—Cape Verde deepwater latticed floater snail. Dimensions are 5, 6, and 4.5mm respectively. Distribution is, respectively, LUS, KEL, and WAFR.

Genera *Manzonia* and *Onoba*. In the photograph, left, *Manzonia crassa* (Kanmacher, 1798)—umbilical cleft floater snail. Right, *Onoba aculeus* (Gould, 1841)—slender-waisted floater snail. Both 4mm. Distribution is KEL, LUS.

Genus *Rissoa*: in the photograph, from right to left, *Rissoa membranacea* (J. Adams, 1800)—membranous floater snail; *Rissoa violacea lilacina* Récluz, 1843—spotted floater snail; *Rissoa guerinii* Récluz, 1843 – pointed floater snail. Dimensions, are 8, 5, and 6mm respec-

tively. Distribution: LUS, KEL.

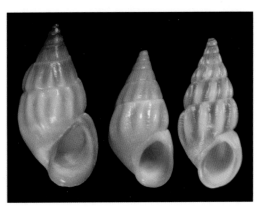

Tornidae

SACCO, 1869
circular snails

Micro-mollusks with almost round, compressed shells. Principally in warmer maritime zones. A common species in Europe.

Tornus subcarinatus

(MONTAGU, 1803)
keeled circular snail

D: 2.5mm. S: distorted, compressed shell. Large body whorl. Broad umbilicus. O: defined spirals, crossed by finer, radial ribs. C: yellowish-white or white. H: d1; areas with coarser sand and pebbles. W: KEL, LUS. R: 1. NB: quite a common species throughout Europe where there is shell sand.

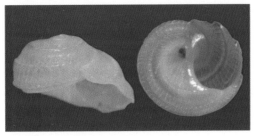

Truncatellidae

J.E. GRAY, 1840
Shells usually less than 10mm tall. Cylindrical, smooth, or ribbed, without an umbilicus. The spire falls off in mature specimens to be replaced by a partition. Worldwide distribution, found on the upper shore.

STROMBOIDEA

RAFINESQUE, 1815

Solidly built, medium-sized to extremely large shells, measuring between 20 and 330mm. The final whorl is large. The aperture's outer lip often flares out into a distinctive wing shape and can develop short or long finger-like projections. The columellar side may be callused. The siphonal canal may be either short or distinctly elongated (genus *Tibia*). Corneous operculum with an eccentric nucleus. The mollusk's head has tentacles, eyes on stalks, and quite a long proboscis (siphon). Found in shallow water, mostly in warmer maritime zones.

Aporrhaiidae

J.E. GRAY, 1850
pelican's foot shells

Shells with an enlarged, wing-like outer lip from which finger-like projections radiate. Radial rows of nodules on the whorls. Atlantic and Mediterranean.

Aporrhais pespelecani

(LINNAEUS, 1758)
common pelican's foot

D: 45mm. S: thick shell. A pointed spire with 10–12 quite convex whorls. The final whorl is markedly wider and ends in finger-like extensions. O: whorls bear blunt tubercles. C: dirty white to pale orange. Aperture and callus usually glossy white. H: d1–2; in shallow as well as slightly deeper water. W: KEL, LUS. R: 1.

Aporrhais serresianus

(MICHAUD, 1828)
Serre's pelican's foot

D: 50mm. S: robust shell with pointed spire, with tapering fingers projecting from the outer lip. Long, narrow siphonal canal projects from the lowest point. O: spirals covered in blunt tubercles. C: amber; aperture and callus glossy creamy white. H: d3–4; deep to very deep water. W: KEL, LUS. R: 1.

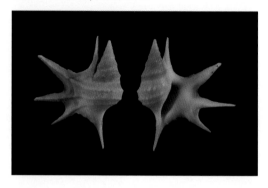

Rostellariidae

GABB, 1868
tibias

Tibia curta

(SOWERBY, 1842)
Indian tibia

D: 140mm. S: thick shell with up to 15 quite level whorls. Siphonal canal straight or slightly bent, approximately 1/6 of the total length. Outer lip has several short projections. O: spire has axial ribs, lower part of body whorl has subtle spirals. C: coffee color, very glossy. Aperture interior white. H: d1–2. W: INDP; from Yemen to southern India. R: 2.

Tibia fusus

(LINNAEUS, 1758)
shinbone tibia

D: 230mm. S: pointed, awl-shaped shell with convex whorls and a long, thin, extended siphonal canal that is sometimes as long as the rest of the shell. Outer lip has 5 short, narrow projections. At the top of the aperture a further short channel for the anal siphon. O: the spire has axial ribs and spiral ornament. Only lower half of body whorl has spirals. C: yellowish-white to tawny brown. Aperture usually lighter. H: d2; deeper water. W: INDP. R: 2–3. NB: the aperture in the species *T. melanocheilus* A. Adams, 1854 – dark-mouthed tibia – is dark purple to brown.

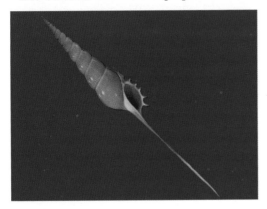

Seraphidae

GRAY, 1853
lance shells

Terebellum terebellum

(LINNAEUS, 1758)
terebellum conch

D: 70mm. S: thin, torpedo-shaped shell, rolled up like a cylinder. The outer lip is not flared and lacks the indentations typical of Strombidae. O: smooth and glossy. C: yellowish-white with variable patterns of brown blotches, dashes, and stripes. Sometimes has zigzag or zebra markings. H: d1; shallow water. W: INDP. R: 1. NB: able to shoot quickly through water and move quickly below sand.

Strombidae

RAFINESQUE, 1815
true conches (and others)

Although this family has only a few genera, these contain some hundreds of species that, for the most part, are distinctively shaped and colored. Most species are found in the Indo-Pacific region. The animals live on sand or mud and feed on algae and detritus. The shells often range from solidly built to thick-shelled and have an enlarged, flaring outer lip. The front (bottom) of the aperture rim shows a slight recess called the stromboid notch through which the animal's left eye-stalk protrudes. The initial whorls of the spire have radial ribs. Subsequent whorls show varices and rounded tubercles, particularly along the shoulder. Subtle spiral ornament is often visible too. In the genus *Lambis* – spider conches – several finger-like projections grow out of the outer lip. Extremely large and heavy shells occur within the genus *Strombus* – true conches – some of which are eaten. The operculum is narrow, crescent-shaped, toothed on one side and too small to seal off the aperture. It is used for locomotion and as a defensive weapon, explaining the name "fighting conch" given to some species. One species, the pink conch or queen conch, *Tricornis gigas* (also known as Strombus gigas), has been protected and may not be traded or imported.

Genera include: *Canarium, Conomurex, Dolomena, Doxander, Euprotomus, Gibberulus, Labiostrombus, Laevistrombus, Lambis, Lentigo, Mirabilistrombus, Strombiconus, Strombus, Tricornis, Varicospira.*

Canarium urceus

(LINNAEUS, 1758)
little bear conch

D: 45mm. S: pointed shell. Angular spire and convex body whorl. Aperture not very enlarged. The inner and outer lips meet at a point at the top of the aperture and are of equal thickness. O: shoulder tubercles and subtle spirals, particularly at the base. C: variable: apricot to dark brown with blotches or stripes. Inner and outer lips usually orange, columellar side sometimes has a brownish-black border. H: d1; shallow water, on sandy or muddy substrates. W: INDP. R: 1.

Conomurex decorus

(RÖDING, 1791)
Mauritian conch

D: 55mm. S: robust shell with a fairly straight-sided spire with a small, pointed apex. Aperture only slightly enlarged, outer lip thickened and bent inward. O: virtually smooth, sometimes subtle spirals. C: creamy white or light brown, with mottling in dark brown, wavy vertical bands. Aperture interior glossy white, orange, or pinkish-red. H: d1; on sand. W: INDP; Indian Ocean. R: 1.

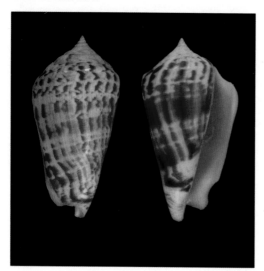

Conomurex luhuanus

(LINNAEUS, 1758)
strawberry conch

D: 70mm. S: upside-down cone shape with a rather compressed spire. Aperture nearly as tall as the body whorl. O: subtle spirals or smooth. C: inner lip black (callused side), aperture flesh-colored or red. H: d1; shallow water, often in considerable numbers. W: INDP. R: 1.

Doxander campbelli

(GRIFFITH & PIDGEON, 1834)
Campbell's conch

D: 50mm. S: shell with a quite pointed spire and an enlarged aperture with a rounded top segment. O: subtle spirals and tubercles. C: white, often with coffee-colored markings. H: d1. W: AUS. R: 1.

Doxander vittatus

(LINNAEUS, 1758)
vittate conch

D: 75mm. S: pointed, elongated shell. Outer lip only slightly enlarged, curves in at an angle to meet inner lip at the top of the aperture. An angular shoulder around the suture. O: spiral and axial ribs on the first whorls. C: gray-white with brown blotches and spiral stripes or else a more uniform amber. H: d1–2; often in slightly deeper water. W: INDP; southern China to Fiji. R: 2.

Euprotomus bulla

(RÖDING, 1798)
bubble conch

D: 60mm. S: thick shell with a wide outer lip. O: coarse tubercles, reasonably wide spirals. Siphonal canal bent outward. C: exterior gray-white with brown blotches. Aperture orange-pink, callus and outer lip white. H: d1; on sand. W: INDP; from Samoa westward. R: 2.

Euprotomus vomer

(RÖDING, 1798)
vomer conch

D: 80mm. S: pointed shell with rather sharply angled whorls. Outer lip extends at an angle,

slightly twisted away, ending at the top in a finger-like projection. O: nodulose spirals and shoulder tubercles. Ridges (lirae) often fan out in the aperture. C: gray-white or apricot, often with orange or brown spots and blotches. Callus and edge of outer lip paler, aperture interior often darker, not necessarily including the apertural folds. The callus often bears a large, dark brown patch halfway up. H: d1; shallow water. W: INDP; southwestern part of the Pacific Ocean. R: 2.

Labiostrombus epidromus

(LINNAEUS, 1758)
swan conch

D: 45mm. S: thick shell with tall, pointed spire. Enlarged, curved outer lip. O: nodules and axial ribs on spire, body whorl virtually smooth. C: white with amber patches and radial zigzags. Aperture white. H: d1. W: INDP. R: 2.

Laevistrombus canarium

(LINNAEUS, 1758)
dog conch

D: 65mm. S: solid to thick shell. Enlarged aperture, almost as tall as the body whorl. O: virtually smooth. C: often a pattern of extremely fine, brown zigzags on a white background. H: d1; shallow water. W: INDP. R: 1.

Lambis chiragra

(LINNAEUS, 1758)
chiragra spider conch

D: 150mm. S: robust, thick shell. The enlarged aperture always has 6 solid, finger-like projections. These are curved, including the lowermost (the siphonal canal). Only the uppermost projection is (nearly) straight. O: blunt tubercles on the whorls and clear grooves. C: creamy white with brown speckled pattern. Interior apricot with very clear columellar folds, often darker in color. H: d1; shallow water, on coral reefs and sand. W: INDP. R: 1. NB: in the species *L. arthritica* (Röding, 1798) – arthritic spider conch – which closely resembles this one, the shell is even thicker and the grooves within the inner lip and elsewhere are a very deep brownish-black.

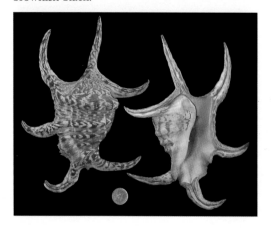

Lambis crocata crocata

(LINK, 1807)
orange spider conch

D: 130mm. S: thick shell with thick outer lip. 7 smooth, finger-like projections. The lower 5, including the siphonal canal, are sharply curved. O: blunt tubercles and grooves. C: apricot, speckled brown. Aperture smooth without grooves, orange. H: d1; shallow water, on reefs. W: INDP. R: 2. NB: the rarer subspecies *L. crocata pilsbryi* (Abbot, 1961) – Pilsbry's spider conch – has notably longer "fingers."

Lambis digitata

(PERRY, 1811)
elongate spider conch

D: 140mm. S: thick shell. The greatly thickened outer lip has 7–9 short, blunt projections. O: tubercles and grooves. C: creamy white with amber markings. H: d1–2. W: INDP. R: 3.

Lambis lambis

(LINNAEUS, 1758)
common spider conch

D: 190mm. S: thick shell with extended outer lip. 7 or more finger-like projections. Siphonal canal fairly short and slightly curved. O: broad tubercles on the whorls and clear grooves. C: exterior creamy white to pale pink with coffee-colored markings. Interior glossy yellow-pink. H: d1; shallow water, on reefs and coral sand. W: INDP. R: 1. NB: female and male specimens differ. For example, males are smaller and have shorter "fingers."

Lambis millepeda

(LINNAEUS, 1758)
millipede spider conch

D: 100mm. S: thick shell. Enlarged aperture with 9 large finger-like projections and often a few smaller ones as well. The uppermost projections are slightly longer, as is the siphonal canal. O: spiral grooves and blunt tubercles on the whorls. C: yellowish-white to orange with brown patches. Aperture interior pink with dark grooves. H: d1; shallow water, on coral reefs and sand. W: INDP. R: 1.

Lambis scorpius scorpius

(LINNAEUS, 1758)
Scorpio conch

D: 150mm. S: thick shell. The outer lip always has 7 curved, finger-like projections, all of which are nodulose, including the siphonal canal. O: grooves and blunt tubercles. C: amber with dark brown patches. H: d1; shallow water, coral reefs. W: INDP; southern part of the Pacific Ocean. R: 1. NB: the subspecies *L. scorpius indomaris* Abbot, 1961 – lesser Scorpio conch – lives in the Indian Ocean and has slightly shorter projections.

Lambis truncata

(LIGHTFOOT, 1786)
giant spider conch

D: 350mm. S: extremely thick shell. The apex is blunt and rounded. The outer lip usually has 7 virtually straight projections (sometimes more). O: blunt tubercles and grooves. C: amber with brown patches. Interior smooth, glossy white without grooves. Inner-lip callus often mauve. H: d1; shallow water on coral reefs and sand. W: INDP; Indian Ocean. R: 1. NB: the largest *Lambis* species. The subspecies *L. truncata sebae* (Kiener, 1843) has a more pointed apex and only lives in the southwestern part of the Pacific Ocean and the Red Sea.

Lambis violacea

(SWAINSON, 1821)
violet spider conch

D: 90mm. S: thick shell. Outer lip has many projections. Siphonal canal slightly curved, other projections almost straight. Outer-lip interior has many very fine folds or grooves. O: tubercles on the whorls and nodulose spirals. C: amber, often with a marbled pattern. Violet to purple deep within the aperture, otherwise porcelain white. H: d2; fairly deep water. W: INDP; Mauritius. R: 4.

Lentigo granulatus

(SWAINSON, 1822)
granulated conch

D: 75mm. S: pointed, relatively slender shell. Outer lip thickened. O: clear spirals and tuber-

cles. Outer-lip interior has granulose folds. C: variable, usually yellowish-white to pink with brown flecks or vertical bands. H: d1; on sandy or rocky substrates in slightly deeper water. W: PAN. R: 1.

Lentigo lentiginosus

(LINNAEUS, 1758)
silver conch

D: 80mm. S: robust, squat shell. Thickened outer lip, serrated at the base. O: exterior entirely covered in nodulose spirals and tubercles. C: purplish-brown flecks and russet spots and lines on a silver-gray background. Outer lip with alternate brown and white stripes. Interior apricot. H: d1; shallow water on coral sand. W: INDP; New Guinea. R: 1.

Mirabilistrombus listeri

(GRAY, 1852)
Lister's conch

D: 130mm. S: very pointed shell with fanciful, wing-shaped outer lip. O: initial whorls have clear axial ribs and subtler spirals. Ornament becomes fainter on body whorl. C: cream or white with a brown zigzag pattern. Sometimes paler bands on a dark background. Aperture white. H: d2; in somewhat deeper water. 70–100m. W: INDP; Bay of Bengal. R: 3. NB: once a greatly sought-after collector's item, now far less rare.

Strombus gracilior

SOWERBY, 1825
eastern Pacific fighting conch

D: 80mm. S: upside-down cone-shape, thickened outer lip, shorter than the body whorl. Angular whorls. O: smooth with blunt, shoulder tubercles. C: apricot, often a lighter band of color in the middle of the body whorl and over the shoulder tubercles. Aperture white, edge of the outer lip and callus a glazed orange-red. H: d1; on sand and mud. W: CAL, PAN. R: 1. NB: defends itself by striking with the foot and operculum.

Strombus pugilis

GMELIN, 1795
West Indian fighting conch

D: 80–90mm. S: robust shell. Upper outer lip angular. O: spiked tubercles on the whorls. C: apricot, callus and inner lip darker orange. H: d1; shallow water, on sand and sea grass. W: CAR; Florida to Brazil. R: 1. NB: defends itself aggressively with its foot and operculum.

Tricornis costatus

(GMELIN, 1791)
milk conch

D: 130mm. S: large, robust to thick shell. O: clearly defined shoulder tubercles and rough, undulating spirals. C: apricot or pink, exterior has subtle, brown markings. Interior glossy orange or pink, sometimes milky white. H: d1. W: CAR. R: 1.

Tricornis gallus

(LINNAEUS, 1758)
rooster tail conch

D: 125mm. S: large, solid species but light in weight. A long, narrow projection extends from the upper part of the outer lip, reaching far beyond the apex. O: 3–5 rough tubercles on the body whorl and very coarse, undulating spirals. C: amber with brown markings. Aperture and callus apricot or pink. H: d1. W: CAR. R: 1.

Tricornis gigas

(LINNAEUS, 1758)
pink conch; queen conch

D: 300mm. S: a large, solid shell with a greatly enlarged aperture that is as wide and tall as the rest of the shell (sometimes taller). O: well-defined, sometimes pointed shoulder tubercles. Nodules also present on body whorl. C: creamy white or apricot; aperture and callus pale or deep pink. H: d1; littoral and slightly deeper water on a sandy substrate. W: CAR. R: 2. NB: protected status: has long been collected in many places for food, causing a sharp decline in the number of adult animals. Sometimes produces (pink) pearls.

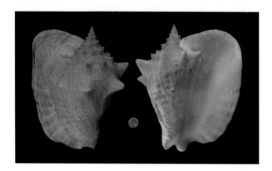

Tricornis goliath

(SCHRÖTER, 1805)
goliath conch

D: 330mm. S: thick, heavy shell. Extremely wide aperture, extending high above the body whorl. Depressed spire. O: slight tubercles. C: yellow-

ish-white or beige flecked with brown. Peach-colored interior. Flaky, yellowish-white periostracum. H: d1–2; deep water on sand. W: CAR; Brazil. R: 3. NB: largest of all the strombs, extremely sought-after by collectors.

Tricornis latissimus

(LINNAEUS, 1758)
broad Pacific conch

160mm. S: thick, heavy shell. Extremely wide aperture, extending far above the body whorl. Depressed spire. O: slight shoulder tubercles and indistinct axial ribs, especially on the upper part of the outer lip. C: light to dark brown with irregular flecks. Aperture interior milky white, sometimes very pale pink. H: d1; sublittoral up to approx. 20m. W: INDP. R: 3.

Tricornis peruvianus

(SWAINSON, 1823)
Peruvian conch

D: 130mm. S: thick shell, aperture greatly enlarged, extending far above the spire. O: exterior has coarse, undulating spirals. Blunt, but prominent, shoulder tubercles. Folds within the aperture. C: brown and gray-white markings. Aperture interior and callus on inner lip a very glossy apricot. H: d1; intertidal zone. W: PAN. R: 2.

Tricornis raninus

(GMELIN, 1791)
hawk-wing conch

D: 100mm. S: solid shell with a blunt spire and callused aperture extending above the apex. O: very blunt shoulder tubercles and rough, undulating spirals on the exterior. C: amber, speckled in brown. Aperture interior glazed apricot to lilac. H: d1; shallow water. W: CAR. R: 1.

Tricornis sinuatus

(LIGHTFOOT, 1786)
sinuous conch

D: 100mm. S: robust shell with somewhat angular spire whorls. Aperture roughly as high as the apex, partly merging with the spire. O: slight tubercles, blunt ribs fan out across outer lip ending in finger-like projections. C: creamy

white with orange to coffee-colored markings. H: d1; on coral sand. W: INDP. R: 2.

Tricornis taurus

(REEVE, 1857)
bull conch

D: 90mm. S: thick, compact shell, somewhat squat. Heavily callused outer lip with one long and one short projection from the upper quadrant. O: a few very large and several less distinct tubercles. C: yellowish-white, speckled with orange. Callus very glossy, orange and merging somewhat into the spire. H: d1; slightly deeper water, on coarse coral sand. W: INDP; Marshall Islands. R: 4. NB: a rare, much sought-after species.

Tricornis tricornis

(LIGHTFOOT, 1786)
three-knobbed conch

D: 100mm. S: quite a solid shell with an enlarged, triangular aperture, extending at an angle in the upper part into a long, finger-like projection. O: 3 very thick, wide tubercles on the body whorls in addition to many smaller ones. C: creamy white mottled with amber.

Aperture interior white. H: d1; shallow water. W: INDP; the Red Sea, Gulf of Aden. R: 1.

Struthiolariidae

P. FISCHER, 1884
ostrich foot shells

Solid, conical or spire-shaped with nodulose ribs and finer spirals. The aperture often somewhat callused but only slightly enlarged (see also Aporrhaiidae) without projections. Broad columellar callus. The animals live buried in sand or silt and, among other places, are found in New Zealand and Australia. A few genera: *Perissodonta, Struthiolaria, Tylospira.*

Struthiolaria papulosa

(MARTYN, 1784)
large ostrich foot

D: 65mm. S: robust, heavy shell with a rather pointed spire. Callused outer lip, curving outward. Thick, glossy callus on inner lip, often also extending above the aperture. O: a row of fairly blunt tubercles encircles the periphery of the whorls. Otherwise, the surface shows fine spi-

rals. C: amber with white and dark brown vertical markings. Aperture and callus cream-colored. H: d1–2; littoral, sublittoral and deeper water. W: AUS; New Zealand. R: 2. NB: worldwide there are fewer than 10 species of ostrich foot. *S. papulosa* is the largest species.

VANIKOROIDEA

J.E. GRAY, 1840
A separate superfamily in which both small spirally wound shells (including the family Vanikoridae) and cap-shaped shells (family Hipponicidae) appear.

Caledoniellidae

ROSEWATER, 1969
Micro-mollusks with thin, flattened spiral shells with a broad, final whorl. No operculum. These snails have a sucker-like mesopodium with which to attach themselves to, for example, crustaceans. Australia and New Zealand.

Haloceratidae

WARÉN & BOUCHET, 1991
Micro-mollusks with a discoid or top-shaped shell with a few whorls. Defined spiral ornament and faint ribs. A deep, wide umbilicus. In deep water to a depth of approximately 3500m.

Hipponicidae

TROSCHEL, 1861
(horse's) hoof shells

Cap-shaped shells with apex curved toward the margin or overhanging it. Ribs and, in places, spirals. Smooth interior. Horseshoe-shaped muscle scar. The animals live attached to rocks, coral, crustaceans, and shellfish. The shell margin adapts to the shape of the surface to which it attaches. Widely distributed throughout warmer maritime zones. Can measure more than 50mm, but is usually smaller. A few genera: *Antisabia, Cheilea, Hipponix, Malluvium, Sabia.*

Cheilea cicatricosa

(REEVE, 1858)
candle-wax hoof shell

D: 30mm. S: thin shell, roughly circular perimeter. A projecting, crescent-shaped plate within, white in color. O: very rounded, concentric ribs, in appearance as if candle wax had dripped onto the shell and hardened. Very fine transverse lines cross the ribs. C: creamy white. H: d1; sublittoral, attached to a hard substrate. W: INDP; Arabian Sea. R: 2.

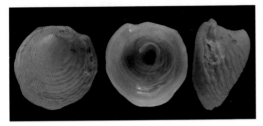

Cheilea equestris

(LINNAEUS, 1758)
false cup-and-saucer shell

D: 30mm. S: thin to solid, cap-shaped shell, sometimes circular. A semicircular, white plate within the shell. O: irregular ribs radiate from the apex, varying in definition. Sometimes nodulose. C: creamy white to yellowish-white. H: d1; sublittoral, attached to a hard substrate. W: CAR, INDP, PAN, PER. R: 1.

Sabia conica

(SCHUMACHER, 1817)
conical horse's hoof shell

D: 10mm. S: thick, cap-shaped shell. Top overhangs the margin, often slightly to one side. O: coarse, flattened, irregular ribs. C: exterior cream or amber, sometimes with russet mottling. Interior orange-brown. H: d1; sublittoral, on other shells and other hard substrates. W: INDP. R: 1.

Vanikoridae

J.E. GRAY, 1840
vanikoro shells

Quite thick, wide, conical shells, measuring up to about 20mm. Large, final whorl. Both spirals and ribs. Broad, slanted aperture, usually with a defined umbilicus. Thin outer lip. Corneous operculum. In the littoral and sublittoral of tropical and subtropical zones, amid rocks, on sand and mud, and in the vicinity of corals, in particular. Also in deeper water. Only a few genera, including: *Larsenia, Macromphalus, Megalomphalus, Talassia, Vanikoro*.

Vanikoro ligata

(RÉCLUZ, 1844)
ligate vanikoro

D: 30mm. S: an almost spherical shell with a large body whorl and an enlarged, almost circular aperture. Clear, wide, cleft-like umbilicus. O: fine spiral ornament. C: white, periostracum amber. H: d1; sublittoral on rocks and reefs. W: INDP. R: 1.

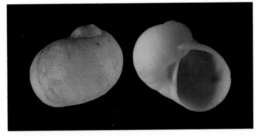

CALYPTRAEOIDEA

LAMARCK, 1809
Limpet-like or spiral in construction. The animals are chiefly protandrously hermaphroditic; juvenile specimens are male, becoming female at a later stage.

Calyptraeidae

LAMARCK, 1809
slipper shells; cup-and-saucer shells, etc.

Either more or less spirally wound shells or else more cap-like in appearance, between 20 and 60mm. The inner walls of the whorls are partially reduced, creating a spiral-shaped plate that can be folded over the umbilicus to produce a funnel shape (genus *Crucibulum*). Flatter species possess a horizontal plate that covers part of the aperture rim (genus *Crepidu-*

la). The animals live attached to rocks or other shellfish. Some species (*Crepidula fornicata*) form chains of 10 or more snails, one on top of the other. On the top are small, sexually mature males, while at the bottom are the (larger) females. Hormonal changes turn males into females as they descend the chain. Found in all warm and temperate maritime zones.

A number of genera: *Calyptraea, Crepidula, Crepipatella, Crucibulum, Maoricrypta, Sandalium, Sigapatella, Siphopatella, Trochita.*

Calyptraea chinensis

(LINNAEUS, 1758)
Chinese cup-and-saucer

D: 6mm. S: fairly thin shell in the shape of a flattened coolie hat. Interior has a white, partially twisted partition plate, which covers part of the aperture. Circular aperture that grows to fit the surface it rests on. O: irregular growth lines. Sometimes also with small nodules. C: white. Glazed interior. H: d1; littoral and sublittoral of rocky coasts, attached to rocks, shells, or other hard substrates. W: KEL, LUS. R: 1.

D: 50mm. S: solid, cap-shaped shell. The apex is curled round to one side; the final whorl is much larger than the one preceding it. The aperture is half covered by a white plate. Adapts to its attachment surface in terms of shape. Both squat and elevated specimens. O: only coarse growth lines. C: amber to pink, with purplish-brown flecks. Shiny pink aperture. H: d1; attached to a hard substrate in the littoral and sublittoral. W: KEL, LUS, VIR. R: 1. NB: at the end of the nineteenth century, accidentally introduced with imported oysters from the North American east coast to southern and western Europe, where it has now become commonplace (competes with oysters and mussels for food and territory).

Crepidula plana

SAY, 1822
eastern white slipper

D: 40mm, often smaller. S: very flat, cap-shaped shell. Underside has a white plate. O: only concentric growth lines. C: white. H: d1; sublittoral, usually amid other shells. W: CAR, VIR. R: 2; less common in the Caribbean. NB: almost never forms chains.

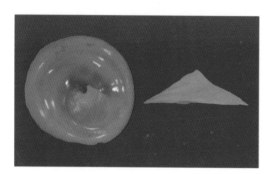

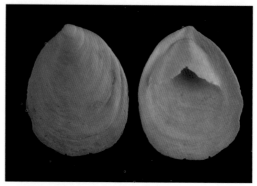

Crepidula fornicata

(LINNAEUS, 1758)
Atlantic slipper

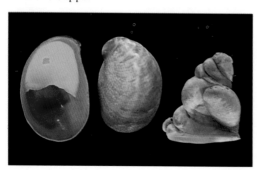

Crucibulum scutellatum

(WOOD, 1828)
shield cup-and-saucer

D: 50mm. S: circular to oval, cap-shaped shell. Adapts shape to its attachment surface. Interior has a twisted, plate-like projection. O: usually has undulating, folded ribs and, sometimes, transverse ribs. C: yellowish-white to white, interior white to light brown. H: d1–2; sublittoral of rocky coasts and deeper, attached to a hard substrate. W: PAN; Mexico to Ecuador. R: 1.

Trochita dhofarensis

TAYLOR & SMYTHE, 1985
Dhofar trochita

D: 40mm. S: solid, rather flat, cap-shaped shell. Interior has a partly twisted partition. Perimeter roughly circular. O: irregular, rounded ribs, radiating from the apex. C: amber with russet patches. Interior russet. H: d1; on a hard substrate. W: INDP; Arabian Sea. R: 3.

CAPULOIDEA

J. FLEMING, 1822
The larvae in the superfamily Capuloidea are different in form to those seen in Calyptraoidea, although similarities exist between their mature shells.

Capulidae

J. FLEMING, 1822
cap shells

Recent research has shown that a group of snails, which previously had always been classified in a separate family, namely Trichotropidae J.E. Gray, 1850, actually belonged within Capulidae. Capulidae are cap-shaped shells. Their first whorls are flattened and coiled. The final whorl is large and expanded into a funnel shape. They have a smooth interior and may also have partitions, causing some species to resemble Calyptraeidae. The periostracum is thick and either pilose or velvety. Shells from the former Trichotropidae are more spirally wound with an enlarged, often

rounded, aperture rim, lattice ornament and an extremely pilose periostracum with long hairs. These animals attach to rocks or bivalves, from which they steal food with their long siphons. Occurrence in all maritime zones, especially in slightly deeper water.

Capulus ungaricus

(LINNAEUS, 1758)
fool's cap

D: 50mm. S: cap-shaped, thin shell. Shape is variable: both elevated and flattened specimens. Apex curls backward. Aperture rim adapts to its attachment surface. O: spiral ribs and grooves radiate from the apex, interspersed with growth lines. C: yellowish-white, orange, or pink. Interior often glossy pink. Tawny periostracum, quite thick and fibrous. H: d2–4; sublittoral to deep water, attached to rocks and shells. W: KEL, LUS. R: 2.

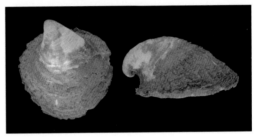

XENOPHOROIDEA

TROSCHEL, 1852
A relatively small group with distinctive characteristics. The animals cement small stones, shell valves, shell fragments, and other material to their own shells.

Xenophoridae

TROSCHEL, 1852
carrier shells

Roughly circular, squat to tent-shaped shells, measuring from 25mm to 110mm. Robust to extremely fragile shells, with or without delicate or coarse ornament. The animals collect bivalve shells, gastropod shells, or pebbles, which are arranged and attached on their own shells radially. Elongated shells are attached on one side like spines; shell valves are usually attached to the edge with the inner side uppermost. Whether the snail collects gastropods, bivalves, or stones all depends on the material available in its environment. Species from the genera *Onustus* and *Stellaria* have a wider umbilicus and cement objects to their shells only rarely.

Onustus exutus

(REEVE, 1842)
barren carrier shell

D: 90mm. S: exceptionally thin shell. A paper-thin, keel-shaped perimeter grows from the underside of the whorls. The base is greatly flattened with a large, circular umbilicus. Only rarely carries attached material. O: irregular, oblique spirals, low plate-like structures and growth lines. C: creamy white to apricot, shiny underside. H: d1–2; sublittoral and somewhat deeper water. W: INDP, JAP. R: 3.

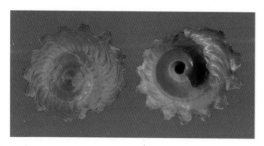

Onustus indicus

(GMELIN, 1791)
Indian carrier shell

D: 75mm. S: thin shell with a flattened base. A paper-thin, keel-shaped perimeter growing from the base. O: flattened underside with a circular umbilicus. Attached material only on the first whorls. C: creamy white to light brown. H: d1; sublittoral, on a sandy substrate. W: INDP. R: 3.

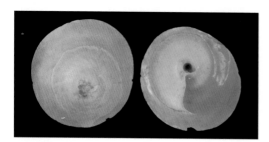

Onustus longleyi

(BARTSCH, 1931)
Longley's carrier shell

D: 130mm (including the perimeter). S: squat, conical shell with an extremely enlarged, wide, paper-thin underside in a keel shape, which is usually partially damaged. Deep, round umbilicus. O: underside with fairly flat, plate-like growth lines. Subtle to defined rhomboid ornament on top of the keeled perimeter. C: creamy white. H: d2–3; mostly in deep water. W: VIR. R: 4. NB: good specimens are rare.

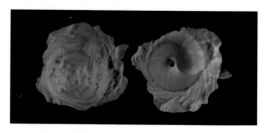

Stellaria solaris

(LINNAEUS, 1764)
sunburst carrier shell

D: 75mm (up to 110mm including projections). S: fairly thin shell with a flattened cone. Below each whorl a keel of flattened spines. Flat underside; wide, round umbilicus. Attached material absent, or only on the first whorls. O: underside has strong, wavy transverse grooves. C: creamy white to amber. H: d1–3; sublittoral to (mostly) deeper water. W: INDP. R: 3. NB: sought after by collectors. Considered very rare before the Second World War. Nowadays, caught regularly.

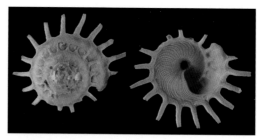

Xenophora conchyliophora

(VON BORN, 1780)
Atlantic carrier shell

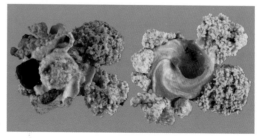

D: 50mm. S: solid, compressed shell, usually covered in a lot of material, including stones and calcified algae. O: no umbilicus. C: amber or orange-brown. H: d1; sublittoral, rocky and sandy coasts. W: CAR, VIR. R: 1.

Xenophora corrugata

(REEVE, 1842)
rough carrier shell

D: 50mm. S: thin, top-shaped shell with angular whorls. Attached material, especially on the spire (stones, shells). Umbilicus open only in young specimens. O: underside has undulating spirals covered in small nodules. C: cream to pale yellow. H: d1–2; sublittoral and deeper water, along sandy coasts. W: INDP; Red Sea, Arabian Sea. R: 2.

Xenophora crispa

(KÖNIG, 1825)
Mediterranean carrier shell

D: 50mm (usually smaller). S: quite solid, squat, conical shell. Mostly gravel and shell fragments attached. O: Underside has undulating spirals covered in very fine nodules. C: creamy white. H: d2–3; sublittoral and mostly rather deeper water. W: LUS, WAFR. R: 4. NB: a sought-after European species. West African types are taller and show coarser ornament on the base.

Xenophora japonica

KURODA & HABE, 1971
Japanese carrier shell

D: 50mm. S: quite solid, slightly domed shell without umbilicus. O: subtle, transverse grooves fan out on underside. C: creamy to milky white. H: d2–3; deep water on sand. W: JAP. R: 3.

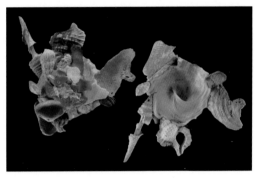

Xenophora mekranensis konoi

HABE, 1953
tent-shaped carrier shell

D: 60mm. S: disproportionately tall shell with a fairly flat underside. Narrow umbilicus. O: undulating spirals covered in fine nodules on underside, the most distinct of these around the umbilicus. C: white to cream, glossy white aperture. H: d1–2; sublittoral and deeper water on sand. W: INDP, JAP. R: 2–3.

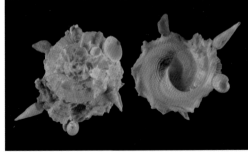

Xenophora neozelanica

SUTER, 1908
Australian carrier shell

D: 60mm. S: robust, conical shell, slightly domed underside. Cleft-like umbilicus or absent. O: faint, vaguely nodulose spirals and wavy transverse ribs on underside. Stones often attached. C: creamy white to amber. Aperture callus sometimes pale orange. H: d2–3; deep water along rocky and sandy coasts up to approx 150m. W: AUS. R: 3.

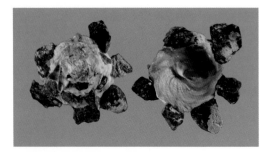

Xenophora pallidula

(REEVE, 1842)
pallid carrier shell

D: 65mm. S: conical shell. Flat underside. Umbilicus very small or absent. O: faint spirals and fanning, radial growth lines on underside. C: pale white or cream. H: d2–3; deep water. W: JAP, INDP, ZAFR. R: 2. NB: particularly noted for the large quantity of material sometimes attached.

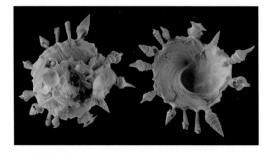

VERMETOIDEA

RAFINESQUE, 1815
Irregularly wound, tubular shells attached to rocks, corals, or other mollusks.

Vermetidae

RAFINESQUE, 1815
worm shells

Vermetidae are often confused with tubeworms, but tubeworms do not have a shiny interior, while Vermetidae tubes do. Moreover, Vermetidae have a spirally wound first whorl, a disengaged shell with a shell wall composed of three layers, and a circular aperture, often with cleft in it. The operculum is small, corneous or wholly absent (genus *Serpulorbis*). Special glands in the foot produce slime threads used to trap micro-organisms. The animals form colonies and live in all warmer maritime regions, mostly in the intertidal and sublittoral zones.

Serpulorbis arenarius

(LINNAEUS, 1767)
Mediterranean worm shell

D: 200mm. S: whorls circular in cross-section, aperture up to 15mm. O: exterior has subtle, keel-shaped longitudinal ribs with finer spirals and irregular growth lines in between. C: yellowish-white or light brown. H: d1; littoral and sublittoral. W: LUS, WAFR. R: 2. NB: the specimen shown survived almost a year in a seawater aquarium.

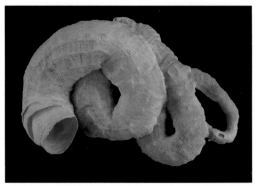

CYPRAEOIDEA

RAFINESQUE, 1815
The shape of these shells differs markedly from that of "ordinary" shells. Instead of the normal, spirally wound shape, where whorls increase in size with age, in adult cowries the newest whorl grows over previous whorls (producing a convoluted spire). The final whorl, the body whorl, is very large. The shell is ovate and on one side has a curved, convex "back." The other side is flatter and through it runs a long, cleft-like aperture with a canal visible at either end of the shell. The outer edge is callused; the outer lip is turned inward. The outer and inner lips almost always show teeth or folds. There is no operculum. The surface is typically smooth with a characteristic, glossy, porcelaneous layer of enamel. This layer and the coloration are created by the thin mantle that surrounds the shell on either side. A mantle line is produced in the (coloration) pattern where the mantle flaps meet each other.

There is wide variation in color and markings. Large areas of color are often present in certain positions, such as a dark spot of color close to the apex, "terminal blotches" at both ends, and dorsal marks on the dorsal side. Immature specimens are thinner and less solid and have an elongated shape. Former whorls can still be seen in such specimens and the wider aperture has no teeth. Most species are smooth. Only a few have any ornament.

Hundreds of species are known, measuring 5–150mm. The animals are nocturnal and feed on algae, various sessile organisms, and carrion. They occur mainly in warmer seas, principally in the Indo-Pacific region. Owing to their captivating appearance, cowries are sought-after collectors' items. Rare species can command high prices. The word "porcelain" derives from these sea snails. Because of their rounded shape, they were known as "porcellana" from the Latin porcella or "little pig." When the shiny glaze of Chinese porcelain was seen in Europe for the first time, people thought that it had been made from these animals' shells!

(In the photograph: *Cypraea pantherina* Lightfoot, 1786 – the panther cowrie – creeps over rocks. The mantle partly encases the shell. Underwater photograph P.L. van Pel.)

Cypraeidae

RAFINESQUE, 1815
cowries

Regarding the general shape of these shells, refer to the previous description of the superfamily. Differences of opinion exist about the classification of the species. Species are often divided into subfamilies according to shape, ornament, coloration, and bodily features: Bernayinae Schilder, 1927; Cypraeinae Rafinesque, 1815; Cypraeovulinae Schilder, 1927; Erosariinae

Schilder, 1924. Additionally, species are divided into various separate genera, such as: *Annepona, Austrocypraea, Barycypraea, Bernaya, Bistolida, Blasicrura, Chelycypraea, Cribrarula, Cypraea, Cypraeovula, Erosaria, Erronea, Ipsa, Leporicypraea, Luria, Lyncina, Macrocypraea, Mauritia, Monetaria, Naria, Neobernaya, Nesiocypraea, Notadusta, Notocypraea, Palmadusta, Proadusta, Purpuradusta, Pustularia, Schilderia, Siphocypraea, Staphylaea, Talparia, Trona, Umbilia, Zoila, Zonaria.* A conservative approach has been taken with all of the cowrie species dealt with here and, as such, they have been placed alphabetically under the genus *Cypraea* Linnaeus, 1758, according to their species name.

Cypraea achatidea

SOWERBY, 1837
agate cowrie

D: 35mm. S: somewhat inflated shell. Teeth often indistinct. O: smooth. C: creamy white or light brown with irregular, dark brown speckling, sometimes lighter. Canal rims and encircling margin apricot. Base (the underside with the aperture cleft) and aperture white. H: d3–4; deeper water. W: LUS. R: 3. NB: the most sought-after species of cowrie from the Lusitanian fauna zone.

Cypraea albuginosa

GRAY, 1825
Albugine cowrie

25mm. S: ovate shell. Small, subtle aperture teeth. O: smooth. C: small, irregular, orange-brown to purplish-brown rings on a grayish-white background. Base and teeth white. H: d1; shallow water under rocks. W: CAL, PAN; Gulf of California, Panama to Ecuador. R: 1.

Cypraea angustata

GMELIN, 1791
plump cowrie

D: 35mm. S: ovate shell, slightly inflated. Sharp, defined aperture teeth. O: smooth. C: shiny, beige to apricot, only the margin has a pattern of round, dark brown speckles. H: d1; littoral and sublittoral. W: AUS; Tasmania. R: 2.

Cypraea annulus

LINNAEUS, 1758
gold-ringer cowrie

D: 25mm. S: ovate shell, slightly compressed. Fairly coarse teeth. O: smooth. C: a bluish-green wash over center of exterior encircled by a thin, golden-yellow ring. Margin, base, and teeth white. H: d1; littoral and sublittoral, coral reefs. W: INDP. R: 1. NB: once used as currency.

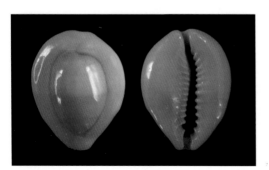

Cypraea arabica

LINNAEUS, 1758
Arabian cowrie

D: 80mm. S: compressed, pear-shaped shell. Quite a lot of relatively large teeth in the aperture. O: smooth. C: background cream-colored to orange-brown with chestnut markings and lines, somewhat reminiscent of Arabic script. Margin speckled in lilac or brown. H: d1; on coral reefs. W: INDP; northwestern part of the Indian Ocean, also in the Red Sea. R: 1.

Cypraea argus

LINNAEUS, 1758
eyed cowrie

D: 80mm, sometimes larger. S: oblong, cylindrical shell. O: smooth. C: light brown with 4 paler, transverse bands. Dorsal side covered in dark brown rings, ranging from small to large (the eyes). H: d1; coral reefs. W: INDP; eastern part of the Indian Ocean to the Philippines. R: 2–3.

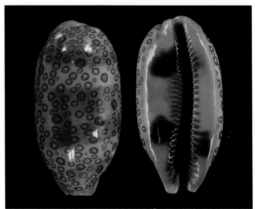

Cypraea asellus

LINNAEUS, 1758
Asellus cowrie

D: 20mm. S: ovate, somewhat elongated shell. O: smooth. C: white with 3 black-brown bands crossing the back. Teeth and base white. H: d1; coral reefs under rocks. W: INDP; from eastern Africa to the Philippines. R: 2.

Cypraea aurantium

GMELIN, 1791
golden cowrie

D: 110mm. S: large, convex, ovate shell. O: smooth. C: exterior a uniform golden yellow to orange-red. Canal extremities paler. Base white, teeth apricot. H: d1; 10–20 meters deep in holes and crevices in coral reefs. W: INDP; from the Philippines to Polynesia. R: 3; relatively rare. NB: used as a status symbol by Polynesian chiefs and others in positions of authority.

Cypraea bistrinotata

M. SCHILDER & F.A. SCHILDER, 1937
bistrinotata cowrie

D: 20–25mm. S: thin, inflated shell, from either end of which extends a "snout" (the canal). O: surface slightly pustular. C: apricot with 3 rows of brown mottling and various smaller speckles on the margin. Base pale yellow, often with 4 brown patches. H: d1; under rocks, on coral reefs. W: INDP; Polynesia and the Philippines. R: 3. NB: the subspecies shown is *C. bistrinotata mediocris* Schilder & Schilder, 1938.

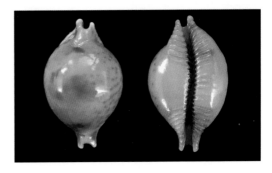

Cypraea camelopardalis

PERRY, 1811
giraffe cowrie

D: 60–70mm. S: ovate, inflated shell. O: smooth. C: brownish-gray with grayish-white speckles of differing sizes. Canal extremities and base paler or white. Black layer on teeth. H: d2–3. W: INDP; Red Sea and Gulf of Aden. R: 3.

Cypraea capensis

GRAY, 1828
Cape cowrie

D: 25mm. S: inflated shell, underside somewhat flattened. Outer lip extends beyond the body whorl on one side. Quite coarse teeth. O: dorsal side has medium-sized lateral ribs, finer ones on the base. C: dorsal side grayish-pink with irregular, rusty markings in the middle. Base gray-white. H: d2–3; deeper water. W: ZAFR.

R: 3. NB: one of the few true cowries with any ornament.

Cypraea caputdraconis

MELVILL, 1888
dragon's head cowrie

D: 25mm. S: shell with an inflated body whorl. Flat base. O: smooth. C: upper surface dark brown with small, paler speckles in an oval area in the center. Clear mantle line. Base is a uniform dark brown, teeth paler or white. H: d1. W: INDP; Easter Island. R: 2.

Cypraea caputserpentis

LINNAEUS, 1758
serpent's head cowrie

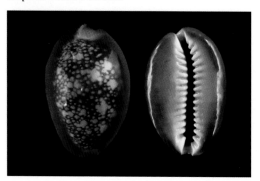

D: 25–30mm. S: upper side has an elevated central section with flatter margins. Base very flattened. O: smooth. C: upper surface brown, an oval area in the center with paler speckles and dots. Canal extremities and base pale orange-brown, teeth yellowish-white to white. H: d1; shallow water, coral reefs. W: INDP; from East Africa to the middle of the Pacific Ocean. R: 1. NB: is among the most commonplace and familiar of species.

Cypraea carneola

LINNAEUS, 1758
carnelian cowrie

D: 65mm. S: ovate shell with quite fine teeth. O: smooth. C: amber to light brown with a few orange-brown transverse bands. Often (although certainly not always) a lilac ring surrounds this. Teeth and aperture interior also lilac. Margin often has indistinct, coffee-colored patches. H: d1; littoral and sublittoral, coral reefs. W: INDP; Red Sea, Indo-Pacific region. R: 1.

Cypraea caurica

LINNAEUS, 1758
caurica cowrie

D: 70mm. S: ovate shell with very distinct teeth. Margin often slightly impressed. O: smooth. C: blue-green with very irregular pattern of amber to brown speckles. Margin has rather larger brown speckles. Sometimes also with one or more markings at the canal extremities. H: d1; sublittoral and littoral. W: INDP; western Pacific Ocean. R: 1. NB: common, exceptionally variable species, various subspecies and colored varieties.

Cypraea cervinetta

KIENER, 1843
Panamanian deer cowrie

D: 75mm. S: elongated, almost cylindrical shell. Fairly coarse teeth, especially in the outer lip. O: smooth. C: beige-amber to light brown, speckled with irregular, white dots and with a few wide, dark brown transverse bands. Clear, paler mantle line. Teeth set off against dark brown indents. H: d1; littoral and sublittoral. W: CAL, PAN. R: 2.

Cypraea cervus

LINNAEUS, 1771
Atlantic deer cowrie

D: 100–170mm. S: oblong-cylindrical shell, fairly distinct teeth. O: smooth. C: light to dark brown with irregular, grayish-white speckles. Clear, pale gray mantle line. Base lighter. Teeth set off against dark brown indents. H: d1; sublittoral. W: CAR; Florida, the Bahamas, Brazil. R: 3. NB: the world's largest species of cowrie.

Cypraea cinerea

GMELIN, 1791
Atlantic gray cowrie

D: 30mm. S: ovate, slightly inflated cowrie. Defined teeth. O: smooth. C: beige-amber, apricot to pink, sometimes with dark speckles. Often with a few wide, dark pink bands. Base and teeth white. H: d1; rocky coasts, reefs. W: CAR. R: 2.

Cypraea cribraria

LINNAEUS, 1758
sieve cowrie

D: 45mm. S: oval shell with distinct teeth. O: smooth. C: upper surface a glossy orange-brown with large, white spots, usually round. Margin and canal extremities white, base and teeth also white or pale sepia. H: d1; sublittoral, reefs. W: INDP. R: 2.

Cypraea depressa

GRAY, 1824
depressed cowrie

D: 50mm. S: ovate, compressed shell with a flat base and domed back. Teeth quite defined. O: smooth. C: upper side russet, speckled pale gray or white, dark brown speckled margin. Base amber or white, edges speckled with brown. Teeth set off against dark brown indents. H: d1; sublittoral, coral reefs. W: INDP. R: 1.

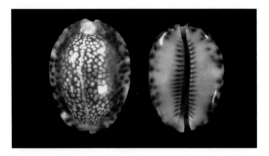

Cypraea diluculum

REEVE, 1845
daybreak cowrie

D: 30mm. S: ovate, slightly inflated shell with fairly strong teeth. O: smooth. C: a few white or light brown transverse bands (consisting of V-shaped markings, often creating a herringbone pattern) against a purplish-brown background. Part of the base shows the same pattern or is speckled dark brown against white. Outer lip always white. H: d1; sublittoral, coral reefs. W: INDP; east coast of Africa. R: 1.

Cypraea eburnea

BARNES, 1824
ivory-white cowrie

D: 45mm. S: elongated oval shell with defined teeth. O: smooth. C: milky white without any

other coloration. H: d2; coral reefs, under rocks. W: INDP; southeastern part, from New Guinea to the Fiji Islands. R: 2.

Cypraea erosa

LINNAEUS, 1758
eroded cowrie

D: 35mm. S: ovate, slightly inflated, shell. Clearly defined teeth. O: upper side smooth; ribbed and granulose at either end of the canals. C: light brown with small, white speckles. Base pale beige to off-white. H: d1; coral reefs, shallow water. W: INDP; eastern coast of Africa to Polynesia. R: 1.

Cypraea friendii

GRAY, 1831
Friend's cowrie

D: 75mm. S: elongated shell, pointed posterior. Extended aperture. Delicate teeth. O: smooth. C: base and margin dark brown, upper side paler with golden-yellow and dark brown markings. H: d2–3. W: AUS. R: 3. NB: several forms.

Cypraea fultoni

SOWERBY III, 1903
Fulton's cowrie

D: 65mm. S: slightly pear-shaped shell, tapering to a "spout" at one end. Rather indistinct teeth. O: smooth; faintly granulose on the base. C: amber, paler on the upper side with a few markings composed of golden-brown, wavy lines haphazardly intersecting. Margin speckled brown. Creamy white base. H: d3–4. W: ZAFR. R: 5. NB: is among the rarest of cowries. For many years known mainly from the stomach contents of deep-sea fishes.

Cypraea globulus

LINNAEUS, 1758
chick-pea cowrie

D: 20mm. S: much inflated, ovate shell. The aperture extended to the front and rear. O: smooth, sometimes with pustules. C: golden-yellow, sometimes speckled dark brown and with several larger, brown spots on the base. H: d1; shallow water, living on corals. W: INDP. R: 2.

Cypraea granulata

PEASE, 1862
granulated cowrie

D: 40mm. S: ovate shell. Extremely fine teeth. O: underside has clear transverse ribs that continue around to the upper surface over the margin, but become fainter in the center of the shell. Also covered in pustular projections. C: orange-brown. Pustules and ribs often outlined in orange. H: d1; reefs. W: INDP; Hawaii, Marquesas Islands. R: 3–4.

Cypraea guttata

GMELIN, 1791
great spotted or drop-covered cowrie

D: 60mm. S: relatively slender shell, pointed extremities. O: ribbed base, ribs becoming fainter as they run over onto the margin. Smooth shiny back. C: teeth folds and grooves light to dark brown. Upper side orange with blotches and finer speckling in pale yellow to white. H: d3. W: INDP, JAP. R: 3–4. NB: sought-after species among collectors.

Cypraea helvola

LINNAEUS, 1758
honey cowrie

D: 25mm. S: oval, slightly compressed shell with distinct teeth. O: smooth, sometimes small, pustular projections on the margin. C: apricot to brownish-red, very glossy. Usually with orange, brown, and pale gray patches. Canal extremities often slightly lilac. Base and teeth honey-yellow or orange. H: d1; littoral and sublittoral, rocky coasts and coral reefs. W: INDP. R: 1.

Cypraea hesitata

IREDALE, 1916
undecided cowrie

D: 100mm. S: oval, compressed shell. Slightly curved aperture, projecting at either end. Delicate teeth. O: smooth, slightly folded at each end. C: amber with darker golden-brown speck-

ling. Base and teeth white. H: d2; deeper water. W: AUS. R: 3.

Cypraea isabella

LINNAEUS, 1758
Isabelle cowrie

D: 45mm. S: elongated, cylindrical shell with very delicate teeth. O: smooth. C: upper side beige to amber, sometimes with transverse bands and in most cases with vertical, broken lines of brown to black dots, flecks and stripes. Base and teeth white. 2 orange blotches at the canal extremities continuing into the aperture cleft. H: d1; sublittoral of coral reefs. W: INDP. R: 1. NB: varies in shape, with plump specimens as well as slender ones.

Cypraea lamarcki

GRAY, 1825
Lamarck's cowrie

D: 40mm. S: oval, slightly inflated shell with strong teeth. O: smooth or subtly granulose. C: spattered with gray-white dots on a greenish-gray or ochre background. Margin has larger, dark brown blotches. Base and teeth white. H: d1; littoral and sublittoral, usually on mud. W: INDP. R: 2.

Cypraea leucodon

BRODERIP, 1828
white-toothed cowrie

D: 85mm. S: ovate, greatly inflated shell. Very strong teeth. O: smooth. C: upper side apricot with large, round, white spots. Base and teeth pale amber. H: d3–4; deepwater species. W: INDP. NB: long considered one of the world's very rarest cowries.

Cypraea limacina

LAMARCK, 1810
Limacina or slug-like cowrie

D: 25mm. S: elongated, oval shell. Very strong teeth. O: surface covered in fine, indistinct, pustular nodules. C: upper side dark brown with pale or white spots. Canal extremities orange-brown. H: d1; sublittoral, under rocks. W: INDP. R: 1. NB: shown in the photograph is the subspecies *C. l. facifer* Iredale, 1933 – the handsome Limacina cowrie.

Cypraea lurida

LINNAEUS, 1758
lurid or fallow cowrie

D: 45–65mm. S: elongated, oval, inflated shell. O: smooth. C: upper side gray-brown with 2 paler transverse bands, extremities orange, each of which has 2 black blotches. Paler colored base. H: d1–2; sublittoral and deeper. W: LUS, WAFR. R: 3.

Cypraea lynx

LINNAEUS, 1758
lynx cowrie

D: 65mm. S: inflated, ovate shell with fairly fine teeth. O: smooth. C: upper side has brown and orange speckling, sometimes green, varying in size. Base paler in color, orange teeth. H: d1; coral reefs, rocky coasts. W: INDP; east coast of Africa to Polynesia. R: 1.

Cypraea mappa

LINNAEUS, 1758
map cowrie

D: 75mm. S: inflated, ovate shell with fine teeth. O: smooth. C: yellow, brownish-gray to pale pink with a pattern of brown stripes and blotches and a pale mantle line with rounded tributaries branching from it. Viewed as a whole, it resembles a well-worn, burnt map. H:

d1; coral reefs, under large pieces of coral. W: INDP; east coast of Africa to Polynesia. R: 1.

Cypraea marginalis

DILLWYN, 1827
margin cowrie

D: 30mm. S: wide, oval shell. Strong teeth. O: smooth; slight nodulose ornament at extremities. C: gray-green with both white speckles as well as rather larger, brown, encircling blotches. H: d2. W: INDP, ZAFR. R: 3.

Cypraea marginata

GASKOIN, 1849
broad-margined cowrie

D: 60mm. S: angular shell, pinched and flattened at the extremities. Very flat base. Fine teeth. O: subtly granulose at the flattened extremities, often pitted. C: creamy white with light brown blotches, or darker with golden-brown blotches. Base and teeth white. H: d1–3; amid corals and sponges. W: AUS. R: 4–5. NB: rare, sought-after Australian species.

Cypraea mauritiana

LINNAEUS, 1758
humpback or chocolate cowrie

D: 90mm. S: wide, heavy shell with a humped back. The sides make an angle with the flat base. O: smooth. C: margin and base chocolate brown. Back often paler with pale, round blotches and a golden mantle line. H: d1; littoral and sublittoral, under rocks and on reefs. W: INDP. R: 1.

Cypraea moneta

LINNAEUS, 1758
money cowrie

D: 35mm. S: solid shell with flattened sides, often granulose. Slightly expanded aperture extremities. Quite distinct teeth. O: smooth. C: variable, usually a glossy yellowish-green, often with a golden-yellow mantle line or ring. 2–3 greenish-gray bands often cross the center of the back as well. A uniform band of pale yellow

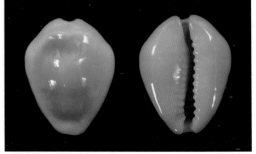

or white surrounds this. Base and aperture also a uniform white. H: d1; sublittoral, rocky coasts, reefs. W: INDP; east coast of Africa to the Galapagos Islands. R: 1. NB: very common species; once used as currency.

Cypraea mus

LINNAEUS, 1758
mouse cowrie

D: 50mm. S: thick shell with protruding outer lip. O: surface slightly granulose. Teeth only subtly indicated. C: amber with light and dark brown blotches. Back has irregular area of dark blotching. Teeth darker. H: d1–2; sublittoral and slightly deeper water. W: CAR; Venezuela, Colombia. R: 2.

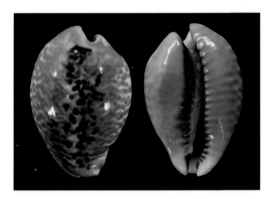

Cypraea nivosa

BRODERIP, 1827
cloudy or snowy cowrie

D: 60mm. S: elongated, oval shell. Quite fine teeth. O: smooth. C: amber with gray-brown to gray, cloudy blotches. H: d1; shallow water. W: INDP; northwestern part. R: 3. NB: once rare, now found in large numbers.

Cypraea ocellata

LINNAEUS, 1758
ocellate cowrie

D: 25mm. S: ovate shell. Strong teeth. O: smooth. C: orange-brown back covered in black and white spots like eyes. Gray mantle line. Base paler, sometimes speckled. H: d1; littoral and sublittoral, under muddy stones. W: INDP; northern part of the Indian Ocean. R: 1.

Cypraea onyx

LINNAEUS, 1758
onyx cowrie

D: 45mm. S: ovate, inflated shell. Quite strong teeth. O: smooth. C: a deep, dark brown upper side with a gray sheen and often slightly muted, golden yellow bands or blotches. H: d1; reefs and muddy bottoms. W: INDP; western Pacific Ocean. R: 2.

Cypraea pantherina

LIGHTFOOT, 1786
panther cowrie

D: 85mm. S: shows similarities with the famous tiger cowrie, *C. tigris*, but is smaller and sleeker.

Aperture cleft is more sharply curved, sunken apex, slightly beaked extremities. O: smooth. C: blotches are smaller and more regular on an even off-white to golden-brown background. H: d1; deeper water. W: INDP; only in the Red Sea and the adjoining Gulf of Aden. R: 3.

Cypraea pulchella

SWAINSON, 1823
pretty or beautiful cowrie

D: 40mm. S: elongated, oval shell. Slightly pointed. Delicate teeth extend to make grooves on the base. O: smooth back, finer grooves on the base. C: gray-yellow with light brown speckles and large, irregular, golden-brown to dark brown blotches. Teeth and grooves brown. H: d1–2. W: INDP. R: 2–3.

Cypraea pulchra

GRAY, 1824
lovely cowrie

D: 50mm. S: oval, inflated shell. O: smooth, fine grooves extend from the aperture and quickly fade out. C: dorsal side gray-brown to amber. 2 black blotches at each extremity. The base is more lightly colored, teeth set off against brown indents. H: d1; sublittoral on coral reefs.

W: INDP; Arabian Sea and Red Sea. R: 3.

Cypraea pyrum

GMELIN, 1791
pear cowrie

D: 50mm. S: oval to pear-shaped shell. Strong teeth. O: smooth. C: upper side blotched golden-brown to russet, sometimes with paler transverse bands. Margin and base apricot, teeth white. H: d1–2; sublittoral and rather deeper water. W: LUS, WAFR. R: 3.

Cypraea rosselli

COTTON, 1948
Rossell's cowrie

D: 50mm. S: triangular shell. Flattened extremities. Flat base with strong teeth. O: smooth. C: deep, dark brown. Upper side a fiery golden-brown. H: d2–3. W: AUS. R: 4–5. NB: an extremely rare, valuable cowrie.

Cypraea sakuraii

HABE, 1970
Sakurai's cowrie

D: 50mm. S: oval shell with slightly protruding outer lip. Fine teeth. O: smooth. C: cream with an orange sheen to it. Irregular, russet blotches. At least 1 slightly larger, brown blotch in the center. Base white. H: d2–3; 70–250m. W: JAP. R: 3.

Cypraea scurra

GMELIN, 1791
jester cowrie

D: 45mm. S: slender, elongated, cylindrical shell. O: smooth. C: light brown with a pattern of round, gray-brown spots. Gray mantle line. Margin has dark brown blotches. Pale base. Russet teeth. H: d1–2; sublittoral and deeper water. W: INDP. R: 2.

Cypraea spadicea

SWAINSON, 1823
date or chestnut cowrie

D: 60mm. S: inflated, ovate shell. Quite delicate teeth. O: smooth. C: milky white. Back shows an irregular golden-brown blotch edged black-brown. Base and teeth milky white. H: d1; sublittoral, under rocks, to approx. 20m. W: CAL. R: 2.

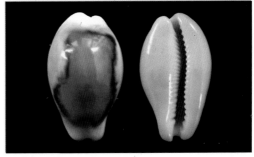

Cypraea spurca

LINNAEUS, 1758
dirty or Atlantic yellow cowrie

D: 35mm. S: elongated, oval shell with quite defined teeth. O: smooth, slightly enlarged margin with subtle nodules. C: golden-yellow to brown with subtle stippling. Margin pale beige to amber with dark brown speckles. Base and teeth pale beige to amber. H: d1–2; rocky coasts in deeper water. W: KEL, LUS; Mediterranean Sea and the adjoining part of the Atlantic Ocean. R: 2.

Cypraea talpa

LINNAEUS, 1758
mole or talpa cowrie

D: 80mm. S: elongated, cylindrical shell. Fine teeth. O: smooth. C: light brown to black-brown, crossed by 2–4 wide, golden-brown bands. Base, margin and teeth black-brown. H: d1; littoral and sublittoral, coral reefs. W: INDP. R: 1.

Cypraea tessellata

SWAINSON, 1822
checkerboard cowrie

D: 40mm. S: squat, slightly inflated shell with a distinctively narrow, almost straight, aperture. Fine teeth. O: smooth. C: pale beige to pink, crossed by a few pink bands and usually flanked by 4 almost square, dark brown blotches. Extremities white, base with alternate white and apricot blotches. Teeth orange-brown. H: d2; on coral reefs, hidden under stones and in rocky crevices in deep water. W: INDP; limited to the area surrounding Hawaii. R: 4. NB: much sought-after by collectors.

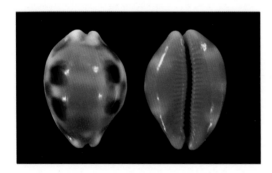

Cypraea teulerei

CAZENAVETTE, 1845
Teulere's cowrie

D: 55mm. S: thick shell with a fairly compact shape. Relatively wide aperture projecting out beyond the humped back. Vague, indistinct

teeth. O: smooth, or here and there granulose. C: gray-yellow with slight gray-brown blotches. Centered on the upper side is an area of much darker brown patterning. Base and aperture very light brown to white. H: d2; rocky coasts. W: INDP; only in southern Oman. R: 3–4.

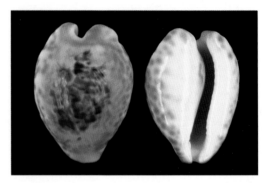

Cypraea tigris

LINNAEUS, 1758
tiger cowrie

D: usually 90mm, but sometimes as much as 150mm. S: ovate shell. O: smooth. C: variable, usually with a pattern of dark brown to black spots and blotches on a pale background. Base and teeth white. Clear golden-yellow mantle line. H: d1; from shallow to deep water, under corals, wherever food is present (polyps). W: INDP. R: 1. NB: the most familiar of all the cowries, found in many souvenir shops at coastal resorts.

Cypraea ventriculus

LAMARCK, 1810
ventral cowrie

D: 50mm. S: thick, rotund shell. Quite strong teeth. O: smooth. C: very pale pink central area on the back with a few darker golden-yellow to russet bands crossing to the margin, often encircled by a violet ring. Base paler. H: d1; littoral and sublittoral, coral reefs. W: INDP. R: 2–3.

blotches faded. Teeth usually set off against dark indents. H: d1–2; sublittoral, up to 150m. W: CAR. R: 2.

Cypraea vitellus

LINNAEUS, 1758
Pacific deer cowrie

D: 90mm. S: inflated, ovate shell. Strong, colorless teeth. O: smooth. C: pale gray to dark brown back with grayish-white spots. Paler base. H: d1–2; littoral, sublittoral and deeper, coral reefs and rocky coasts. W: INDP. R: 1. NB: most specimens are paler brown than the specimen shown.

Cypraea ziczac

LINNAEUS, 1758
zigzag cowrie

D: 20mm. S: oval, slightly inflated cowrie. Quite fine teeth. O: smooth. C: back crossed by 3 white bands with a V-shaped zigzag pattern. Brown-speckled base and margin. H: d1–2; sublittoral and deeper water, coral reefs. W: INDP; east coast of Africa to Tahiti. R: 2–3.

Cypraea zebra

LINNAEUS, 1758
zebra cowrie

D: 90mm. S: fairly large, cylindrical shell. Quite fine teeth, appearing stronger due to coloration. O: smooth. C: upper side light brown, crossed by vague, dark brown bands. Entire surface covered in gray-white spots, some of which are darker within, especially on the base. Base

Ovulidae

J. FLEMING, 1822
shuttle shells, egg shells, etc.

Pear- to shuttle-shaped shells (fusiform), often extended and pointed at the ends, sometimes markedly so. Although these shells often resemble Cypraeidae, the internal construction of the body differs greatly and their shells have different characteristics. Often, colorful patterns are absent and the thickness of the exterior enamel is sharply reduced. Even the way in which the whorls are coiled is different. Only subtle teeth appear in the aperture. These animals live mostly on soft corals, such as *Gorgonaria, Madreporaria, Alcyonaria.* (In the photograph: *Cyphoma gibbosum* (Linnaeus, 1758) – the flamingo tongue – grazing on soft coral. Underwater photograph P.L. van Pel.) Mostly in tropical waters. Subfamily: Ovulinae J. Fleming, 1822 with various genera, including: *Aperiovula, Calpurnus, Cymbovula, Cyphoma, Diminovula, Hiatavolva, Margovula, Neosimnia, Ovula, Phenacovolva, Primovula, Prionovolva, Procalpurnus, Prosimnia, Pseudosimnia, Simnia, Volva.*

Calcarovula longirostrata

(SOWERBY, 1828)
long-snouted volva

D: 65mm. S: elongated, cylindrical shell with a cleft-like aperture that is widest below the centerline. No teeth. Both aperture extremities are long, pointed extensions and slightly curved. O: smooth. C: creamy white to palest pink. H: d2–3; on soft corals in rather deeper water. W: JAP. R: 3. NB: specimens can have virtually straight extensions as well as sharply curved ones.

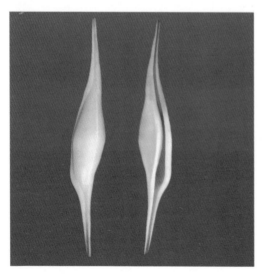

Calcarovula tokioi

(CATE, 1973)
Tokio's volva

D: 65mm. S: elongated, cylindrical shell with a cleft-like aperture. No teeth. Both aperture extremities are extended but less so than in *C. longirostrata.* O: smooth, or with reasonably defined growth lines. C: pale pink, often a darker rose-red at the extremities. H: d2–3; on *Gorgonia* corals in rather deeper water. W: INDP, JAP; southwestern part of the Pacific Ocean. R: 3.

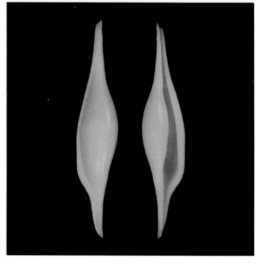

Calpurnus verrucosus

(LINNAEUS, 1758)
umbilical ovula

D: 30mm. S: roughly rhomboid shell. O: a round, pustular callus at either end. Outer lip has quite strong teeth. C: white, a mauve patch at either end. H: d1; coral reefs. W: INDP; Madagascar to Polynesia. R: 1.

Cyphoma gibbosum

(LINNAEUS, 1758)
flamingo tongue

D: 30mm. S: oval, somewhat cylindrical shell. No teeth in the aperture. O: smooth with a wide, but very rounded, rib crossing the center. C: creamy white to apricot, paler in the center. Aperture interior also apricot. H: d1–2; sublittoral and deeper, on reefs and rocks where soft corals grow. W: CAR; North America to the West Indies. R: 1. NB: in the living animal, the shell is partly enveloped by a black-edged mantle with yellow (giraffe-like) blotches.

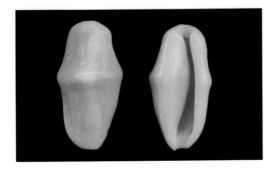

Inflatovula sinensis

(SOWERBY, 1874)
Chinese ovula

D: 25mm. S: cowrie-shaped shell with the outer lip stretching just beyond the body whorl. O: The inner lip has clear columellar folds. C: smooth. H: d2–3; deeper water. W: INDP, JAP; China Sea, Taiwan. R: 3.

Neosimnia spelta

(LINNAEUS, 1758)
Mediterranean pointed cowrie

D: 20mm. S: relatively robust shell, pointed to tapering, with callused, curled outer lip. No teeth.

O: smooth, sometimes stronger growth lines. C: cream to purplish-brown, the same color as the soft corals on which it feeds. H: d1–2; sublittoral and deeper, on *Gorgonaria* corals. W: LUS; Mediterranean Sea and adjoining part of the Atlantic Ocean. R: 2.

Ovula ovum

(LINNAEUS, 1758)
common egg cowrie

D: 90mm. S: ovoid shell with an extended, slightly curved outer lip, especially at the anterior end. O: smooth. C: glazed white exterior, brown within. The living animal is black with bright, golden-yellow markings. H: d1; coral reefs, on black sponges. W: INDP. R: 1. NB: the closely similar *O. costellata* (Lamarck, 1810) – pink-mouth ovula – is smaller (40mm) and pink inside. From the east coast of Africa and the Red Sea to Tonga.

Volva volva

(LINNAEUS, 1758)
shuttle volva

D: 120mm. S: cowrie-shaped shell, but the aperture is wider and very greatly extended and extruded at both ends. O: subtle transverse grooves. C: pale pink, orange-pink aperture interior. H: d1; sublittoral on coral reefs. W: INDP; east coast of Africa to Polynesia. R: 2.

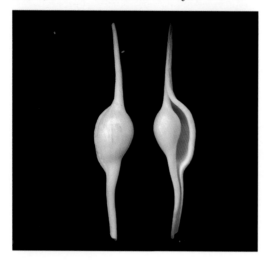

Pedicularidae

J.E. GRAY, 1853
pseudo-cowries

Recently separated from Ovulidae. The animals live mostly on and in soft corals. Genera: *Cypraeogemmula, Jenneria, Pseudocypraea.*

Jenneria pustulata

(LIGHTFOOT, 1786)
Jenner's cowrie

D: 25mm. S: cowrie-shaped shell with unusual ornament. O: upper side has defined, rounded, pustular nodules. Base has strong ribs running across to the aperture, where they form teeth. C: gray-white or brown with orange-red pustules. Gray-brown ribs on the base. H: d1; coral reefs and rocky coasts. W: PAN. R: 2.

Pedicularia californica

NEWCOMB, 1864
Californian cap cowrie

D: 12mm. S: initially a wound shell, later becoming irregular and opening out into a wide aperture with a cap-like appearance. O: first whorls have a fine, net-like ornament. Later whorls have fine spirals. C: creamy white to pink. H: d1–2; attached to coral polyps, such as *Allophora californica*. W: CAL. R: 2.

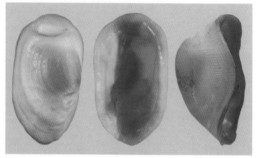

VELUTINOIDEA

J.E. GRAY, 1840
On the basis of a similar larval stage and parallels both anatomically and in behavior, the outwardly very different families of Velutinidae and Triviidae have been grouped together within the superfamily Velutinoidea.

Eratoidae

GILL, 1871
erato shells

Robust smooth shells, resembling those of Marginellidae. Clear, aperture teeth. Genera: *Erato, Hesperato.*

Erato voluta

(MONTAGU, 1803)
European erato

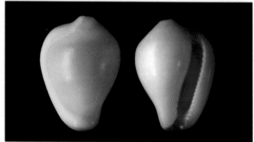

D: 8mm. S: robust shell with a blunt apex and curled outer lip with teeth. Vague teeth in inner lip as well. O: smooth. C: glossy white, cream, light brown or even purplish-brown. Sometimes with dark brown or purple blotches at either end of the aperture. H: d1–2; lives amid sea squirts (Ascidiacea). W: KEL, LUS. R: 2.

Triviidae

TROSCHEL, 1863
trivia shells (and others)

Solid, rounded, bean-shaped or fusiform shells, in appearance resembling Cypraeidae with an equally narrow, cleft-like aperture, usually toothed. Quite small, 5–20mm. Outer lip always curling inward. Just as with Velutinidae, the animals feed on sedentary sea squirts, which they suck out with their proboscis. Found in all temperate and warmer seas in the West Indies, Atlantic Ocean and Indo-Pacific region. Few genera: *Niveria, Pusula, Trivia, Triviella, Trivirostra.*

Pusula pedicula

(LINNAEUS, 1758)
coffee-bean trivia

D: 15mm. S: coffee-bean-shaped shell with a narrow cleft-like aperture. O: transverse ribs and a narrow longitudinal groove, on either side of which the ribs are slightly more inflated. C: back light brown with 3 dark blotches in irregular pairs. H: d1; sublittoral under large rocks. W: CAR, VIR; Florida to the West Indies. R: 1.

Pusula solandri

(SOWERBY, 1832)
Solander's trivia

D: 15mm. S: coffee-bean-shaped shell with a cleft-like aperture. O: solid, transverse ribs di-

vided in the middle by a broad, longitudinal groove. On either side of this the grooves inflate into bud-like nodules. C: mauve to dark brown. Ribs and groove paler. H: d1–2; sublittoral, to deeper water under rocks. W: CAL, PAN, PER. R: 1.

Trivia arctica

(PULTENEY, 1799)
arctic trivia

D: up to 12mm. S: solid, convex shell in the shape of a ribbed coffee bean. A narrow, cleft-like aperture on the base. O: ribs and grooves run across the whole shell. C: grayish-pink to pink, no dorsal blotches. Base and interior white. H: d1–2; rocky coasts, under stones. Littoral, 100m or more. W: KEL, LUS. R: 1. NB: the European cowrie, *T. monacha* (Da Costa, 1778) has 3 dark blotches (see photograph, specimen far right). Its distribution is roughly the same.

Triviella aperta

(SWAINSON, 1828)
gaping trivia

D: 20mm. S: solid, inflated shell. Base has a relatively wide aperture. O: ribs and grooves run across the whole shell, a vague longitudinal groove runs down the center. C: grayish pink to pink, base paler or white. H: d1–2; sublittoral to slightly deeper water. W: ZAFR. R: 1.

Velutinidae

J.E. GRAY, 1840
velutinid shells

Extremely thin-shelled and ear-shaped with a greatly expanded final whorl. No umbilicus. Species from the subfamily Lamellariinae; the outer lip rim is curled over. The mantle largely covers the shell in the living animal. The animals have different sexes. However, the species from the subfamily Velutininae can be both hermaphroditic as well as protoandrously hermaphroditic. Carnivorous snails, living off sedentary sea squirts, such as Tunicata. Found in both warmer and colder seas: the Arctic, the Antarctic, the North Atlantic Ocean, and the Pacific Ocean off the coast of Australia.

Velutina velutina

(MÜLLER, 1776)
smooth velutina

D: 15mm. S: very thin shell. The final whorl is very large and partly closes off the previous whorl. O: usually with a generally fine lattice ornament. The periostracum is often ribbed as well. C: mauve with a felty, amber periostracum. Glossy aperture. H: d1–3; sublittoral to deep water. W: KEL, LUS. R: 1.

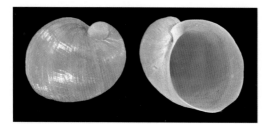

NATICOIDEA

FORBES, 1838
Large, familiar group of carnivorous sea snails. The shells have a fairly uniform appearance. The animals plough through the soft, sandy sea floor, searching for prey, predominantly bivalves. These are bored through with a drilling organ attached to the end of the proboscis, creating circular holes in the victim's shell. The drilling is done mechanically but is assisted by an acidic liquid substance produced by a special gland. The victim's shell is held tight by a dilated part of the propodium. The location of the borehole depends on the way in which the prey is being held. Many species mostly hunt at night at low tide. These animals have different sexes. Eggs are deposited in flat, semicircular bands reinforced by grains of sand. The group has a worldwide range, with the largest number of species found in tropical regions, mostly in shallow water.

Naticidae

FORBES, 1838
moon snails

Mostly robust, semicircular to ovoid, smooth and often glossy shells. The final whorl is large. In many cases, a clear, circular or widened umbilicus is visible, which may be partly closed. The aperture is in the shape of a half-moon. Naticidae is divided into several subfamilies. The subfamily Ampullospirinae Cox, 1930 only contains fossil species. Members of the subfamily Naticinae Forbes, 1838 have a corneous, calcified operculum and an open umbilicus. The subfamily Polinicinae J.E. Gray, 1847 contains species with a corneous operculum without any calcification and often a partly covered umbilicus. The subfamily Sininae Woodring, 1928 contains species with a more ear-shaped, thinner shell, where the operculum is clearly smaller than the aperture. Taken together, these subfamilies contain various genera, including: *Benthobulbus, Bulbus, Choristes, Cochlis, Eunaticina, Euspira, Friginatica, Globisinum, Glossaulax, Glyphepithema, Lunaia, Mammilla, Natica, Naticaria, Neverita, Payraudeautia, Polinices, Proxiuber, Sinum, Stigmaulax, Tanea, Uberella.*

Conuber conicus

(LAMARCK, 1822)
conical moon snail

D: 25mm. S: robust shell with a fairly high spire. Umbilicus partly callused. O: smooth. C: amber, dark brown callus on inner lip and surrounding the umbilicus. H: d1–2; sublittoral and rather deeper water. W: AUS. R: 3.

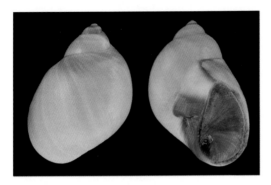

Euspira catena

(DA COSTA, 1778)
European necklace moon snail

D: 40mm. S: fairly thick shell with inflated whorls that quickly increase in size. Blunt spire, half-moon aperture. Corneous operculum. Deep, round umbilicus next to aperture. O: smooth. C: glossy yellow-gray or light brown, often a row of dark brown spots on top of the whorls. H: d1–2; sublittoral and deeper waters of sandy coasts. W: KEL, LUS. R: 1. NB: the species shown right in the photograph is *E. nitida* (Donovan, 1804). (The same distribution, measuring up to 15mm.) Both species are responsible for the boreholes found in European bivalves.

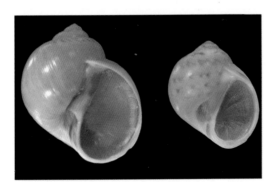

Globularia fluctuata

(SOWERBY, 1825)
wavy moon snail

D: 50mm. S: fairly thin shell with a relatively large aperture. Sharp apex. No umbilicus. Inner lip callused. O: smooth, only growth lines. C: amber with paler, or white, zigzags. Callus

white and dark brown. H: d1–2; deeper water. W: INDP. R: 1–2.

Glyphepithema alapapilionis

(RÖDING, 1798)
butterfly moon snail

D: 30mm. S: somewhat angular, compact shell with a large, half-moon aperture. Squat spire and apex. Umbilicus extremely wide; a well-defined, wavy umbilical callus within. O: smooth, only growth lines. C: amber to gray-brown. 4 pale or white bands on the final whorl with alternate dark brown and white dashes. Aperture and umbilicus white to dark brown. H: d1; sublittoral, shallow water on sand. W: INDP. R: 2–3.

Lunatia heros

(SAY, 1822)
common northern moon snail

D: 90mm. S: round shell with an elevated spire. Half-moon aperture. Deep umbilicus. O: defined growth lines only. C: yellowish-gray, on

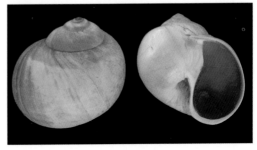

rare occasions with colored flecks around the suture. H: d1; littoral and sublittoral on sand. W: ARC, KEL, VIR. R: 2. NB: is among the largest species in the family.

Mammilla melanostoma

(GMELIN, 1791)
black-mouth moon snail

D: 50mm. S: reasonably solid, elongated, oval shell with very level whorls. Very large body whorl; wide, half-moon aperture. Umbilicus largely covered by callus. O: smooth. C: amber with vague dark brown blotches, sometimes in bands. Inner lip and callus dark brown to black. H: d1; shallow water on sand. W: INDP. R: 1.

Mammilla simiae

(DESHAYES, IN DESHAYES & MILNE EDWARDS, 1838)
simi moon snail or monkey sand shell

D: 40mm. S: fairly solid, oval shell with a low spire and a large half-moon aperture, angled at the top. Thick callus from the inner lip covers the umbilicus almost completely. O: smooth, only growth lines. C: amber to dark brown, usually with a wide, white band just below the centerline and sometimes a second band below the suture. H: d1–2; sublittoral and deeper. W: INDP. R: 1.

Natica acinonyx

MARCHE-MARCHAD, 1957
African berry moon snail

D: 25mm. S: somewhat compressed shell with a half-moon aperture. Very large, wide umbilicus with a clear, wavy callus within. O: smooth, only growth lines. C: white to amber with light to dark brown, rounded spots. H: d2–3; deeper water. W: WAFR; Senegal, the Gambia. R: 4.

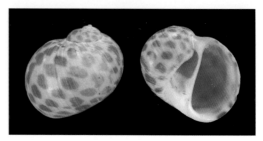

Natica fanel

REECLUZ, 1844
Fanel moon snail

D: 25mm. S: oblong shell with slightly angular whorls. Raised spire. Broad, open umbilicus; around it a rounded umbilical callus. O: smooth, glossy. C: russet spots and blotches that sometimes merge together on a white to yellow-gray background. H: d1; on sand in shallow water. W: WAFR. R: 2.

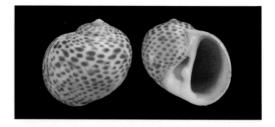

Natica fasciata

(RÖDING, 1798)
solid moon snail

D: 25mm. S: round shell with a low spire and blunt apex. Ovate aperture and a narrow umbilicus, partly covered by callus. O: smooth. C: amber to (usually) chestnut brown, often with a wide, paler band of color. H: d1; shallow water on sand. W: INDP; southwestern part. R: 1.

Natica stellata

HEDLEY, 1913
starry moon snail

D: 50mm. S: solid shell with round, convex whorls. Fairly blunt spire. Half-moon aperture and a deep umbilicus partly covered by a tongue-shaped callus. O: smooth. C: golden-yellow with white, cloudy blotches. H: d1; coarse sand and broken shells up to 20m. W: INDP, JAP. R: 2.

Natica vitellus

(LINNAEUS, 1758)
calf or banded moon snail

D: 40mm. S: slightly elongated shell with a rather large aperture. Spire barely raised. Clear umbilicus; round, vague umbilical callus. Calcareous, thickened operculum. O: smooth, glossy. C: dark brown with lighter bands of color. Underside of body whorl and aperture pale yellow to white. H: d1; shallow water. W: INDP. R: 1.

Naticarius canrena

(LINNAEUS, 1758)
colorful Atlantic moon snail

D: 50mm. S: asymmetric oval shell with a slightly raised spire. Blunt apex. Teardrop-shaped umbilicus with a strong, umbilical callus around it. O: smooth. C: amber with a pattern of paler striped bands and dark brown dashes and wavy lines. Lower part of body whorl usually paler or white. H: d1–2; deeper water, up to 60m. W: CAR. R: 3.

Naticarius hebraea

(MARTYN, 1784)
Hebrew moon snail

D: 43mm. S: round shell with a flattened apex and half-moon aperture. The umbilicus is wide with a thick, round umbilical callus. Thick, calcareous operculum. O: smooth, only growth lines. C: variable, usually gray-brown with irregular, russet dashes, dots, and lines. Sometimes almost a uniform color, in rare cases zigzagged. H: d1–2; from 10m to considerably deeper water. W: LUS, WAFR. R: 1. NB: common Mediterranean species, regularly washed ashore and found in fishing waste.

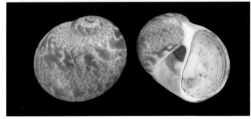

Naticarius onca

(RÖDING, 1798)
China moon snail

D: 30mm. S: solid, obliquely distended shell. Raised spire, convex whorls. Large, half-moon aperture. Very wide umbilicus with an umbilical callus in the center. C: white with 5 rows of chocolate-colored spots. H: d1; sublittoral, on sand. To a depth of 20m. W: INDP, JAP. R: 2.

Naticarius stercusmuscarum

(GMELIN, 1791)
fly-specked moon snail

D: 40mm. S: large, solid, round shell or with a slight oblique distension. Spire barely raised, blunt apex. Large, half-moon aperture. Very wide umbilicus with a very prominent umbilical callus in the center. O: smooth, sometimes distinct growth lines. C: russet dots on a white to pale gray background. H: d1; slightly deeper water, up to approx. 50m. W: LUS, WAFR. R: 2. NB: a popular Mediterranean species among collectors.

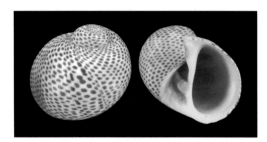

Neverita albumen

(LINNAEUS, 1758)
egg-white moon snail

D: 50mm. S: very distended shell with a very flat underside. Underside callused, umbilicus ending in a twisted umbilical groove. O: smooth. C: upper side glossy amber, underside and aperture white. H: d1–2; shallow to deeper water, on sand. W: INDP. R: 1.

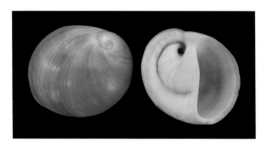

Neverita incei

(PHILIPPI, 1853)
Ince's moon snail

D: 25mm. S: distended shell, flat underside. Umbilicus covered by a large callus plug. Corneous operculum. O: smooth with stronger growth lines. C: white, aperture and umbilical plug sometimes dark brown, otherwise white. Russet operculum. H: d1; sublittoral. W: AUS. R: 2.

Neverita josephinia

RISSO, 1826
Josephine's moon snail

D: 30mm. S: slightly distended shell, somewhat flattened underside. Umbilicus partly covered by a bud-like callus plug. Corneous operculum. O: smooth, polished. C: cream to yellowish-gray. Aperture and (occasionally) callus plug amber. H: d1; sublittoral in sand. W: LUS, WAFR. R: 1.

Polinices aurantius

(RÖDING, 1798)
golden moon snail

D: 45mm. S: very thick, elongated, oval shell, somewhat distended, with a blunt, flattened spire. Half-moon aperture, thickened lip. Umbilicus almost entirely covered by callus. O:

polished smooth, glossy. C: orange, mouth and callus white. H: d1; sublittoral, up to approx. 20m. W: INDP. R: 2.

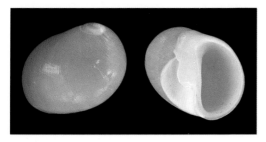

Polinices lacteus

(GUILDING, 1834)
Caribbean milk moon snail

D: 25mm. S: very thick, elongated, oval shell, somewhat distended, with a very flattened spire. Half-moon aperture, crescent-shaped umbilicus, often slightly callused. O: smooth, glossy. C: milky white. H: d1; sublittoral, shallow water. W: CAR. R: 1.

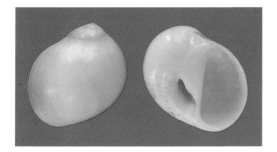

Sinum bifasciatum

(RÉCLUZ, 1851)
West African ear moon snail

D: 30mm. S: thin, distended shell with an extremely large body whorl and an ear-shaped aperture. O: distinct spirals over the whole shell. C: cream to yellowish-white. H: d2; deeper water. W: WAFR. R: 1.

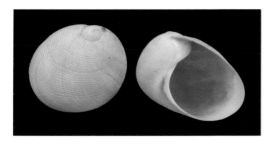

Sinum perspectivum

(SAY, 1831)
(white) baby-ear moon snail

D: 40mm. S: very thin shell with a flattened profile, extremely large body whorl with an ear-shaped aperture. O: subtle spirals, sometimes crossed by faint axial ribs. C: milky white, light brown periostracum soon worn away. H: d1; littoral and sublittoral, on sand. W: CAR. R: 1.

Tanea lineata

(RÖDING, 1798)
lined moon snail

D: 40mm. S: solid shell with round, convex whorls. Fairly squat spire. Half-moon aperture, deep umbilicus with a central, semicircular callus. O: smooth. C: creamy white to amber with diagonal, russet to dark brown, slightly wavy stripes. H: d1; sublittoral and deeper, on sand and mud, up to 50m. W: INDP, JAP. R: 2.

TONNOIDEA

SUTER, 1913
A distinctive superfamily that contains a huge variety of forms. The snails have a long, pleurembolic proboscis and feed on sea urchins, crustaceans and other small sea creatures. In addition to a few smaller families of deep-sea species (Laubierinidae Warén & Bouchet, 1990; Pisanianuridae Warén & Bouchet, 1990), the group also contains several well-known families, including a number of the largest species of snail on earth, such as the huge *Charonia tritonis* – the trumpet triton – measuring over 400mm.

The families Bursidae, Cassidae, Cymatiidae, and Tonnidae can all produce asparagine amino acids, sulfuric acid, and neurotoxins from their salivary glands. These are used to paralyze their victims and weaken their shells or carapaces.

Bursidae

THIELE, 1925
frog shells

Thick, coarsely ornamented shells. Similarities with Ranellidae (tritons) in terms of appearance. Often ornamented with defined nodules or spines. Often with varices (thick "scars" from former apertural lips). The siphonal canal at the base of the aperture is short. A second canal (the anal canal) lies at the top of the aperture. Indo-Pacific region, Atlantic Ocean, Mediterranean Sea. Fairly small family with only a few genera: *Bufonaria, Bursa, Crossata, Marsupina, Tutufa.*

Bufonaria echinata

(LINK, 1807)
spiny frog shell

D: 50mm. S: thick shell with a fairly pointed apex. Thick outer lip. Narrow, relatively long siphonal canal. O: both wide and finer spirals covered in beads and nodules. C: Outer lip and varices have spines. H: d1–2. W: INDP. R: 2.

Bufonaria elegans

(BECK IN SOWERBY II, 1836)
elegant frog shell

D: 75mm. S: reasonably thick shell with a quite pointed apex. Thickened outer lip. Narrow siphonal canal. O: mostly finer spirals, especially on the base with nodules. Outer lip and varices have short spines. C: amber, often with

dark brown, spiral bands. H: d1; littoral and sublittoral. W: INDP; Indian Ocean. R: 1.

Bufonaria nobilis

(REEVE, 1844)
noble frog shell

D: 55mm. S: thick shell with somewhat angular whorls. Thickened outer lip with teeth within. Inner lip also has folds and nodules. O: fine spirals covered in small nodules and broad, subtle axial ribs and varices. C: amber. The spirals are usually speckled alternately light and dark brown. H: d1; sublittoral, coral reefs. W: INDP. R: 2.

Bufonaria rana

(LINNAEUS, 1758)
common frog shell

D: 75mm. S: fairly solid, obliquely distended shell. Varices at the sides of each whorl. Pointed apex. Thickened outer lip with teeth within. Narrow, relatively long, siphonal canal. O: wide and finer spirals combined, covered in nodules. Outer lip and varices have small, slightly curved spines. C: amber to brown.

Aperture white. H: d1–2; sublittoral and deeper water. W: INDP. R: 2.

banding. H: d1–2; sublittoral and deeper water. W: CAR, INDP. R: 2.

Bursa corrugata

(PERRY, 1811)
gaudy or corrugated frog shell

D: 50mm. S: very thick shell with greatly thickened outer lip. O: coarse tubercles and varices. Callused inner and outer lips containing granulose nodules. C: amber. Aperture paler. H: d2; deeper water. W: CAL, CAR, PAN. R: 2.

Bursa lamarckii

(DESHAYES, 1853)
Lamarck's frog shell

D: 50mm. S: thick, rotund shell. Rather blunt apex. Outer lip much thickened. Siphonal canal is narrow, long, and straight. Anal canal is long and extruded like a vent. Former anal canals projecting from the varices create a spiny effect. Inner and outer lips have teeth and nodules. O: strong spirals and very strong tubercles, which in turn are covered in smaller nodules. C: amber with dark brown blotches. Aperture chocolate-brown. H: d1; coral reefs and rocky coasts. W: INDP; southwestern part. R: 3.

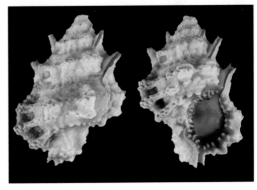

Bursa granularis

(RÖDING, 1798)
granulate frog shell

D: 50mm. S: solid shell, fairly slender with rounded whorls. O: delicate and defined spirals covered in round nodules and granulose ornament. Larger tubercles in places. Varices on either side of the whorls. Granulose ornament mostly below the body whorl, around the siphonal canal. C: amber with light and dark

Marsupina bufo

(BRUGUIÈRE, 1792)
chestnut frog shell

D: 50mm. S: thick, obliquely distended shell with a much thickened outer lip and several varices. The anal canal is long and projects out somewhat like a vent. Strong teeth within outer lip. O: the entire shell is covered in spiraling, pustular growths that are reminiscent of the warts on a toad or frog. C: amber to chestnut brown. H: d1. W: CAR. R: 2.

the inner lip is smooth without the subtle folds seen in *B. bubo*. O: nodulose, spiny spirals, strong varices. C: creamy white to light brown. Aperture usually has a russet edge. H: d1–2; sublittoral and deeper water. W: AUS, INDP. R: 1.

Bursa bubo

LINNAEUS, 1758
giant frog shell

D: 180mm. S: very thick, pointed shell. Whorls with very angular shoulders. O: nodulose spirals, varices, and in between 6–8 larger, blunt tubercles. C: creamy white with light and dark brown blotches. H: d1–2; sublittoral and deeper water. W: INDP. R: 1.

Tutufa rubeta

(LINNAEUS, 1758)
ruddy frog shell

D: 150mm. S: thick shell with a much thickened outer lip and a short, slightly curved siphonal canal. Fairly long, defined anal canal. Inner and outer lips with folds and denticles (granulose bumps). O: coarse nodules, defined spiral ribs, finer on the underside. Very thick, nodulose varices. C: amber with lighter and darker bands and blotches. Aperture reddish. H: d1–2; sublittoral and deeper water. W: INDP. R: 1–2.

Tutufa bufo

(RODING, 1798)
red-mouth frog shell

D: 150mm. S: solid shell with pointed apex and angular whorls. Narrow siphonal canal: quite long and often slightly bent aside. The callus on

Cassidae

LATREILLE, 1825
helmet shells, bonnet shells

Quite solid to thick shells, with a relatively narrow aperture. The outer lip is thickened. The siphonal canal is short and curves backward.

Often with very glossy, colored callus on the columellar side. Radial ornament, spiral ribs, and shoulder knobs. Often nodulose varices as well. The shells of some species may differ according to sex. For example, male specimens of *Cassis cornuta* have longer knobs along the shoulder. Found in warmer climates, in shallow water on sand. Some species (genus *Oocorys*) live to depths of over 1000m. Their food includes sea urchins, whose spines are bent back by the foot, while the proboscis spreads acids over the surface. There are three subfamilies. The subfamily Cassinae Latreille, 1825 mostly contains large, heavy, colorful species. The operculum is oval with a slightly convex nucleus. In most cases, the siphonal canal is either straight or slightly curved. The subfamily Oocorythinae P. Fischer, 1885 mostly contains deepwater species. The subfamily Phaliinae Beu, 1981 contains various smaller species, often with rather thinner shells. The aperture is wider and has a restricted siphonal canal with a clear backward curve or twist that usually ends in a tubular construction. The operculum is fanshaped, the nucleus to one side of the center. Male specimens are often smaller than females. These include the genera: *Casmaria, Cassis, Cypraecassis, Dalium, Echinophoria, Galeodea, Hadroocorys, Herculea, Phalium, Sconsia, Semicassis.*

Casmaria erinacea

(LINNAEUS, 1758)
common bonnet

D: 50mm. S: solid shell with a quite pointed spire. Outer and inner lips very thickly callused. Top of whorls have an obliquely angled shoulder. O: slight shoulder knobs and more distinct growth lines. 4–6 small projections at base of the outer lip. C: Pale pink with orange-brown blotches or lines. Periphery of outer lip checkered dark brown on white. Creamy white callus. H: d1; sublittoral. W: INDP. R: 1.

Cassis cornuta

(LINNAEUS, 1758)
horned helmet

D: 220mm. S: very thick shell. Very wide shield, callused covering the entire apertural side. Enlarged outer lip. O: defined knobs, very fine spirals and faintly pitted. C: grayish-yellow. Callus deep orange, especially in the inner recess of the aperture. H: d1; up to 20m. W: INDP. R: 1. NB: much used in the tourist trade.

Cassis fimbriata

QUOY & GAIMARD, 1833
fringed helmet

D: 75mm. S: a stocky shell. Flattened spire. Thickened outer lip. Varices sometimes present. O: fine axial ribs and spirals. Also stronger axial ribs covered in angular nodules. C: apricot with russet blotches. Spirals often striped or checkered. Outer lip also sometimes checkered. H: d1–3; from sublittoral to deep water. W: AUS. R: 1.

Cassis madagascariensis

(LAMARCK, 1822)
emperor helmet

D: 300mm. S: thick shell. Flat spire. Extensive parietal shield. O: defined knobs and slight spirals. Folds and teeth on inner and outer lips. C:

gray-brown, bright orange callus with black between the columellar folds. H: d1; shallow water. W: CAR. R: 2.

Cassis nana

(TENISON-WOODS, 1879)
dwarf helmet

D: 40mm. S: solid to thick shell. Flat spire with a pointed apex. Greatly enlarged parietal shield next to inner lip. Teeth within inner and outer lips. O: up to 5 rows of small knobs. C: apricot. H: d2–3; deep water, up to 240m. W: AUS. R: 2. NB: smallest helmet shell on earth.

Cassis tuberosa

(LINNAEUS, 1758)
king helmet

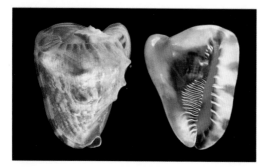

D: 150mm. S: thick shell. Flattened spire. Greatly expanded parietal shield, often ending in a vaguely wing-shaped fold on the left-hand side. O: coarse knobs and fine, rhomboid ornament. Strong teeth on inner and outer lips. C: gray-brown, callus deep orange with brownish-black folds between teeth. Several dark blotches on each varix. Checkered outer lip. H: d1; shallow water. W: CAR. R: 2.

Cypraecassis rufa

(LINNAEUS, 1758)
bull's-mouth helmet

D: 150mm. S: thick shell. Thickened outer lip. Greatly expanded parietal shield. O: very fine teeth on inner and outer lips. Wide, nodulose spirals with much finer spirals in between. Axial ribs underneath. C: russet with orange callus, often with dark vertical banding. H: d1; sublittoral, coral reefs. W: INDP. R: 1. NB: used in making cameos.

Cypraecassis testiculus

(LINNAEUS, 1758)
reticulated cowrie helmet

D: 65mm. S: solid, oval shell. Blunt spire with a sharp apex. Convex whorls without shoulders. Very wide parietal shield. Inner and outer lips have a great many teeth. O: densely clustered axial ribs like pleats, bisected by slight spiral ribs, sometimes somewhat nodulose. C: orange to rose-red with gray, russet, and orange blotches, usually grouped in bands. Orange callus, checked with russet blotches on outer lip rim. H: d1; littoral, shallow water. W: CAR. R: 1.

Phalium areola

(LINNAEUS, 1758)
checkerboard bonnet

D: 65mm. S: fairly solid shell with a pointed spire. Thickened outer lip with teeth within. Part of inner lip has columellar folds. O: very fine spirals, a single varix. C: gray-white, with a checkerboard pattern of dark brown blotches. H: d1; sublittoral, on sand and mud. W: INDP; from east coast of Africa to Melanesia. R: 2.

Phalium bandatum

(PERRY, 1811)
banded bonnet

D: 75mm. S: a solid shell with a pointed spire. Convex whorls with clearly angular, sloped shoulders. Thickened outer lip. Parietal shield ends halfway up the body whorl. O: tightly grouped shoulder knobs. Varices in some places. Older whorls have several nodulose spirals. C: grayish-yellow with 4–5 bands of rectangular, orange blotches. H: d1–2; sublittoral and deeper, 10–50m, on sand. W: AUS, INDP, JAP. R: 1.

Phalium fimbria

(GMELIN, 1791)
fimbriate bonnet

D: 75mm. S: solid, elongated oval shell. Very pointed spire and whorls with angular, sloped shoulders. O: wide, undulating axial ribs and nodulose spirals on the shoulders. C: amber. Orange-brown folds. Edge of parietal shield and outer lip have russet blotches. H: d1–2; deeper water. W: INDP. R: 3–4.

Phalium flammiferum

(RÖDING, 1798)
striped bonnet

D: 90mm. S: solid shell with a reasonably pointed spire. Whorls have sloped shoulders.

Parietal shield callus extends over only part of the body whorl. Strong teeth within the outer lip. O: smooth spirals, clearest on the shoulders and around the columella. C: cream with amber to russet, radial bands. H: d1–2; sublittoral and deeper, up to 100m. W: INDP, JAP. R: 2.

Phalium glaucum

(LINNAEUS, 1758)
gray bonnet

D: 90mm. S: solid shell with a pointed spire. Strong varices apparent. A few nodulose projections at the base of the aperture. O: smooth, slight shoulder fold and vague, small shoulder nodules. C: gray to purplish-brown. Callus pale orange. H: d1–2; sublittoral and deeper water, on sand. W: INDP. R: 2.

Semicassis saburon

(BRUGUIÈRE, 1792)
Saburon bonnet

D: 50mm. S: solid shell with inflated whorls. Pointed spire, shallow sutures between whorls. outer lip curled over and thickened – has fine teeth. O: clear, flattened spirals. Granulose nodules around columella. C: grayish-white with a purple sheen. Brown-orange blotches set in rows. H: d1–2; 10–100m. W: LUS, WAFR. R: 1.

Semicassis undulata

(GMELIN, 1791)
Mediterranean bonnet

D: 100mm. S: fairly solid shell. Pointed spire, convex whorls, no shoulders. Callus often restricted to the base of the body whorl. O: defined spirals with deep grooves in between. Often coarsely granulated callus in inner lip. Strong teeth and folds within outer lip. C: gray-brown, alternately checkered with creamy white and russet blotches. H: d1–2; 5–100m. W: LUS, WAFR, ZAFR. R: 3.

Personidae

J.E. GRAY, 1854
distorted whelks

Thick, roughly ornamented shells with a strange, misshapen appearance. Only the spire is evenly wound. The first aberration or distortion appears at the fourth or fifth whorl. Distortions are due to the necessity for whorls to grow over the expanded former aperture (varix) and parietal shield of the previous whorl. Lattice ornament. Aperture lips more or less drawn together with a strong varix at the outer lip. Apertural rim has teeth and nodules, and folds on the columellar side. Callus greatly extended in some species. Columella folds merge into the siphonal canal. Periostracum can either be very thick or thin, membranous or velvety. Indo-Pacific region, Caribbean region. Few genera: *Distorsio, Distorsionella, Distorsomina, Personopsis.*

Distorsio anus

(LINNAEUS, 1758)
common distorsio or old-lady shell

D: 70mm. S: very thick shell. Very short siphonal canal. Pointed spire. Oblique varices create a sort of frill around the whole apertural side. O: spiral and axial ribs, very strong, blunt knobs. Folds and teeth in inner and outer lips. C: creamy white with brown bands and blotches. H: d1; coral reefs. W: INDP. R: 2.

Distorsio clathrata

(LAMARCK, 1816)
Atlantic distorsio

D: 65mm. S: thick shell. Pointed spire, long siphonal canal. Callus extends over only part of the inner lip. O: lattice ornament, the axial ribs are slightly stronger. Nodules at intersections. C: cream to pale yellow. Periostracum grayish-brown, fibrous. H: d1–2; deep water to approx. 150m. W: CAR; North Carolina to Brazil. R: 2.

Distorsio kurzi

PETUCH & HARASEWYCH, 1980
Kurz's distorsio

D: 35mm. S: thick, severely distorted shell. Often entirely oblique growth. Very pointed spire and a narrow, quite long, siphonal canal. Extensive parietal shield (callus). O: spirals, coarse and fine nodules. Callus and inner lip very granulose and nodulose. Inner and outer lips with strong

teeth: 1 dominant tooth in outer lip. C: russet. H: d1–3; deep water. W: INDP. R: 3.

Distorsio reticularis

(LINNAEUS, 1758)
reticulate distorsio

D: 60mm. S: thick shell, not exceptionally distorted. Long, narrow, straight siphonal canal. Pointed spire. Quite convex whorls and deep suture. O: even lattice ornament. Varices not very prominent. Very strong teeth and folds in outer lip. C: amber, often with russet bands. H: d1–2; deeper water. W: INDP. R: 3

Ranellidae

J.E. GRAY, 1854
tritons, etc.

Mostly solid to thick shells varying in shape, often with an ovoid aperture and siphonal canal of variable length. Usually strongly ornamented: spiral and axial ribs, nodules, and often strong varices (former apertures). The periostracum is thick, scaly and, sometimes, hairy. Aperture without anal canal as in Bursidae. Thickened outer lip, teeth within. Columellar callus present usually with folds. Found in tropical and subtropical seas. Most species live in the intertidal zone and on the continental shelf on rocky coasts, coral reefs, and sand. Dimensions of 15–400mm. There are two subfamilies. The subfamily Cymatiinae Iredale, 1913 contains species often with more angular whorls and flattened to very markedly developed varices, often with one on every second whorl. The varices do not form a regular pattern. The subfamily Ranellinae J.E. Gray, 1854 contains species that usually display rounded whorls. Varices connect directly with the ones on the whorls above, or are only slightly out of line. All together, only a few genera: *Argobuccinum, Biplex, Cabestana, Charonia, Cymatium, Fusitriton, Gyrineum, Halgyrineum, Ranella, Sassia*.

Biplex perca

PERRY, 1811
maple-leaf triton

D: 50mm. S: thick shell, slightly distorted. Almost circular aperture. Long siphonal canal. Strong finlike projections on either side of the shell. O: spiral and nodulose axial ribs, varices. C: amber, spirals and nodules paler. H: d1–2; deeper water. W: INDP; western part. R: 1. NB: sometimes used as an oil lamp.

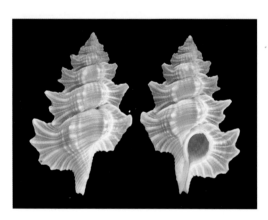

Charonia tritonis

(LINNAEUS, 1758)
trumpet triton

D: 330mm. S: extremely large shell. Pointed apex, extremely large final whorl, ovate aperture. O: up to 2 thin varices per whorl. Wide and narrower spirals with deep grooves in between. Strong knobs on spiral ribs on top of whorls. Nodulose spirals also elsewhere. Fine

folds on inner lip with some more defined ones on the outer lip. C: apricot with an irregular pattern of dark brown blotches. H: d1; shallow water, coral reefs. W: AUS, INDP, JAP. R: 1. NB: used as a trumpet in some places.

Cymatium hepaticum

(RÖDING, 1798)
black-striped triton

D: 50mm. S: thick shell with a rather blunt apex. Strong teeth in inner and outer lips. O: thick varices. Axial and spiral ribs with nodules in between. C: orange-brown with dark brown to black bands and white flecks in places. H: d1; coral reefs. W: INDP. R: 3.

Cymatium lotorium

(LINNAEUS, 1758)
black-spotted triton

D: 90mm. S: very thick shell. Rather blunt apex. O: Very coarsely nodulose varices. Flattened spirals. Strong teeth and folds within outer lip. C:

orange-brown to dark brown. Varices and outer lip checkered white and dark brown. H: d1; coral reefs, shallow water. W: INDP. R: 3.

Cymatium pileare

(LINNAEUS, 1758)
common hairy triton

D: 75mm. S: solid, slender shell. Angular whorls. Elongated, oval aperture ending in a fairly long siphonal canal. O: several wide varices. Ornament varies markedly. Usually a fine, net-like pattern. C: apricot with dark brown and white blotches and bands. A very thick, brown, hairy periostracum is present in living animals. H: d1; shallow water. W: CAR, INDP. R: 1.

Gyrineum gyrinum

(LINNAEUS, 1758)
tadpole triton

D: 25mm. S: thick, squat shell. Slightly distended. O: strong varices on either side. Defined

axial ribs crossed by finer spiral ribs. C: white with wide, dark brown bands. H: d1; sublittoral, under coral rubble. W: INDP. R: 1.

Tonnidae

SUTER, 1913
tun shells

Round, cask-shaped shells with a low spire and a large, broad body whorl. In proportion to their size, these shells are relatively thin and light with clear spiral ribs. The rim of the outer lip is only barely thickened. A deep siphonal canal at the base of the aperture. Colored creamy white to brown, often with blotches or bands of color. The animals have a large foot, a wide proboscis, hook-shaped jaws, and a strong radula, which they use to tear large chunks from their prey to devour whole. Found in tropical and temperate maritime regions, from fairly shallow water to great depths. Only a few genera: *Eudolium, Malea, Tonna*.

Eudolium pyriforme

(SOWERBY, 1914)
pyriform false tun or cask tun

D: 55mm. S: elongated shell with convex whorls and an oval aperture, slightly pointed at the top. In fully mature specimens, the outer lip can be slightly thickened, with slight folds within. O: fairly low spirals, broken up by growth lines. C: amber. Often a checkered pattern of light and slightly darker patches on the spirals. H: d2–3; deeper water. W: INDP, JAP. R: 1.

Malea pomum

(LINNAEUS, 1758)
Pacific grinning tun

D: 65mm. S: thick, elongated shell with a narrow aperture. Thickened, crenulated outer lip, outline wider below than above, with strong teeth and folds within. Callus extends from inner lip over body whorl. Columellar folds. O: wide spiral ribs, angular below the suture, with shallow grooves in between. C: cream with orange-red to brown blotches. Aperture and callus yellowish-white. H: d2–3. W: INDP. R: 2–3. NB: like *M. ringens*, named after its prominent teeth.

D: 170mm. S: thick, compact shell with a narrow aperture. Greatly thickened outer lip covered in strong teeth and folds. 2 strong bud-like growths either side of a central notch in the columella and a nodulose callus that extends out over the body whorl. O: wide, rounded spirals. C: early whorls amber, otherwise milky white or cream. H: d1–2; sublittoral and deeper water. W: PAN. R: 2.

Tonna allium

(DILLWYN, 1817)
costate tun

D: 90mm. S: thin, inflated shell with a fairly pointed spire. Faint umbilical channel, columellar folds. Crenulated outer lip. O: wide, raised, sharp ribs, becoming finer at the base, crossed by axial ribs. C: milk-white to amber, spirals often light brown on a white background. H: d1–2; sublittoral and deeper water. W: INDP. R: 2.

Malea ringens

(SWAINSON, 1822)
grinning tun

Tonna deshayesii

(REEVE, 1849)
Deshayes' tun

D: 110mm. S: thin, slightly elongated shell with convex, gently shouldered whorls separated by a deep suture. Crenulated outer lip. O: flat, spiral ribs with narrower grooves in between. C: creamy white to amber with irregular brown stripes or white dashes in a roughly radial pattern. H: d1; sublittoral. W: INDP. R: 1.

Tonna dolium

(LINNAEUS, 1758)
spotted tun

D: 100mm. S: a thin, squat shell with an extremely narrow umbilical cleft. O: wide spiral ribs, often with several finer grooves in between and very fine axial ribs. C: gray-brown or white. A checkered pattern of light and dark brown blotches on the spirals. H: d1–2; mostly in deeper water. W: AUS, INDP. R: 2.

Tonna galea

(LINNAEUS, 1758)
giant tun

D: 250mm. S: thin, but robust, cask-like shell with a low apex and an extremely large final whorl. Slightly thickened outer lip, crenulated due to the spiral ribs. Deeply channeled suture between whorls. O: alternate wide and narrow spirals on whorls. C: amber, aperture white. H: d1–2; sublittoral and deeper up to approx. 50m. W: CAR, LUS, WAFR. R: 3. NB: now a protected species.

Tonna maculosa

(DILLWYN, 1817)
Atlantic partridge tun

D: 90mm. S: thin, elongated shell. Top angle of the large aperture is pointed. Crenulated outer lip. Narrow umbilicus, crevice-like. O: flat spiral ribs. C: lilac-brown with light and dark brown dashes and spots. Apex often mauve. Aperture often edged white. H: d2; deeper water. W: CAR. R: 2.

Tonna perdix

(LINNAEUS, 1758)
Pacific partridge tun

D: 130mm. S: thin shell with a very large, elongated aperture. Crenulated outer lip. Narrow umbilicus, crevice-like, with a wide spiral rib around it. O: regular, flat spiral ribs. C: lilac-brown with light and dark brown dashes and spots. Aperture white. H: d1–3; deeper water, on sandy substrate. W: INDP. R: 2.

Tonna sulcosa

(VON BORN, 1778)
banded tun

D: 110mm. S: thin, relatively small shell with convex whorls with a deeply channeled suture in between. Thickened outer lip with folds and teeth. O: flat spirals with very narrow, shallow grooves in between. C: milky white with russet to dark brown bands. H: d1–3; mostly in deep water. W: INDP, JAP. R: 2.

Tonna tesselata

(LAMARCK, 1816)
tessellate tun

D: 130mm. S: thin shell with a slightly raised spire. Deeply channeled suture between spire whorls. O: wide or narrow spiral ribs quite widely interspaced. C: creamy white to amber. Russet dashes on spirals. Aperture usually brown. Grayish-yellow periostracum, usually abraded. H: d2–3; usually in deeper water. W: INDP, JAP. R: 1.

FICOIDEA

MEEK, 1864
Nowadays, Ficidae are placed in their own superfamily, together with the deepwater family Thalassocyonidae F. Riedel, 1994 (not discussed further). This is partly due to differences in form and anatomy and also because this group already existed in the Paleocene, which is to say long before Tonnoidea existed.

Ficidae

MEEK, 1864
fig shells

Thin, yet robust shells with an upside-down pear shape (indeed, they are fig-shaped). The spire is quite blunt, while the aperture is large and wide, gradually leading downward to a long siphonal canal. The surface has a delicate lattice ornament, or else is dominated by spiral ribs. No operculum or varices. The mantle can cover the entire shell. These animals plough through the sandy seafloor searching for food. They do not secrete acids when catching prey. Principally found in shallow, tropical waters. Only one genus: *Ficus.*

Ficus eospila

(PÉRON & LESUEUR, 1807)
spotted fig shell

D: 50mm. S: thin shell with somewhat convex whorls with a shallow suture in between. Outer lip thin. O: sharp, even spiral ribs, crossed by finer axial ribs. C: pale apricot or cream with russet to dark brown blotches. H: d1–2; deep water. W: AUS. R: 2–3.

Ficus ficus

(LINNAEUS, 1758)
common fig shell

D: 100mm. S: thin shell with rounded spire. Aperture not thickened or only slightly. O: intersecting axial ribs and spiral ribs create a coarse, woven texture. C: amber with faint, lighter perpendicular bands offset with russet blotches. Aperture violet/purple. H: d1–2; sublittoral and deeper, up to approx. 100m. W: INDP, JAP. R: 2.

prox. 100m. W: INDP, JAP. R: 1–2.

Ficus filosa

(SOWERBY, 1892)
threaded fig shell

D: 75mm. S: thin shell with a fairly flat spire and a clear, if shallow, suture. O: very even ornament of interlaced, narrow axial and spiral ribs. C: apricot, often with light brown stripes. H: d2–3; deep water. W: INDP, JAP; East and South China Sea. R: 4.

Ficus variegata

RÖDING, 1798
true or variable fig shell

D: 75mm. S: thin, but robust shell with convex whorls, a broad body whorl and a wide aperture. The outer lip may be slightly thickened. O: very closely grouped, fine, flat spiral ribs, crossed by even fainter growth lines. C: greenish-brown with silver-gray dashes and vertical bands, and russet spots that may follow the spiral ribs. Aperture purplish-brown to violet. H: d1; sublittoral to approx. 20m. W: INDP, JAP. R: 1. NB: one of the few fig shells from shallow waters.

Ficus gracilis

(SOWERBY, 1825)
graceful fig shell

D: 150mm. S: thin, relatively slender shell with a long siphonal canal, somewhat convex whorls, and a slightly raised spire. O: very fine, closely interlaced lattice of axial and spiral ribs. Spiral ribs often slightly dominating axial ribs. C: golden brown with russet dashes and stripes. H: d1–2; sublittoral and deeper water, up to ap-

CARINARIOIDEA

DE BLAINVILLE, 1818
heteropods: pelagic gelatinous gastropods

(Synonym: Heteropoda Lamarck, 1812.) Snails with a pelagic lifestyle: animals that spend their whole lives swimming or floating through plankton. The upward and downward movement of a "fin" at the front of the foot makes them active swimmers. Their shells are reduced, thin, or entirely absent. They eat jellyfish, the larvae of other sea snails, and other zooplankton. Worldwide distribution in all warmer maritime zones. A few families. Species from the family Atlantidae Rang, 1829—atlantids—have spirally wound shells with an operculum, often with a keel and up to 11mm across, into which the animal is able to withdraw completely. Genera: *Atlanta, Oxygyrus, Protatlanta*. Species from the family Carinariidae De Blainville, 1818 have extremely fragile, cap-shaped shells with a wide aperture, somewhat flattened on either side, much smaller than the very lengthy animals (measuring up to 500mm). No operculum. A few genera: *Cardiapoda, Carinaria, Pterosoma*. The family Firolidae Rang, 1829 contains species which are completely without shells. Genera: *Firoloida, Pterotrachea*.

INFRAORDER PTENOGLOSSA

J.E. GRAY, 1853
This infraorder contains 3 superfamilies of carnivorous snails. The radula is adapted to carnivorous activity and contains many similarly shaped denticles, progressively larger the closer they are to the side. Most species have a proboscis which folds inward (acrembolic).

TRIPHOROIDEA

J.E. GRAY, 1847
Tiny, slender shells that grow either clockwise or counterclockwise and have both spiral and radial ribs. The protoconch is composed of several whorls. The base of the aperture contains a siphonal canal. Usually smaller than 10mm. Most species live parasitically on sponges. Principal occurrence in relatively shallow, tropical and temperate maritime zones. Some species found in deep water up to depths of 1000m.

Cerithiopsidae

H. & A. ADAMS, 1853
miniature cerith shells

Principally micro-mollusks. Slender shells that grow clockwise. In appearance, similar to some genera from Triphoridae. Worldwide distribution, mostly feeding on sponges. Intertidal zone to depths of thousands of meters. Subfamilies: Aliptinae Marshall, 1978; Cerithiopsinae H. & A. Adams, 1854; Eumetulinae Golikov & Starobogatov, 1975. Various genera, including: *Cerithiopsida, Cerithiopsidella, Cerithiopsis, Dizoniopsis, Eumetula, Euseila, Potenatomus, Seila, Stilus, Tubercliopsis, Zaclys*.

Cerithiopsis tubercularis

(MONTAGU, 1803)
brown miniature cerith

D: 7mm. S: thick, spire-shaped shell with up to 14 whorls. Short siphonal canal at the base of the aperture. No umbilicus. O: delicate lattice ornament. Nodules where spiral and axial ribs intersect. C: dark or chestnut brown. The protoconch is usually paler in color, as are the nodules and columella. H: d1–2; sublittoral to depths of over 100m, amid sponges, such as *Halichondria*. W: KEL, LUS. R: 1.

Triforidae

JOUSSEAUME, 1884
Spire-shaped shells that grow in a clockwise orientation. Nodulose spiral ornament. Small aperture with a bent siphonal canal. Live on sponges. A few genera, including: *Ataxocerithium* and *Cerithiella*.

Triphoridae

J.E. GRAY, 1847
counterclockwise shells

Principally micro-mollusks. The shells grow counterclockwise and have a lattice ornament with nodulose spirals. The siphonal canal is short and bent. A small aperture with a notch or small channel at the top. Worldwide occurrence, parasitically attached to sponges, usually in shallow water under rocks and coral. Sometimes found at depths of many hundreds of meters. Divided into several subfamilies. Laiocochlinae Golikov & Starobogatov, 1987 and Triphorinae J.E. Gray, 1847 grow counterclockwise. Adelacerithinae Marshall, 1984 and Metaxiinae Marshall, 1977 grow clockwise. A great many genera, including: *Cheirodonta, Cos-*

motriphora, Euthymella, Inella, Laiocochlis, Marshallora, Mastonia, Metaxia, Monophorus, Obesula, Seilarex, Similiphora, Strobiligera, Tetraphora, Triphora, Viriola.

A well-known European species is seen to the left in the photograph: *Marshallora adversa* (Montagu, 1803) – brown counterclockwise shell – (an SEM image and a detailed view of the apex showing its complex structure). Two tropical species are shown (center and right): *Tetraphora princeps* (Sowerby, 1904) from the Philippines and *Viriola corrugata* (Hinds, 1843) from Australia. These last two are large in comparison with the rest of the family.

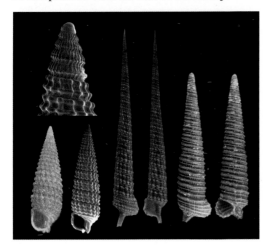

JANTHINOIDEA

LAMARCK, 1812
The two families classified within this superfamily are quite different from each other ecologically. All of them are carnivorous with a ptenoglossa radula. Their food includes jellyfish, sea anemones and corals. Most species are protoandrously hermaphroditic.

Aclididae

G.O. SARS, 1878
spike shells

Micro-mollusks. Colorless shells, slender and spired with up to ten whorls, sometimes convex, with spiral and/or axial ribs. The inner lip is slightly recurved with a narrow, crevice-like umbilicus behind it. Species look like those from the family Eulimidae, but can be told apart by the radula structure and the lack of a penis. They occur in all warm and temperate seas, usually in deep water. Only a few genera, including: *Aclis, Awanuia, Discaclis, Thaleia.*

Aclis minor

(BROWN, 1827)
small spike shell

D: 6mm. S: thin, awl-shaped shell with up to 10 convex whorls. Oval aperture with a deep, defined umbilicus next to it. O: clear spirals, mostly in the middle of the whorls. However, the whorls can also be virtually smooth. C: cream to white. H: d1–2; on muddy sand or gravel at 15–150m. W: KEL, LUS. R: 2.

Epitoniidae

BERRY, 1910
wentletraps

Thin shells, yet because of their structure often very robust. The aperture opens to the right. Shells range from pointed spires to rounded cones, usually with closely connected whorls. In many species, ornament comprises distinctive, radial ribs or lamellae. Various other types of ornament appear as well, ranging from a smooth finish to delicate lattice. The aperture is usually circular. The name "wentletrap" derives from Dutch and means "spiral staircase."
Worldwide distribution. Most species live in relatively shallow water, although species do exist in the abyssal zone (the deep sea). The food of Epitoniidae consists of sea anemones (*Actinia* species) and corals. Many animals produce secretions that turn deep purple or violet when exposed to air and light. Divided into several subfamilies: Epitoniinae Berry, 1910; Nystiellinae Clench & Turner, 1952; Pseudonininae Bertolaso & Palazzi, 1994. A great many species in a variety of genera, including: *Acirsa, Amaea, Cirsotrema, Claviscala, Cycloscala, Cylindriscala, Eglisia, Epitonium, Gyroscala, Laeviphitus, Murdochella, Opalia, Opaliopsis, Punctiscala, Stylotrochus.*

Amaea ferminiana

(DALL, 1908)
ferminiana wentletrap

D: 40mm. S: fairly robust shell. O: axial and spiral ribs cross, making a lattice. C: amber. Axial ribs sometimes a little paler. H: d2–3; in deeper water. W: PAN. R: 4.

Amaea magnifica

(SOWERBY, 1844)
magnificent wentletrap

D: 100mm. S: very large, thin shell. O: both spirals and thin axial ribs, which are usually less dominant. C: white. H: d3; deep water. W: JAP. R: 4. NB: rare, sought-after by collectors.

Cirsotrema rugosum

KURODA & ITO, 1961
rugose wentletrap

D: 70mm. S: very pointed shell with a large number of strongly shouldered whorls. O: narrow, bladelike axial ribs that curve upward at the top of the whorl. A sharp spiral rib links together all the ribs at the base of the body whorl. C: white. H: d2–3. W: JAP. R: 3–4. NB: a rare, sought-after species.

Cirsotrema varicosum

(LAMARCK, 1822)
varicose wentletrap

D: 40mm. S: robust shell with a thickened outer lip. O: varices apparent. Between these, distinctively patterned, gossamer-thin layers of calcium, reminiscent of finely woven lacework. C: chalky white. H: d2; deeper water. W: JAP. R: 3.

Epitonium clathratulum

(KANMACHER, 1798)
white wentletrap

D: 13mm. S: small, fragile shell with up to 12 convex whorls. Circular aperture coincides with a rib. O: up to 20 sharp ribs on the final whorl, often oblique. C: cream to white, no marks. H: d1–2; sublittoral and deeper. Found on sandy and rocky coasts on anemones. W: KEL, LUS. R: 2.

Epitonium clathrus

(LINNAEUS, 1758)
common European wentletrap

D: 35mm. S: thin, awl-shaped shell with up to 12 convex whorls. Its first whorls are usually broken off. Circular aperture coincides with an axial rib. No umbilicus. O: thin axial ribs, joining up with the ribs above. The area in between is smooth. C: glossy, porcelain-white, often with russet spots. H: d1–2; parasite of anemones. W: KEL, LUS. R: 1.

Epitonium pallasi

(KIENER, 1838)
Pallas' wentletrap

D: 25mm. S: thin shell, although made quite strong by its ribs. Deep suture. Narrow, deep umbilicus. O: evenly arranged axial ribs. Outer lip always coincides with a rib. C: amber, ribs paler. H: d1; sublittoral. W: INDP. R: 1. NB: looks like the common European wentletrap, but adults are smaller.

Epitonium scalare

(LINNAEUS, 1758)
precious wentletrap

D: 60mm. S: thin shell with fairly broad whorls. Extremely deep, open suture. A broad, open umbilicus. O: ribs evenly interspaced with wide spaces in between. C: white, sometimes pale pink to pale amber. H: d1. W: INDP. R: 2. NB: one of the most famous of all shells. Once exceptionally rare and worth huge sums. Fakes were even made from rice paper. Nowadays, commonly available.

149

Epitonium turtonis

(TURTON, 1819)
Turton's wentletrap

D: 35mm. S: quite a slender, solid shell with up to 15 fairly rounded whorls. Circular aperture that coincides with a rib. No umbilicus. O: 9–12 flat, axial ribs on the final whorl, some of which are clearly enlarged. Fine spiral ornament visible between the ribs. C: light to dark brown with purplish-brown blotches. H: d1–2; sublittoral and deeper, sandy and rocky coasts. W: KEL, LUS. R: 2. NB: specimens from the Mediterranean Sea are often larger and darker in color than specimens from more northerly climes (Denmark, Sweden).

Gyroscala lamellosa

(LAMARCK, 1822)
lamellose wentletrap

D: 30mm. S: thin, pointed shell. O: thin, blade-like ribs. Another bladelike spiral rib runs around the base of the final whorl, connecting the axial ribs that run through it. C: whorls purplish-brown or paler. All ribs white. H: d1–2; sublittoral and deeper water. W: CAR, INDP, LUS, WAFR. R: 2.

Janthinidae

LAMARCK, 1812
purple sea snails

Thin, squat to top-shaped shells. Very light-weight. Violet or colorless. All these animals are pelagic without exception and hang suspended by the foot under a self-made "raft" of mucus-covered air bubbles. Their egg capsules also float attached to these rafts. The animals feed on other floating organisms, such as sea-snail larvae and jellyfish colonies (Siphonophora). They occur in the warmer parts of all maritime zones. These animals, and the rafts on which they float, are sometimes seen washed ashore in huge numbers following storms. Few species in two genera: *Janthina, Recluzia*.

Janthina janthina

(LINNAEUS, 1758)
common purple sea snail or janthina

D: 40mm. S: thin shell with fairly level whorls and a markedly angular aperture. O: low, wavy spirals and more defined growth lines. C: often creamy white to pale lilac on top of the whorls, dark purple below. H: pelagic. W: worldwide distribution, both cold and warm maritime environments. R: 1.

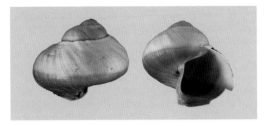

Janthina prolongata

DE BLAINVILLE, 1822
elongate janthina

D: 25mm. S: thin shell with convex whorls and an angular, wide aperture. O: very delicately lined or checkered with coarser growth lines.

C: pink to lilac, especially at the base of whorls. H: pelagic species (floats in the sea). W: worldwide, all warmer maritime zones. R: 3. NB: specimens with an intact outer lip are rare.

EULIMOIDEA

PHILIPPI, 1853

A relatively large group of sea snails that has adapted to an entirely parasitic lifestyle. These snails' hosts include sea urchins and sea cucumbers. Most species have a long proboscis. Instead of a radula, they have a special siphon within the esophagus.

Eulimidae

PHILIPPI, 1853
eulimids

Principally, fairly small shells, usually in the form of slender cones. Some groups have shells that are more inflated and convex, like bullets. The spire often leans to one side, giving the shell a bent appearance. The surface is polished and very glossy, usually white or glassy, and sometimes also amber or russet with bands of color. Only the larger species have an operculum. Most species do not have an umbilicus adjoining the aperture, with the exception of the genera *Microstilifer* and *Niso*. Dozens of genera, including: *Balcis, Curveulima, Ersilia, Eulima, Eulitoma, Haliella, Halielloides, Melanella, Niso, Pelseneeria, Plagyostila, Strombiformis, Thyca, Vitreolina.*

Eulima glabra

(DA COSTA, 1778)
great eulimid

D: 10mm. S: thin shell, resembling a bodkin, with exceptionally flat whorls. Top of aperture

meets at a point, accounting for roughly half the shell's total height. O: smooth. C: amber with 2–6 orange-brown bands. H: d1–3; sublittoral to deep water. W: KEL, LUS, WAFR. R: 2. NB: to the right in the photograph is *Vitreolina philippi* (Rayneval & Ponzi, 1854)—the bent eulimid. 8mm. Same distribution.

Melanella martinii

(A. ADAMS IN SOWERBY, 1853)
thick-shelled eulimid

D: 35mm. S: large, thick, spire-shaped shell. Whorls with slight shoulders. Apex slightly curved. O: smooth. C: glossy white. H: d1; sublittoral to 30m. W: INDP, JAP. R: 2. NB: one of the few large species of eulimid.

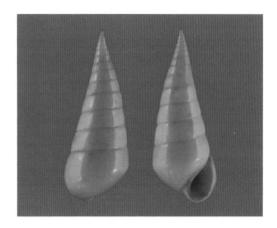

INFRAORDER NEOGASTROPODA

THIELE, 1929

This includes several superfamilies of principally carnivorous snails (active predators or scavengers). Extremely varied shells, often strongly ornamented, with a siphonal canal and a corneous operculum.

MURICOIDEA

RAFINESQUE, 1815

The families Buccinidae, Nassaridae and Volutidae were once classified in separate superfamilies. Nowadays, they are all placed within Muricoidea. These animals are predatory or scavenge, and use a short, or long, siphon, a retractable proboscis and a rachiglossate radula (a radula with two laterals and a single central tooth). Some genera from Buccinidae, Marginellidae and Muricidae secrete an acidic, poisonous substance. This enables them to bore through the shells of other mollusks, with the proboscis sucking up the soft parts through the resulting hole. In Ancient Rome, a purple dye was obtained from some species of murex and whelk to color imperial robes and religious apparel. The liquid that these snails secrete from a special gland is initially clear, but changes color as a reaction to sunlight from yellowish-green to a deep violet-purple.

Buccinidae

RAFINESQUE, 1815
whelks, Neptunes, and others

Conical or fusiform shells. Whorls often have a relatively defined shoulder. A siphonal canal is present. This is often elongated and may be bent outward, but may also be short and blunt. The columella is without folds and usually smooth. The shell surface has radial or spiral ribs. Radial ribs often have shoulder tubercles. Carnivorous snails, in most cases scavengers. A number of species are able to bore holes into other mollusks (genus *Cominella*). Divided into a number of subfamilies: Buccininae Rafinesque, 1815 – whelks; Photinae J.E. Gray, 1857 – phos whelks; Pisaniinae Tryon, 1881 and Volutopsiinae Habe & Sato, 1972. Fasciolariinae, Melongeninae, and Nassariinae are sometimes treated as subfamilies of Buccinidae. The family is distributed across all maritime zones, from tropical to temperate and colder regions. Various species also live in the Arctic, often in deeper water. All together, these comprise many dozens of genera, including: *Babylonia, Bartschia, Belomitra, Beringius, Buccinulum, Buccinum, Burnupena, Caducifer, Cantharus, Chauvetia, Colus, Cominella, Engina, Hindsia, Kryptos, Liomesus, Mohnia, Nassaria, Neptunea, Northia, Phos, Pisania, Retimohnia, Searlesia, Siphonalia, Tacita, Trajana, Troschelia, Volutopsius.*

Babylonia japonica

(REEVE, 1842)
Japanese Babylon

D: 75mm. S: thick shell with inflated, gently shouldered whorls. A fold borders the umbilical groove adjoining the inner lip. O: smooth surface apart from the umbilical fold. C: yellowish-white with distinctive, dark brown markings, consisting of small spots in the whorl midsection and larger blotches in bands above and below this. H: d1; usually in slightly deeper water to approx. 20m. W: JAP. R: 1.

Babylonia spirata

(LINNAEUS, 1758)
spiral Babylon

D: 45mm. S: very thick shell with fairly flattened whorls. Very deeply channeled suture, creating sharply shouldered whorls. Wide umbilical groove with an umbilical fold alongside. O: surface appears smooth to the eye but has very delicate axial grooves. C: white with rose-red to amber blotches. White-callused inner lip. Tawny periostracum. H: d1–2; muddy substrate, up to approx. 60m. W: INDP. R: 1.

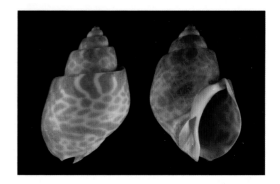

Buccinum undatum

LINNAEUS, 1758
common northern or edible European whelk

D: 120mm. S: large, thick shell with convex whorls. The apex is relatively pointed. The oval aperture ends in a short siphonal canal. O: horizontal ribs crossed by clear growth lines. Wide, wavy axial ribs, especially on upper part of whorls. C: yellowish-white or brown, often with dark blotches or bands. H: d1–3; mostly on soft, muddy substrates, sublittoral and deeper. W: KEL (both sides of the Atlantic Ocean), LUS. R: 1. NB: eggs are small, rubbery balls laid stuck together in a yellowish-white clump.

These often wash ashore, sometimes with young whelks still contained within.

Colus gracilis

(DA COSTA, 1778)
slender colus

D: 60mm. S: solid, slender shells with fairly level whorls. The apex is pointed with the protoconch being slightly wider than the whorl that follows it and thus bud-like. The elongated, oval aperture ends in a long, bent siphonal canal. O: fine, spiral ribs. C: white to cream. The amber periostracum is thin and membranous and soon abrades after it is dried. H: d2–4; sandy or muddy substrates at depths of 30 to 800m. W: ARC, KEL. R: 2. NB: Jeffreys' colus, *C. jeffreysianus* (Fischer, 1868), closely resembles this species but does not have the same bud-like apex.

Nassaria amboynensis

(WATSON, 1881)
banded phos

D: 25mm. S: pointed shell with convex whorls and a deep suture. Thickened outer lip with folds and teeth within. Inner lip also toothed. Long, slightly bent, siphonal canal. Narrow

anal canal at top of aperture. O: fine spiral ribs run across and between wide axial ribs. C: white with broad, russet bands. H: d1; sublittoral. W: INDP. R: 2.

Neptunea antiqua

(LINNAEUS, 1758)
ancient Neptune

D: 200mm. S: thick shell with convex whorls. Fairly pointed apex, protoconch usually broken off. Pear-shaped aperture, ending in a nearly straight siphonal canal. O: subtle spirals. C: yellowish-white to light brown. Aperture apricot. H: d2–4; in deep water from 15 to 2000m. W: ARC, KEL. R: 1.

Neptunea contraria

(LINNAEUS, 1771)
left-handed Neptune

D: 90mm. S: similar in shape to *N. antiqua*, but completely reversed; aperture opens to the left. O: clearly regular ornament. C: creamy white or amber, outer lip usually somewhat paler. H:

d1–2; from deep water to great depths. W: KEL, LUS; Bay of Biscay, Mediterranean Sea. R: 3.

Neptunea kuroshio

(OYAMA IN KIRA, 1959)
Japanese small Neptune

D: 80mm. S: thick, compact shell with a pointed apex and a long, bent siphonal canal. O: fairly low, but clear, spirals. C: milky white to cream. H: d2–3; deep water to 200m. W: JAP. R: 2.

Phos senticosus

(LINNAEUS, 1758)
common Pacific or thorny phos

D: 40mm. S: thick, pointed shell with convex, shouldered whorls. Thickened outer lip with sharp teeth within. O: thick axial ribs and narrower, sharp spirals. Nodules and scales at in-

tersections. C: amber with dark and light brown bands. H: d1; littoral and sublittoral, especially on sandbars and mud flats in the intertidal zone. W: INDP. R: 1.

Pyrolofusus deformis

(REEVE, 1847)
sinistral Arctic whelk

D: 75mm. S: solid shell wound counterclockwise with a fairly blunt apex and convex whorls. Wide siphonal canal crossing the base of the outer rim. O: defined spirals and wavy, pleated axial ribs that become fainter toward the base. C: amber to cream. H: d2; deeper water. W: ARC, JAP. R: 2. NB: this and other northern species appear infrequently in collections.

Siphonalia cassidariaeformis

(REEVE, 1843)
bonnet whelk

D: 40mm. S: reasonably thick shell with sloped shoulders. Thickened outer lip with clear ridges and teeth within. Long, bent siphonal canal. O: regular spirals and shoulder tubercles. C: amber with dark brown blotches. H: d2; deep water. W: JAP. R: 1. NB: extremely varied in color and form.

Austrofusus glans

(RÖDING, 1798)
New Zealand knobbed whelk

D: 50mm. S: not particularly thick-shelled, but robust. Outer lip only slightly thickened if at all. Long, slightly bent, siphonal canal. O: subtle axial and spiral ribs. Small knobs at intersections, particularly just above the center of the whorl. C: amber, often with some small, brown blotches. H: d1–2; sublittoral and below, on sand. W: AUS; New Zealand. R: 1.

Volutopsius norvegicus

(GMELIN, 1791)
Norwegian volute whelk

D: 100mm. S: robust to thick shell, resembling a *Voluta* in shape. Blunt apex. Convex whorls. Large body whorl. Wide aperture. O: surface almost smooth with defined growth lines. C: creamy white. H: d2–4; lives on echinoderms at

depths ranging from a few hundred meters to over 2000m. W: ARC, KEL. R: 2.

Columbellidae

SWAINSON, 1840
dove shells

Quite small shells, like upturned cones, some with spires more pointed than others. Aperture ranges from fairly narrow to cleft-like. The outer lip is usually thickened and has strong apertural folds and teeth. Often, there are also columellar folds. The siphonal canal is short but evident and open. The shell can be smooth or ornamented, and is often gaudily colored. The outer lip and columella are usually toothed. These lively animals live in the intertidal zone and deeper water. Food consists of algae and detritus. Found principally in warmer maritime zones. Two subfamilies: Columbellinae Swainson, 1840; Pyreninae Suter, 1909. Various genera, including: *Aesopus, Amphissa, Anachis, Columbella, Columbellopsis, Mitrella, Nitidella, Pardulina, Pictocolumbella, Pyrene, Strombina, Zafra.*

Columbella haemastoma

SOWERBY, 1832
bloodstained dove shell

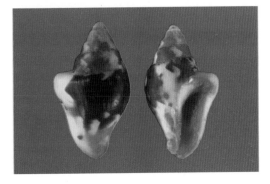

D: 20mm. S: thick shell with a much thickened, flaring outer lip – somewhat wing-shaped and slightly impressed in the center. Strong teeth within. O: smooth, or with very fine spirals. C: chocolate-brown with light brown and white patches. Aperture rim and teeth orange-red. H: d1; sublittoral. W: PAN; Galapagos Islands. R: 2.

Columbella major

SOWERBY, 1832
fat dove shell

D: 30mm. S: thick shell with a pointed spire. Thickened outer lip bends outward slightly. Strong teeth within and also on the inner lip. O: fine axial grooves. C: chocolate- to coffee-brown, with light brown or white blotches. Often a larger white patch on the shoulder close to the outer lip. H: d1; sublittoral. W: PAN, PER. R: 1.

Columbella mercatoria

(LINNAEUS, 1758)
common dove shell

D: 20mm. S: thick shell with a blunt apex and squat spire. Outer lip much thickened with teeth within. O: Clear spiral ribs over the whole shell. C: very variable – pink, yellowish-white,

to dark brown, in all imaginable patterns. H: d1; littoral and sublittoral, under rocks. W: CAR. R: 1.

Columbella strombiformis

LAMARCK, 1822
stromboid dove shell

D: 30mm. S: thick shell with shouldered whorls. In shape, reminiscent of a miniature conch (Strombidae). O: spirals, mostly on the lower half of the shell. C: russet to dark brown with lighter patches. H: d1; sublittoral, under rocks. W: PAN; California to Peru. R: 1.

Parametaria dupontii

(KIENER, 1849)
Dupont's dove shell

D: 27mm. S: thin, but robust shell, rather like a cone shell in shape (Conidae). Outer lip without teeth and only slightly thickened if at all. O: smooth. C: amber to orange with irregular patterns. H: d1; shallow water. W: CAL; California to Mexico. R: 1.

Pictocolumbella ocellata

(LINK, 1807)
lightning dove shell

D: 20mm. S: thick shell with quite rounded whorls. Pointed spire, outer lip much thickened with clear teeth in the midsection within. O: faint spirals, clearest on the underside. C: dark brown to black with white zigzags. H: d1; littoral and sublittoral. W: INDP. R: 1.

Strombina fusinoidea

DALL, 1916
slender strombina

D: 50mm. S: thick, very pointed shell with straight-sided whorls. Much thickened outer lip, no defined teeth within. O: spiral ribs only below the body whorl. C: creamy white with amber blotches. H: d1–2; sublittoral and slightly deeper water. W: CAL, PAN. R: 2.

Strombina maculosa

(SOWERBY, 1832)
blotchy strombina

D: 25mm. S: solid, very pointed shell with straight-sided whorls. Thickened outer lip with strong teeth within. O: low, wavy axial ribs, with sharp knobs close to the shoulder. A second row of knobs in the center of the body whorl. C: creamy white to amber, patterned with dark brown patches. H: d1; sublittoral, muddy substrates. W: CAL, PAN. R: 2.

Coralliophilidae

CHENU, 1859
coral shells, latiaxis shells

A fairly small group, related to Muricidae. Often somewhat compact, strongly ornamented shells, possessing angular whorls with sharp keels, spines, nodules, and other features. The surface itself is covered in fine granules or scales. These animals prey or live parasitically on (or even in) hard corals, gorgonians, or sea anemones. They do not possess a radula. Instead, they have a proboscis with a narrow esophagus. The genus *Latiaxis* mostly lives in deep waters in the Indo-Pacific region. The genera *Coralliophila*, *Rapa*, and their relatives principally live in shallower water, on coral reefs. Few genera. These include: *Babelomurex*, *Coralliophila*, *Latiaxis*, *Magilus*, *Mipus*, *Rapa*.

Coralliophila neritoidea

(LAMARCK, 1816)
violet coral shell

D: 35mm. S: thick shell with a flattened spire and low, irregular whorls, Thickened outer lip with folds within. O: Low spirals. Surface can often be eroded and calcified. C: grayish-white.

Aperture interior glossy violet-pink. H: d1; coral reefs. W: INDP. R: 1.

Latiaxis mawae

(GRAY IN GRIFFITH & PIDGEON, 1834)
Mawe's latiaxis

D: 50mm. S: thick, irregularly shaped shell with a severely flattened spire. Large and small, leaf-like (foliaceous) flanges project and curve upward around the shoulder. Umbilicus gapes open. Wide open siphonal canal. O: distinct growth lines. C: creamy white to pale yellow. H: d2; deeper water. W: JAP. R: 2. NB: very variable in size and shape.

Latiaxis pilsbryi

HIRASE, 1908
Pilsbry's latiaxis

D: 35mm. S: fairly thin shell with a very flat spire. Very flat, foliaceous flanges project around the shoulders. Projections also around

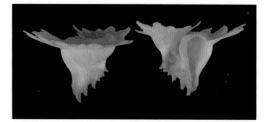

the base of the body whorl. Gaping umbilicus. O: distinct growth lines. C: yellowish-white to cream. H: d2–3; deep water. W: JAP. R: 4. NB: a variety of fancifully shaped *Latiaxis* species are known of in Japanese waters. Most of these are rare and greatly sought-after by collectors.

Rapa rapa

(LINNAEUS, 1758)
rapa snail

D: 60mm. S: thin shell with a severely flattened spire. The siphonal canal is usually wide open, ending in a scoop shape and can be strongly bent to one side. O: strong spiral grooves. C: yellowish-white to cream. H: d1–2; attaches itself on soft corals. Regularly washed ashore. W: INDP. R: 1.

Costellariidae

MCDONALD, 1860
ribbed miters

Pointed, elongated shells with a fairly narrow aperture. Whorls are either rounded or angular, and have axial ribs in most cases. Spiral ribs are also present in most cases. The outer lip may be somewhat thickened and usually contains folds. The columella has three to six strongly developed folds, the lowest usually being the widest. The parietal wall is often callused. In shape, these carnivorous snails resemble Mitridae (miter shells) but are actually more closely related to Muricidae. Species from the genus *Thala* paralyze their prey by injecting poison. They occur in warmer maritime zones, mostly on a sandy substrate and amid rocks and corals. Dozens of species, assigned to only a few genera, including: *Austromitra, Costellaria, Nodicostellaria, Pusia, Thala, Turricostellaria, Vexillum, Zierliana.*

Vexillum plicarium

(LINNAEUS, 1758)
plaited miter

D: 50mm. S: a solid, quite wide, rotund shell.
O: narrow axial ribs and very strong spirals, especially at the base. C: creamy white with wide,
amber bands and narrow, broken stripes from
dark brown to black. H: d1; sublittoral. W:
INDP. R: 1.

Vexillum rugosum

(GMELIN, 1791)
rugose miter

D: 50mm. S: solid shell, angular whorls. Very
delicate columellar folds. O: wide axial ribs and
strong, pleated spirals. C: amber with narrow
russet stripes and wider dark brown bands. H:
d1; sublittoral, on sand. W: INDP. R: 1.

Vexillum regina

(SOWERBY, 1828)
queen miter

D: 60mm. S: a very pointed, slender shell. Slim
aperture. O: axial ribs, becoming fainter at the
base. Spirals across the whole shell, clearest at
the base. C: bands of orange, dark brown, and
creamy white. H: d1; shallow water. W: INDP;
the Philippines. R: 3.

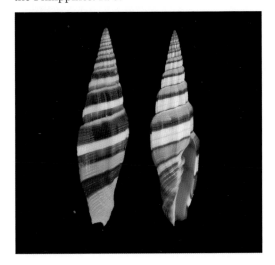

Vexillum stainforthii

(REEVE, 1842)
Stainforth's miter

D: 40mm. S: solid, pointed shell with fairly
rounded whorls. O: Wide, rounded, slightly
wavy axial ribs. Fine spirals. C: white with alternate vertical bands checkered in orange-red
blocks. H: d1; sublittoral, shallow water. W:
INDP; southwestern part. R: 3.

Vexillum taeniatum

(LAMARCK, 1811)
ribboned miter

D: 50mm. S: a solid, slender shell. Quite a long siphonal canal. O: low spirals and rounded axial ribs, becoming fainter below. C: yellowish-white to orange. Lower half of whorl has a creamy white band. Often a dark brown stripe above and below whorls with a further stripe just below the lowest band (not shown). H: d1; shallow water, on sand. W: INDP, JAP. R: 3–4.

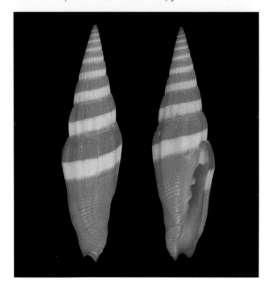

Vexillum vulpecula

(LINNAEUS, 1758)
little fox miter

D: 50mm. S: solid, rather angular shell. Whorls have slightly rounded shoulders. An extra columellar fold higher up on the inner lip. O: low

spirals. Rounded axial ribs soon become fainter. C: variable, orange to creamy white with dark brown bands. H: d1; sublittoral. W: INDP. R: 1.

Cystiscidae

STIMPSON, 1865
margin shells

These shells closely resemble Marginellidae (also called margin shells). However, Cystiscidae absorb their early whorls and columellar folds from within, which Marginellidae do not. The radulae are also different. Cystiscidae mostly have small, white, or uniformly colored, rounded shells. Some of these also have a pattern. The apex is usually flattened or depressed. The surface is smooth or has radial ribs. Varices are sometimes visible. The outer lip is thickened and may be with or without teeth. The columella usually has 2 to 10 folds and spiral grooves on the parietal wall. The animals are predatory and occur in all warmer maritime regions on sandy substrates, from the intertidal zone to deeper water. Divided into subfamilies: Cystiscinae Stimpson, 1865; Granulininae G.A. & H.K. Coovert, 1995; Persiculine G.A. & H.K. Coovert, 1995; Plesiocystiscinae G.A. & H.K. Coovert, 1995. Various genera, including: *Cystiscus, Gibberula, Granulina, Persicula.*

Gibberula oryza

(LAMARCK, 1822)
rice-grain margin shell

D: 5mm. S: small, robust shell. Blunt spire. Narrow aperture. Callused columella. O: smooth, various teeth on inner and outer lips. C: apricot, earlier whorls darker. Columella and outer lip paler or white. H: d1; sublittoral. W: KEL, LUS. R: 2.

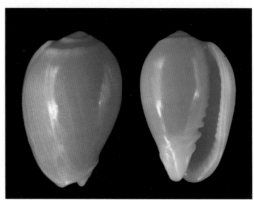

Persicula cingulata

(DILLWYN, 1817)
girdled margin shell

D: 25mm. S: inflated shell, spire bluntly flattened. Thickened outer lip. O: smooth. Inner lip has subtle folds. C: creamy white to yellow with thin, russet oblique to spiral bands. H: d1; sublittoral, shallow water, on sand and mud. W: WAFR. R: 1.

Persicula masirana

ROTH & PETIT, 1972
Omani margin shell

D: 9mm. S: thick, squat shell. Flat spire, apex slightly depressed. Thickened outer lip, straight at the center. O: smooth, very strong teeth in lower inner lip. C: grayish-white with subtle, russet to yellowish-gray blotches. H: d1; sublittoral. W: INDP; Oman. R: 3.

Persicula persicula

(LINNAEUS, 1758)
spotted margin shell

D: 20mm. S: inflated shell. Flat spire. The thickened outer lip extends just above the body whorl. O: smooth, various folds on inner and outer lips. C: apricot with russet spots. H: d1; sublittoral. W: WAFR. R: 3.

Fasciolariidae

J.E. GRAY, 1853
tulip shells, spindle shells, and others

A family with a variety of large shells. Usually roughly fusiform with a siphonal canal ranging from short to extremely long. Whorls usually have spiral ribs, but often have radial ribs as well. Outer lip only slightly thickened if at all, sometimes serrated. The columellar may sometimes have folds. Corneous operculum. Carnivores. Mostly found in tropical seas. Three subfamilies. The subfamily Fasciolariinae J.E. Gray, 1853 contains species often with a slightly curved siphonal canal and usually with columellar folds. Shallow water or on coral reefs. The subfamily Fusininae Wringley, 1927 contains species usually with a long, virtually straight siphonal canal and no columellar folds. From shallow water to deep sea. The subfamily Peristerniinae Tryon, 1880 contains species with smaller, thick shells that are strongly ribbed or nodulose with a short siphonal canal. Three oblique columellar folds. Various genera, including: *Buccinofusus, Dolicholatirus, Fascinus, Fasciolaria, Fusinus, Granulifusus, Latirolagena, Latirus, Leucozonia, Opeatostoma, Peristernia, Pleuroploca, Pseudolatirus.*

Fasciolaria lilium hunteria

(PERRY, 1811)
banded tulip

D: 90mm. S: shell with rounded whorls. Extended siphonal canal, slightly bent. O: virtually smooth, spirals only around the columella. C: gray-yellow, grayish streaks, thin brown spiral lines. H: d1; sublittoral, seaweed forests. W: CAR. R: 1. NB: to the right in the photograph *F. l. branhamae* Rehder & Abbot, 1951.

Fusinus australis

QUOY & GAIMARD, 1833
Australian spindle

D: 100mm. S: thick shell with quite angular whorls. Fairly long siphonal canal. O: strong spirals and axial ribs quick to fade away. C: brown gray, periostracum brown. H: d1; shallow water. W: AUS. R: 1.

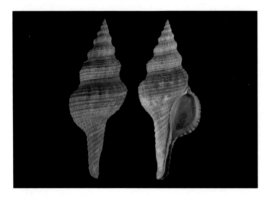

Fusinus colus

(LINNAEUS, 1758)
distaff spindle

D: 170mm. S: solid, slender shell with pointed apex and very long siphonal canal, usually

slightly curved at the end. O: fine spirals. A strong, nodulose spiral in the center of each whorl. C: creamy white to white. Spire and underside of siphonal canal russet. H: d1–2; sublittoral and deeper water. W: INDP. R: 1.

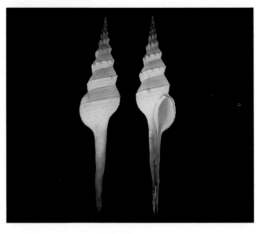

Fusinus nicobaricus

(RÖDING, 1798)
Nicobar spindle

D: 115mm. S: thick shell. Angular, stepped whorls with sloped shoulders. Very long, straight siphonal canal. O: Very strong spirals, slight shoulder nodules. C: white with irregular, russet vertical bands and flecks. H: d1; shallow water. W: INDP. R: 1.

Fusinus rostratus

(OLIVI, 1792)
small Mediterranean spindle

D: 60mm. S: robust shell with very convex whorls. Siphonal canal quite long, either straight or bent. O: folds within outer lip. Spirals and strong, rounded axial ribs. C: apricot to brown, may have slight banding. H: d1–2; sublittoral and slightly deeper water. W: LUS; mainly Mediterranean, also the Canary Islands and the Algarve, Portugal. R: 1. NB: often caught in octopus traps in the Algarve.

Fusinus syracusanus

(LINNAEUS, 1758)
Sicilian spindle

D: 55mm. S: solid shell with angular, stepped whorls with oblique-sloping shoulders. Fairly short siphonal canal, virtually straight. O: wide, axial ribs and finer spirals. C: creamy white with wide, dark brown bands. Shoulders always brown. H: d1–2; sublittoral and deeper to approx. 50m. W: LUS. R: 2.

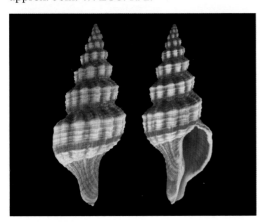

Harpidae

BRONN, 1840
harp shells

Cask-shaped shells with a short spire and a large body whorl. A clear siphonal notch at the base of the outer lip. Typically has strong or less well-defined radial ribs and an often quite distinctive russet and mauve coloration. No operculum. Found on sandy substrates in all tropical and subtropical seas, from the sublittoral to depths of some hundreds of meters. Only a few species, which are much sought-after by collectors. The family is divided into two subfamilies: Harpinae Bronn, 1840 and Moruminae Hughes & Emerson, 1987. One rare, deepwater genus *Astroharpa* and two genera from shallow water: *Harpa* and *Morum*. For many years, the latter genus was classified within Cassidae.

Harpa amouretta

RÖDING, 1798
minor harp

D: 50mm. S: solid, relatively elongated shell. O: sharp, wide ribs that are nodulose or rather angular at the top. C: apricot to pink with a pattern of purplish-brown blotches and bands both on and between the ribs. The apex is lilac. H: d1; littoral and sublittoral, shallow water. W: INDP. R: 1.

Harpa cabritii

(P. FISCHER, 1860)
inflated harp

D: 100mm. S: oval shell, often with a some-what angular and inflated body whorl. O: an-gular, quite prominent axial ribs ending at the shoulder in spiny nodules. C: amber to rose-red with paler and darker bands crossing the ribs. Often V-shaped or triangular patterns between ribs. Glossy callus – creamy yellow or russet – always with 2 dark brown blotch-es. H: d1–2; sublittoral and deeper. W: INDP; from the Red Sea to South Africa. R: 1.

Harpa costata

(LINNAEUS, 1758)
imperial harp

D: 75mm. S: quite a rotund, wide shell with a relatively low spire. O: various closely aligned, angular ribs that end in spiny points at the shoulder creating a "crown" effect. The "siphonal fasciole" (the pleats outside the col-umella made by the edges of the siphonal canal each time it re-forms) is strongly ribbed. C: creamy yellow with light brown bands crossing over and between the ribs. The apex is mauve. Creamy yellow callus with 2 coffee-colored blotches. Aperture interior yellowish-white. H: d1; shallow water. W: INDP; only around Mau-ritius. R: 4–5. NB: this rare harp shell is much sought-after by collectors.

Harpa doris

RÖDING, 1798
rose harp

D: 55mm. S: thin, elongated shell. O: narrow, low ribs, quite well interspaced. The rib tops often have somewhat pointed nodules at the shoulder. Sometimes slight nodules appear elsewhere on the ribs. C: mauve to russet with delicate russet patterns. Usually not as glossy as most other harp shells. H: d1–2; sublittoral and deeper water. W: WAFR; Senegal, Angola,

Cape Verde Islands. R: 4.

Harpa harpa

(LINNAEUS, 1758)
true harp

D: 60mm. S: relatively small, thick shell. Slight-ly raised spire. O: quite elevated, angular axial ribs, forming sharp spines at the shoulder. C: variable. From creamy yellow to russet with brown to mauve patterns. Bands often on ribs. These may consist of thin, brown stripes. Zig-zags often between ribs. Glossy parietal wall always has 3 separate, dark blotches. H: d1; littoral and sublittoral. W: INDP. R: 1.

Harpa major

RÖDING, 1798
major harp

D: 90mm. S: large, thick, rather inflated shell. Fairly deep suture between whorls. O: Reason-ably wide, low axial ribs, less dominating lower down. C: russet with dark brown blotches and bands. Glossy chocolate-brown callus on the parietal wall and columella, with a paler patch breaking this up halfway down. H: d1–2; shallow water, to a depth of approx. 100m. W: INDP. R: 1.

Morum grande

(A. ADAMS, 1855)
giant morum

D: 65mm. S: quite a solid shell like an upturned cone. A much thickened outer lip and a broad parietal shield. O: wide, regularly interspaced spirals, crossed by narrow scaly axial ribs, creating a lattice. C: creamy or yellowish-white with brown bands. Glossy, pure white callus and outer lip. Aperture white. H: d2–3; deep water. W: AUS, INDP, JAP. R: 3–4.

Morum oniscus

(LINNAEUS, 1767)
Atlantic morum

D: 20mm. S: very thick shell with a flattened spire and a pointed apex. The outer lip is much thickened with various ridges. Thick callus spreads out over the parietal wall. O: more or less evenly interspaced, blunt, lumpy nodules.

C: amber or white, often with dark brown blotches. The outer lip and, in particular, the callus are usually magenta with pale spots and blotches. H: d1; sublittoral, coral reefs. W: CAR; Florida to Brazil. R: 1.

Marginellidae

J. FLEMING, 1828
marginellas

Marginellas (also known as margin shells) are glossy shells, often beautifully colored and patterned, with smooth, rounded whorls. In the living animal, the shell is almost entirely covered by the mantle. The apex is usually flattened or depressed. The surface is smooth or has rounded, radial ribs. In almost all cases, the outer lip is thickened to some degree. There are often either delicate or distinct teeth or folds. The columella has three to six often rather strong folds. These animals have no operculum. Two subfamilies: Marginellinae J. Fleming, 1828; Marginelloninae Coan, 1965. The place where the aperture attaches to previous whorls and its relative length are good ways to identify these shells. In the genus Marginella, for example, the spire accounts for approximately a quarter of the total height and the aperture is relatively wide, while in *Closia, Cryptospira,* and *Prunum,* the spire is flattened and the aperture is long and narrow. Many hundreds of species assigned to various genera, including: *Afrivoluta, Balanetta, Bullata, Closia, Cryptospira, Glabella, Hyalina, Marginella, Prunum, Serrata, Volvarina.*

Afrivoluta pringlei

TOMLIN, 1947
Pringle's marginella

D: 75mm. S: elongated, cylindrical shell with a wide, blunt apex. Narrow aperture. Slightly thickened outer lip. 4 strong shelf-like folds on the columella. Upper part of body whorl is misshapen due to a thick, oval callus. O: smooth, sometimes with strong growth lines. C: Reddish- to orange-brown color. Callus amber to cream. H: d2–3; deep water. W: ZAFR. R: 1. NB: classified under Volutidae for many years.

Bullata bullata

(VON BORN, 1778)
bubble marginella

D: 75mm. S: large shell with inflated whorls. Sunken, flattened spire. Thickened outer lip, sometimes with slight folds. O: smooth, glossy. C: beige with subtle, light and dark lines and bands. Aperture white, outer lip rim often amber. H: d1; sublittoral. W: CAR; Brazil. R: 2.

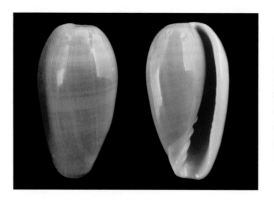

Bullata ventricosa

(G. FISCHER, 1807)
broad marginella

D: 25mm. S: an upturned pear shape with a depressed spire. Apex visible. Top of whorls flat-

tened. Thickened outer lip, sometimes subtly toothed. Completely callused. Oblique columellar folds. O: smooth. C: uniformly white, gray, amber, or apricot with very slight blotching. H: d1; littoral and sublittoral, shallow water on muddy substrates. W: INDP; Southeast Asia. R: 2. NB: sometimes also classified in the genus *Cryptospira*.

Cryptospira elegans

(GMELIN, 1791)
elegant marginella

D: 30mm. S: thick, oval shell with depressed spire. Thickened outer lip, toothed within. 5–7 folds on inner lip. O: smooth, glossy. C: grayish-white, sometimes greenish with radiating stripes of dark gray. Orange columella and outer lip rim. H: d1; sublittoral to approx. 10m. W: INDP. R: 2–3. NB: sometimes known as the "barcode snail" because of its patterning.

Cryptospira strigata

(DILLWYN, 1817)
striped marginella

D: 40mm. S: oval shell with a low, depressed spire covered by callus. Thickened outer lip.

5 strong folds on inner lip. O: smooth, glossy. C: creamy white with shaky, olive-brown vertical lines. Columella sometimes apricot. H: d1; on sand. W: INDP; Southeast Asia. R: 3. NB: sometimes known as the "heart-line marginella" because of similarities to lines on a cardiac monitor.

Glabella pseudofaba

(SOWERBY, 1846)
queen marginella

D: 35mm. S: robust shell with a raised spire accounting for about a fifth of its total height. Relatively narrow aperture. Thickened outer lip with fine teeth within. 3–4 columellar folds. O: angular axial ribs that fade out below. C: cream to pale yellowish-green with rough, reddish- to dark brown blotching and finer purplish-black spots. H: d1–3; fairly deep water. W: WAFR. R: 3.

Marginella cincta

KIENER, 1834
encircled marginella

D: 20mm. S: solid shell with a depressed spire that is largely callused. Outer lip much thick-

ened. 4 columellar folds. O: smooth and glossy. C: creamy white to amber, encircled dorsally by a golden-yellow ring. H: d2; deep water to approx. 80m. W: WAFR. R: 3. NB: renowned and sought-after collector's item, now also known as *Prunum cinctum*.

Marginella denticulata

(LINK, 1807)
toothed marginella

D: 25mm. S: solid shell with a raised spire accounting for a third of the shell's total height. Shouldered whorls. Fairly narrow aperture. Thickened outer lip with clear teeth along its full length. 3–4 large columellar folds. O: Axial ribs with nodular shoulders quickly fading out below. C: cream with purplish-brown blotches and small brown spots. H: d2; deep water to approx. 100m. W: WAFR. R: 2. NB: sometimes also placed in the genus *Glabella*.

Marginella desjardini

MARCHE-MARCHAD, 1957
Desjardin's marginella

D: 50mm. S: solid, elongated shell with a raised spire accounting for a quarter of the shell's total height. Thickened outer lip, sometimes toothed at the center. 4 columellar folds, the lowest is faint. O: smooth. C: orange-pink with 3 darker bands and white spots. H: d2; deep water to approx. 100m. W: WAFR. R: 2–3.

water. W: WAFR; the Gambia, Angola, the Azores, Canary Islands. R: 3.

Marginella glabella

(LINNAEUS, 1758)
glimmende liphoren

D: 30mm. S: solid shell. Raised spire, about a third of the shell's total height. Edge of outer lip is dentate. 4 columellar folds. O: smooth. C: glossy, light reddish-brown with paler markings. H: d2; deep water to approx. 80m. W: WAFR. R: 2.

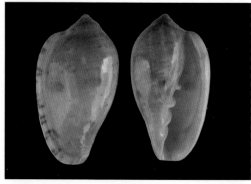

Marginella nebulosa

(RÖDING, 1798)
cloudy marginella

D: 40mm. S: solid shell with a raised spire accounting for a quarter of the shell's total height. Gently shouldered whorls. Aperture widens at the base. Thick outer lip. 3–4 columellar teeth. O: smooth and glossy. C: Usually rather hazy, purplish-brown or gray markings on a creamy white to pure white background. H: d2; deep water to approx. 75m. W: ZAFR. R: 2.

Marginella helmatina

RANG, 1832
Cuming's marginella

D: 35mm. S: solid shell with a raised spire accounting for a sixth of the shell's total height. Fairly wide aperture. Thick outer lip. 3–4 columellar folds. O: smooth. C: grayish-pink with subtle greenish-gray to purplish-brown markings. Often with 2 clear, broken spiral bands. Sometimes the whole shell tends to flamingo pink. Inner and outer lips white. H: d2; deeper

Marginella sebastiani

MARCHE & ROSSO, 1979
Sebastian's marginella

D: 40mm. S: solid shell with a raised spire accounting for a quarter of the shell's total height. Fairly wide aperture. Thick outer lip. 3–4 columellar folds. O: smooth, glossy. C: amber to orange-brown, sometimes slightly darker spiral bands. Yellowish-white to pure white spots on this darker background. H: d1–2; in deeper water. W: WAFR; Senegal, Mauritania. R: 2.

Melongenidae

GILL, 1871
melon conches and others

A small family of large tropical species. Robust shells, often with a somewhat compact body whorl and a gaping siphonal canal that is frequently extended and curved. Often with spiral ribs, shoulder tubercles, and spines. Corneous operculum that is thick and clawlike. Sometimes live in large colonies in sandy and muddy areas, in shallow estuarine water, and calm bays. Carnivorous predators, preying on bivalves, and scavengers. The genus *Busycon* occurs in North America and also contains some naturally sinistral (counterclockwise) species. The genus *Melongena* occurs in Central America, while the genus *Pugilina* occurs in Africa and the Indo-Pacific region. Two subfamilies: Busyconinae Wade, 1917; Melongeninae Gill, 1871. Only a few genera: *Busycon, Hemifusus, Melongena, Pugilina, Volema*.

Busycon canaliculatum

(LINNAEUS, 1758)
channeled whelk

D: 180mm. S: fairly thin-shelled. Has angular whorls with slightly sloping shoulders. Wide aperture, leading below to a narrow, slightly bent or straight, siphonal canal. O: slight spirals and radial ribs. A strong, spiral rib below the shoulder. C: apricot, aperture orange. Periostracum yellowish-gray. H: d1–2; sublittoral and somewhat deeper water. W: CAL (introduced), VIR. R: 1.

Busycon carica

(GMELIN, 1791)
North Atlantic knobbed whelk

D: 200mm. S: thick shell with angular whorls. Quite a wide aperture, extending below into a wide, slightly recurved, siphonal canal. O: slight spirals, very strong shoulder tubercles. C: grayish-brown with russet blotches and radial bands. H: d1; sublittoral to 10m. W: VIR. R: 1.

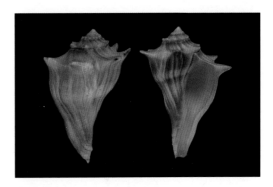

Busycon contrarium

(CONRAD, 1840)
lightning whelk

D: 400mm. S: solid, sinistral shell. Flattened spire, shouldered whorls. Wide aperture, extending below into a siphonal canal that quick-

ly narrows. O: shoulder knobs, strong or finer spirals, and axial ribs that soon fade out below. C: amber with russet blotches. H: d1–2; sublittoral to 50m. W: CAR. R: 2. NB: the species *B. perversum* (Linnaeus, 1758) – the perverse whelk – which is also sinistral, occurs on the northeast coast of Mexico and bears stronger, spiny tubercles.

Busycon spiratum

(LAMARCK, 1816)
pear conch

D: 100mm. S: fairly thin-shelled. Flattened spire, shouldered whorls. Wide aperture, extending below into a recurved siphonal canal. O: clear spirals. C: amber with amber to russet markings. H: d1; sublittoral. W: CAR; Mexico, VIR. R: 2.

Hemifusus crassicaudus

(PHILIPPI, 1848)
thick-tail false fusus

D: 140mm. S: robust shell with quite a pointed spire. Angular, shouldered whorls. Elongated aperture, ending below in a broad siphonal canal. O: strong spirals, spiny shoulder tubercles. C: amber, apricot aperture. H: d1; shallow water, on sand. W: INDP, JAP. R: 1.

Melongena corona

(GMELIN, 1791)
common crown conch

D: 75mm. S: robust shell with convex, shouldered whorls. O: strong shoulder tubercles and spines, often curved upward to create a "crown." Axial and spiral ribs. C: creamy white with dark brown and paler spiral bands and stripes. H: d1; shallow water, mangroves. W: CAR. R: 1. NB: many variations that may be wider or more slender, and spinier or without spines altogether.

Melongena melongena

(LINNAEUS, 1758)
West Indian crown conch

D: 120mm. S: very thick shell. Quite a low spire. Very large, wide, shouldered body whorl. Broad

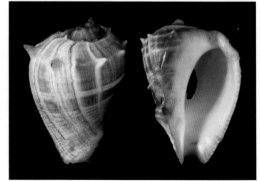

aperture. Callused inner lip extends across the parietal wall to body whorl. O: low spirals, strongest at the base. Blunt to pointed, relatively short, shoulder tubercles. C: amber with purplish-brown bands and blotches. Apex is a uniform purplish-brown. Periostracum is thick, dark brown, and flaky. H: d1; sublittoral to 25m. W: CAR; West Indies. R: 1. NB: the species *M. patula* (Broderip & Sowerby, 1829) – the Pacific crown conch – has more angular whorls and an even thicker periostracum. It occurs from Mexico to Ecuador.

Mitridae

SWAINSON, 1831
miters

Fusiform (shuttle-shaped) shells with generally high spires. With spiral ribs or virtually smooth. Occasionally with axial ribs. The aperture is narrow and meets at an angle at the top. There is a vague siphonal notch at the apertural base. The aperture is dentate or has folds. Three or more oblique columellar folds, the lowest usually being the thickest. No operculum. These animals live on particular species of burrowing worms. They occur in warm and temperate maritime zones, under rocks and coral or buried in the sand. Many species live in the intertidal zone and the sublittoral, while others live in deeper water. Three subfamilies: Cylindromitrinae Cossman, 1899; Imbricariinae Troschel, 1868; Mitrinae Swainson, 1831. Several genera, including: *Cancilla, Charitodoron, Domiporta, Imbricaria, Mitra, Pterygia, Scabricola, Subcancilla, Ziba*.

Domiporta carnicolor

(REEVE, 1844)
horn-colored miter

D: 25mm. S: slender shell with a pointed spire. Columellar folds and fine folds in the outer lip. O: axial and spiral grooves, areas in between are roughly rectangular, creating a rhomboid pattern. C: apricot with white blotches and spots. Rose-red spire. H: d1; sublittoral to 20m. W: INDP, JAP. R: 1.

Domiporta gloriola

(CERNOHORSKY, 1970)
gloriola miter

D: 40mm. S: a solid, slender shell. Fairly convex whorls with little or no shoulders. O: nodulose spirals and fine axial grooves. C: grayish-white with russet and orange dashes and spots. H: d1; sublittoral. W: INDP, JAP; Philippines, Indonesia. R: 1.

Mitra cardinalis

(GMELIN, 1791)
cardinal miter

D: 70mm. S: solid shell with low whorls. O: slight spirals with pitted grooves. C: creamy white with russet spots and broken bands. H: d1; shallow water, on sand. W: INDP, JAP. R: 1.

Mitra incompta

(LIGHTFOOT, 1786)
tessellate miter

D: 120mm. S: robust, very slender shell with slightly convex whorls. O: spirals, cut by finer, radial grooves. C: amber with dark brown stripes and flecks. H: d1; reefs to 40m. W: INDP, JAP. R: 2–3.

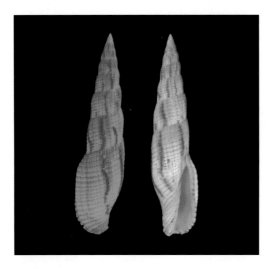

Mitra mitra

(LINNAEUS, 1758)
Episcopal miter

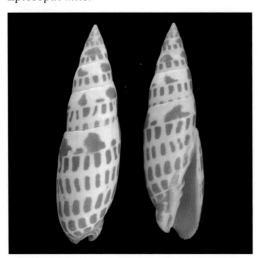

D: 10mm. S: solid, pointed shell. Slightly convex whorls without shoulders. O: smooth. C: creamy white with 4–6 rows of orange blotches. H: d1; sublittoral, on sand. W: INDP, JAP; Galapagos Islands. R: 1.

Mitra papalis

(LINNAEUS, 1758)
papal miter

D: 80mm. S: thick, heavy shell with shouldered whorls. O: spirals, especially at the base next to the columella. Slight or strong shoulder nodules. C: creamy white with irregular orange blotches. H: d1; coral reefs, under rocks and coral rubble. To depth of 30m. W: INDP, JAP. R: 2.

Mitra paupercula

(LINNAEUS, 1758)
poverty miter

D: 25mm. S: solid, slightly rotund shell. Low, un-shouldered whorls. O: smooth or with the

very faintest of spirals. C: russet or brown zebra stripes on a white background. H: d1; littoral and sublittoral, under rocks. W: INDP, JAP. R: 1.

Mitra stictica

(LINK, 1807)
pontifical miter

D: 65mm. S: solid shell with strongly shouldered whorls. O: spirals, sometimes fainter in the center. Slight shoulder nodules. C: white or cream with orange blotches. H: d1; sublittoral, coral reefs. W: INDP, JAP. R: 1.

Pterygia scabricula

(LINNAEUS, 1758)
rough miter

D: 40mm. S: thick, rotund shell with fairly convex whorls. O: strong, slightly nodulose spirals. Pitted grooves. C: apricot with russet and white dashes. H: d1–2; under coral rubble and rocks, sublittoral, to 50m. W: INDP, JAP. R: 2.

Scrabicola fissurata

(LAMARCK, 1811)
reticulate miter

D: 50mm. S: solid, slender shell. Straight-sided to slightly rounded whorls. No shoulders. O: very delicate ornament. C: grayish- or pinkish-brown with a pattern of grayish-white stripes that closely resemble cracks in glass or glazed tiles. H: d1; coral reefs. W: INDP; Indian Ocean. R: 3.

Scrabicola variegata

(GMELIN, 1791)
snake miter

D: 50mm. S: solid, pointed shell. Fairly wide aperture. Flat-sided whorls with a slightly sloping shoulder. O: spirals with pitted grooves. C: creamy white with apricot bands and blotches and a pattern of wavy, russet vertical lines like scales. H: d1; sublittoral. W: INDP; the Philippines, Marquesas Islands. R: 2.

Muricidae

RAFINESQUE, 1815

murex shells (murices), rock shells, and others

An extremely large family, distributed worldwide. Particularly rich in species in the tropics and warmer seas. However, species also occur in cold and temperate maritime zones. They occur in the intertidal zone, on rocks, coral reefs, and on sandy, stony, and muddy substrates. Their food often consists of acorn barnacles and small bivalves. Several genera bore into their victims. Some are considered a threat to cultivated oysters. Muricidae shells are enormously diverse in form, ranging from shells of only 10mm to *Chicoreus ramosus* (Linnaeus, 1758) – the ramose or branched murex – with a shell over 300mm in length. Often thick-shelled with quite convex whorls that may be covered in varices and also spines, scales, ribs, nodules, pleats, and other types of ornament besides. The siphonal canal may be short or extremely long, open or partially closed. The family is divided into several subfamilies: Ergalataxinae Kuroda & Habe, 1971; Muricinae Rafinesque, 1815; Muricopsinae Radwin & D'Attilio, 1971; Ocenebrinae Cossmann, 1903; Rapaninae J.E. Gray, 1853; Trophoninae Cossmann, 1903; Typhinae Cossmann, 1903. All together, these subfamilies contain many dozens of genera with many hundreds of species. Among the most well-known genera are: *Aspella, Bolinus, Boreotrophon, Calotrophon, Ceratostoma, Chicoreus, Concholepas, Cymia, Cytharomorula, Dermomurex, Drupa, Drupella, Ergalatax, Favartia, Hadriania, Haustellum, Hexaplex, Homalocantha, Lataxiena, Morula, Murex, Murexiella, Murexsul, Muricopsis, Naquetia, Nassa, Nucella, Ocenebra, Ocinebrina, Orania, Phyllonotus, Plicopurpura, Poirieria, Pterorytis, Pterynotus, Purpura, Rapana, Stramonita, Thais, Trochia, Trophon, Typhis, Urosalpinx, Vexilla, Xymene.*

Bolinus brandaris

(LINNAEUS, 1758)

purple-dye murex

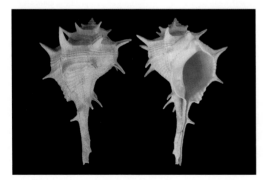

D: 110mm. S: robust shell with a long siphonal canal. O: irregular spirals and strong spines, short and long, on whorls as well as on the outer lip and siphonal canal. C: yellowish-white to light brown. Aperture and inner lip callus a glossy apricot. H: d1; sublittoral. W: LUS, WAFR. R: 1. NB: much used in the past to produce purple dye. Also eaten.

Ceratostoma burnetti

(A. ADAMS & REEVE, 1850)

Burnett's murex

D: 100mm. S: a reasonably solid shell with a pointed spire and a largely closed siphonal canal. Strong, prominent varices. O: Varices have strong, spiral ribs, creating hollow projections. C: amber. Aperture creamy white. H: d1; sublittoral to 20m. W: JAP, INDP; China Sea, Korea. R: 2.

Chicoreus aculeatus

(LAMARCK, 1822)

pendant murex

D: 50mm. S: robust shell with a fairly small aperture. O: undulating spirals and rounded axial ribs and varices. Strong, slightly branched, hollow projections on the varices, the extremities of which often point upward. C: yellowish-white to pink, spines and varices a more intense pink. H: d1–2; deep water. W: INDP, JAP. R: 3.

Chicoreus axicornis

(LAMARCK, 1822)
axicornis murex

D: 75mm. S: thick shell with a small aperture and a very long siphonal canal. O: scaled spirals and rather low axial ribs and varices, the latter having very thick, short and long projections that branch out like antlers. C: amber. H: d1. W: INDP, JAP. R: 2.

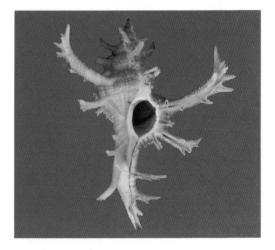

Chicoreus orchidiflorus

(SHIKAMA, 1973)
orchid murex

D: 40mm. S: very thin, fragile shell. Long siphonal canal. O: delicately beaded spirals, rounded axial ribs. Varices bear undulating ribs on very long, exceptionally thin, fin-like flanges with a spiky perimeter. C: pale pink with orange blotches. H: d1–2; deeper water. W: INDP, JAP; Taiwan. R: 3. NB: flawless specimens are greatly sought-after by collectors.

Chicoreus brevifrons

(LAMARCK, 1822)
West Indian murex

D: 120mm. S: thick shell with a fairly long siphonal canal. O: wide, nodulose spiral ribs. In between, narrower, nodulose axial ribs and 3 prominent varices bearing long and short projections. Siphonal canal also spiny. C: grayish-brown to dark brown with paler bands. Aperture cream. H: d1; sublittoral, shallow water. W: CAR. R: 1.

Chicoreus venustulus

REHDER & WILSON, 1975
lovely murex

D: 50mm. S: solid shell with a quite pointed spire and a fairly long, recurved siphonal canal. O: rounded to angular axial ribs. Finer, scaled spirals. Enlarged outer lip. C: orange-pink with brown patches. Creamy white to pure white aperture. H: d1–2; deep water to 125m. W: INDP; the Philippines, Marquesas Islands. R: 4.

Drupa lobata

(DE BLAINVILLE, 1832)
lobate drupe

D: 25mm. S: thick, rotund shell. Fairly blunt spire. Outer lip has finger-like projections. The uppermost of these is the largest and hollowed out for the anal siphon. O: strong, slightly scaled, spirals. Outer lip and columella more strongly scaled. C: grayish-brown. Dark brown to black callus on inner lip and within outer lip. H: d1; shallow water. W: AUS, INDP. R: 1.

Drupa morum

RÖDING, 1798
purple Pacific drupe

D: 25mm. S: thick, rotund shell. Flattened spire. Large body whorl, cleft-like aperture with large folds and teeth on the inner and outer lips. O: strong nodules. C: creamy white, nodules brown to black. Deep purple aperture. H: d1; littoral and sublittoral, reefs. W: INDP, JAP. R: 1.

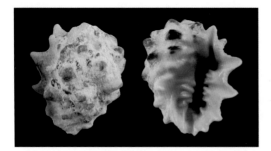

Drupa ricinus

(LINNAEUS, 1758)
prickly Pacific drupe

D: 30mm. S: thick, rotund shell. Blunt spire. Aperture has strong teeth. Inner lip thickly callused. O: nodules plus large and small spines. C: creamy white, nodules and smaller spines

dark brown to black. Aperture white, with a golden orange ring. H: d1; coral reefs. W: INDP, JAP. R: 1.

Drupa rubusideus

(RÖDING, 1798)
strawberry drupe

D: 40mm. S: thick, rotund shell with a flattened spire. Large body whorl, fairly wide aperture. Only small teeth in the aperture. O: strong nodules and vague spirals. C: grayish-white, aperture and callus on inner lip pink. H: d1; sublittoral, deeper reefs. W: INDP, JAP. R: 1.

Haustellum chrysostoma

(SOWERBY, 1834)
gold-mouthed murex

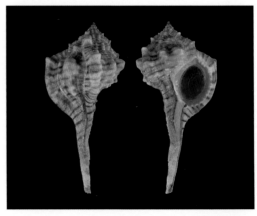

D: 50mm. S: thick, fairly rotund shell. Very long siphonal canal. O: thick spirals. Strong, nodulose axial ribs. C: grayish-white with a golden yellow aperture, or darker brown with a reddish-orange aperture. H: d1; in fairly deep water. W: CAR. R: 2. NB: the form shown is *bellus* Reeve, 1845 – the belle murex – with a much darker, orange-red mouth and darker shell.

Haustellum haustellum

(LINNAEUS, 1758)
snipe's bill murex

D: 125mm. S: solid, compact shell with an exceptionally stretched, thin siphonal canal. Oval aperture. O: strong, rounded axial ribs. C: amber with dark brown blotches and lines. Orange-red aperture. H: d1; sublittoral, 3–20m. W: INDP. R: 1. NB: very similar is the Filipino species *H. vicdani* Kosuge, 1980, shown on the right in the photograph.

Hexaplex cichoreus

(GMELIN, 1791)
endive-like murex

D: 110mm. S: thick shell with a quite convex body whorl. Long siphonal canal. O: wide spirals with finer ones in between. Varices covered in strong projections, often pointing upward. C: creamy white with dark brown bands. Spines dark brown to black. Aperture white or ringed with a thin, red-orange line. H: d1; sublittoral. W: INDP. R: 2.

Hexaplex fulvescens

(SOWERBY, 1834)
giant eastern murex

D: 150mm. S: thick shell with a convex body whorl. O: narrow, irregular spirals and wide axial ribs and varices covered in sharp spines. C: creamy white, sometimes with brown blotches. H: d1; sublittoral and deeper water. W: VIR; North Carolina to Texas. R: 1.

Hexaplex princeps

(BRODERIP, 1833)
prince murex

D: 130mm. S: thick shell. Reasonably long siphonal canal. Oval aperture. O: strong spirals and varices with wide and narrow spines. C: cream with dark brown bands, varices and spines. H: d1–2; sublittoral and deeper. W: PAN. R: 2.

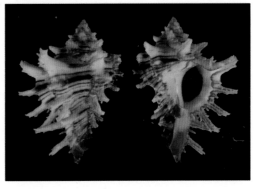

Hexaplex stainforthi

(REEVE, 1843)
Stainforth's murex

D: 60mm. S: thick shell with a closed, reasonably long, siphonal canal. O: irregular spirals and several varices crammed with thorny spines. C: creamy white to light brown, apricot aperture. Blackish-brown spines. H: d1; littoral and sublittoral to 3m. W: AUS. R: 2.

Homalocantha scorpio

(LINNAEUS, 1758)
scorpion murex

D: 50mm. S: thick shell with a blunt spire. Small aperture, very long siphonal canal. O: strong, irregular spirals and axial ribs with broad scales and projections. Spine extremities flattened out and branched, particularly on the outer lip. C: creamy white with dark brown to black ribs and spines. H: d1; sublittoral. W: INDP. R: 1.

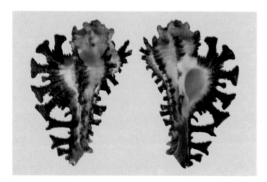

Homalocantha zamboi

(BURCH & BURCH, 1960)
Zambo's murex

D: 50mm. S: thick shell, fairly pointed spire, callused. Small aperture. Very long siphonal canal, often slightly curved. O: irregular ribs with very long, partly hollow, projections, branched or expanded at the ends, sometimes bent back sharply. C: creamy white. H: d1; sublittoral and deeper water. W: INDP; central Philippines. R: 2.

Marchia bipinnatus

(REEVE, 1845)
pinnacle murex

D: 50mm. S: robust shell with an elongated spire but a blunter apex. Angular whorls, long siphonal canal. Flanged varices on body whorl, outer lip greatly enlarged. O: axial ribs. Spiral ribs, strongest on the varices. C: creamy white or amber, aperture violet to pink. H: d1–2; sublittoral and deeper to 50m. W: INDP, JAP. R: 4. NB: sought-after collector's item, sometimes also placed in the genus *Pterymarchia*.

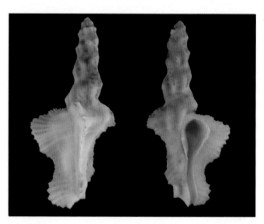

Murex pecten

LIGHTFOOT, 1786
Venus comb murex

D: 100mm. S: solid shell with a quite pointed spire and an extremely long siphonal canal. O: wide and narrow spirals, slight axial ribs (actu-

Much extended apertural margin. O: strong spirals and varices with thick spines. C: creamy white. H: d1–2; sublittoral and deeper water. W: WAFR. R: 2.

Rapana rapiformis

(VON BORN, 1778)
turnip-shaped rapa whelk

D: 90mm. S: relatively thin shell with a very large body whorl. Wide aperture, ending in a short, slightly bent, siphonal canal. Strong folds (lirae) within aperture. Very large, wide umbilicus. O: subtle to strong shoulder tubercles, sometimes spines. Thick and thin spirals. Often spiny projections around the umbilicus. Whole surface finely scaled. C: grayish-brown, aperture orange or cream. H: d1–2; sublittoral and deeper. W: INDP. R: 1. NB: the Japanese species *Rapana venosa* (Valenciennes, 1846) – Thomas' Rapa Whelk – has a thicker shell, but a narrower aperture. It was accidentally introduced to the Black Sea and now occurs commonly in parts of the Mediterranean Sea.

Siratus formosus

(SOWERBY, 1841)
beauty murex

D: 75mm. S: robust shell with a pointed apex and a very long, straight siphonal canal. O: fine

and stronger, nodulose spirals, several varices per whorl, covered in sturdy, sharp spines, usually straight. C: amber to dark brown. H: d1–2; sublittoral and deeper water to 100m. W: CAR. R: 2.

Nassariidae

IREDALE, 1916
nassa mud snails (dog whelks) and others

Robust, ovoid to conical shells. In many cases, the shells have both spiral and axial ribs, which cross and sometimes form a lattice sculpture. The aperture is rounded and ovate. An anal groove lies at the top of the aperture in some species. The siphonal canal is recurved. The outer lip may be thickened and has folds or teeth. The parietal wall is callused and in many instances the columella has folds. A distinctive feature of some species is the extensive parietal shield (callus) that extends well over the earlier whorls. The operculum is corneous, triangular, or oval, often with a serrated edge. The animals scavenge for food. Some species are able to sense food at a distance of many meters thanks to their exceptional olfactory sense. The family occurs in all tropical and temperate seas, from the intertidal zone to a depth of approximately 1250m, often in large numbers. There are three subfamilies. The subfamily Cylleninae Bellardi, 1882 contains species with quite robust shells, a slender shape, and an anal groove at the top of the aperture. The columella is often completely covered in callus and folds. The subfamily Dorsaninae Cossmann, 1901 contains species with thin, spire-shaped shells with rounded whorls. These are smooth, only with limited spirals in the main. Usually shouldered, formed by a clear spiral callus just under the suture. Sometimes shoulder nodules. Aperture gapes wide open at the base. No anal groove. The subfamily Nassariinae Iredale, 1916 contains species usually with robust to thick shells, often rather squat in shape, and with a twisted siphonal canal and an anal groove (far and away the majority of species). All together, several genera, including: *Buccinanops, Bullia, Cyclope, Cyllene, Demoulia, Dorsanum, Hebra, Nassarius.*

Alectrion papillosus

(LINNAEUS, 1758)
pimpled nassa

D: 40mm. S: solid, reasonably pointed shell with fairly rounded whorls. O: spiral and axial ribs cross and, in so doing, create strong, rounded nodules. C: amber to dark brown. Often darker between nodules. Spire often paler or rose-red. H: d1; sublittoral to 10m. W: INDP, JAP. R: 1.

Buccinanops globulosum

(KIENER, 1834)
globular bullia

D: 20mm. S: solid, squat shell with rounded shoulders and a fairly blunt apex. Wide, unthickened outer lip. Heavily callused inner lip. O: smooth. C: grayish-brown with amber bands and blotches. Callus and interior apricot. H: d1; littoral and sublittoral. W: PAN. R: 1.

Bullia rogersi

SMYTHE IN SMYTHE & CHATFIELD, 1981
Omani bullia

D: 20mm. S: thin, inflated shell with fairly rounded whorls. O: a thick, callused spiral rib around the suture. Early whorls have clear spirals, fading out on later whorls. Clear spirals reappear at base of body whorl. C: creamy white to pale amber with russet blotches and wavy, amber, radial stripes. H: d1–2; sublittoral and deeper water. W: INDP; Oman. R: 3.

Bullia semiplicata

GRAY IN GRIFFITH & PIDGEON, 1834
semi-pleated bullia

D: 30mm. S: pointed and thin-shelled, yet still robust. Quite straight-sided whorls with a clear shoulder. O: narrow shoulder spiral, wide axial ribs (with shoulder nodules) that soon fade out below. C: creamy white, light to very dark brown, or light and dark brown bands. H: d1; sublittoral, in sand. W: INDP; Arabian Sea. R: 2.

Bullia vittata

(LINNAEUS, 1767)
ribbon bullia

D: 30mm. S: pointed and thin-shelled, but robust. Fairly rounded whorls, slight shoulder.

O: shoulder has 2 spirals covered in square or round beads. Otherwise, surface cover of fine spiral and radial ribs. C: amber to russet. H: d1; sublittoral, on muddy substrates. W: INDP; Indian Ocean. R: 1.

Demoulia obtusata

(LINK, 1807)
obtuse demoulia

D: 25mm. S: thin, barrel-shaped shell with a pointed apex. Curved whorls with clearly rounded shoulders. O: fine spirals, sometimes shoulder nodules. Periostracum in radial pleats of papery scales. C: yellowish-white, often with brown blotches around the shoulders. Brown periostracum. H: d1; sublittoral and deeper water. W: LUS, the Algarve (Portugal); WAFR. R: 3.

Nassarius distortus

(A. ADAMS, 1852)
distorted or necklace nassa

D: 30mm. S: thick shell with gently shouldered whorls. O: strong axial ribs broken by a spiral groove at the shoulder. Spirals also at base of body whorl. C: gray-green with brown spiral bands and lines. H: d1; sublittoral. W: AUS, INDP. R: 2.

Nassarius incrassatus

(STRÖM, 1768)
thick-lipped dog whelk

D: 14mm. S: robust shell with convex whorls. Oval aperture, greatly thickened outer lip. Parietal shield callus not extensive. Clearly dentate within outer lip. O: lattice ornament. Axial ribs wider than the spaces in between. C: variable: yellowish-white, orange, rose-red, or dark brown, often in bands. Siphonal canal, callus and apertural margin white. A dark blotch within the siphonal canal. H: d1–2; sublittoral and deeper. Rocky coasts to over 150m. W: KEL, LUS. R: 1. NB: In the photograph (right), *N. pygmaeus* (Lamarck, 1822) – the pygmy nassa – is more finely ornamented, has a wider parietal shield, several varices (former thickened apertures) and lacks the dark blotch on the siphonal canal. The same distribution.

Nassarius mutabilis

(LINNAEUS, 1758)
mutable nassa

D: 30mm. S: thin, inflated shell. Somewhat reminiscent of *Tonna*. Convex whorls, wide aperture. Slightly thickened outer lip with folds within. Broad parietal shield (callus). O: fine,

low spirals, fainter at the center of whorls. C: amber with brown and russet blotches. H: d1–2; sublittoral and deeper to 50m. W: LUS, WAFR. R: 1.

Nassarius myristicatus

HINDS, 1844
myristic nassa

D: 12mm. S: thick, compact shell. Pointed apex. Thickened outer lip with several folds. Columellar folds. Callus not extensive. O: thick axial ribs crossed by finer spirals that produce scaly projections where they rise over the axials. C: grayish-brown with paler banding. Scales often picked out in light brown. H: d1–2; sublittoral and deeper water to 50m. W: PAN, PER. R: 1.

Nassarius pyrrhus

(MENKE, 1843)
red-banded nassa

D: 20mm. S: solid shell with fairly low whorls. Pointed apex, pear-shaped aperture. O: spiral and axial ribs create rounded nodules. C: creamy white with brown bands. H: d1; littoral and sublittoral on sand. W: AUS; New Zealand, Tasmania. R: 1.

Nassarius reticulatus

(LINNAEUS, 1758)
netted nassa

D: 35mm. S: thick shell with fairly low whorls. Pointed spire. Pear-shaped aperture ending in a siphonal canal. Small folds on inner and outer lips. Final whorl partly covered by callus. O: horizontal ribs crossed by vertical ones (lattice sculpture). Number and thickness of ribs varies (10–25). C: grayish-white or amber, sometimes with purplish-brown bands. Periostracum flaky, rust-colored. H: d1; in calm areas like lagoons and bays. Sublittoral to a few tens of meters. W: KEL, LUS, WAFR. R: 1. NB: scavengers with strong olfactory senses.

Zeuxis hirasei

KURODA & HABE, 1952
Hirase's nassa

D: 30mm. S: solid, rather full shell with convex whorls and a fairly deep suture. O: first whorls have a delicate lattice sculpture. Narrow, dense, radial ribs dominate on later whorls. However, spirals reappear at the base of the body whorl. C: amber, sometimes with brown bands or blotches. H: d1–2; 20–200m. W: INDP, JAP; Taiwan. R: 3.

Olividae

LATREILLE, 1825
olive shells, ancillas, etc.

A very large, well-known family with cylindrical to more fusiform, smooth, glossy shells. Mostly colored, often in distinctive patterns, which can differ markedly within each species. The spire is generally raised. The aperture is long, usually with a slightly thickened anal notch at the top. There is often a subtle notch at the base of the aperture as well. Often a thick columellar callus, sometimes with folds and grooves. Sometimes there are also spirals above this. Wide distribution throughout all tropical maritime zones. Particularly found in shallow water but also at greater depths. The animals hide in sand during the day but emerge to hunt at night and when the tide turns. They are principally scavengers. Divided into several subfamilies: Agaroniinae Olsson, 1956; Ancillinae Swainson, 1835; Olivellinae Troschel, 1869; Olivinae Latreille, 1825. All together, there are hundreds of species contained within many genera, including: *Agaronia, Amalda, Ancilla, Ancillista, Austrancilla, Baryspira, Belloliva, Cupidoliva, Gracilancilla, Jaspidella, Oliva, Olivancillaria, Olivella.*

Ancilla glabrata

(LINNAEUS, 1758)
golden ancilla

D: 70mm. S: thick, elongated oval shells partly callused. Very wide, curved umbilical groove that appears to be contained within the inner lip. O: 2 grooves wind from the columella at the base of the body whorl. Otherwise smooth. C: pale yellow to apricot, lower part of earlier whorls white. Aperture, umbilicus and spiral grooves also white. H: d1–2; sublittoral and deeper water, sandy substrates. W: CAR; West Indies. R: 2.

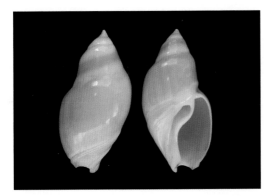

Ancilla lienardi

(BERNARDI, 1858)
Lienardo's ancilla

D: 40mm. S: very thick, elongated oval shell, partly covered by callus. Very deep, curved umbilical groove (wider than in *A. glabrata*) that appears to be contained within the inner lip. Often a wide, white patch of callus above the aperture. O: 2 very deep grooves wind from the columella at the base of the body whorl. Otherwise smooth. C: golden yellow. Aperture, umbilicus, and (sometimes) spiral grooves white. H: d1; deep water. W: CAR; Brazil. R: 3.

Ancilla suavis

(YOKOYAMA, 1922)
delightful ancilla

D: 40mm. S: slender shell with a pointed apex and a narrow aperture, sharply angled at the top. O: smooth. 1–2 very faint spiral folds next to the columella. C: light brown with light and dark brown spiral bands. H: d2–3; deep water to approx. 200m. W: JAP. R: 3.

Ancillista cingulata

(SOWERBY, 1830)
cingulate ancilla

D: 75mm. S: thin shell. Un-thickened outer lip. Subtly shouldered whorls. O: exceptionally fine, netlike ornament. Sometimes keels on spire. C: grayish-brown to honey yellow. Paler suture band. A wide, russet to chestnut-brown band at the base. H: d1; littoral, on sand. W: AUS. R: 2.

Baryspira hinomotoensis

(YOKOYAMA, 1922)
Hinomoto ancilla

D: 45mm. S: thick, pointed shell. Heavily callused spire. O: smooth, several grooves at base. C: amber with golden-brown bands. Pink spire. H: d2–3; deeper water. W: JAP. R: 3.

Oliva australis

DUCLOS, 1835
Australian olive

D: 30mm. S: thick, slender shell. Level whorls. Long, narrow aperture. Fine columellar folds.

O: smooth, slight spirals at base. C: white to cream and a russet, zigzagged pattern. H: d1; sublittoral on sand. W: AUS, INDP. R: 1.

Oliva bulbosa

(RÖDING, 1798)
inflated olive

D: 45mm. S: thick, relatively wide, inflated shell. O: smooth, broad columella callus with vague spirals. C: grayish-white with dark brown zigzags or with wide, brown spiral bands. H: d1. W: INDP. R: 1. NB: many differently colored forms.

Oliva caerulea

(RÖDING, 1798)
purple-mouth olive

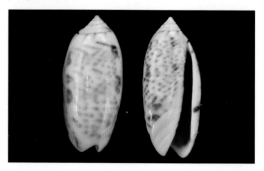

D: 50mm. S: thick, slender shell. Deep suture between whorls. O: smooth, strong columellar folds. Rest of inner lip sometimes also has fine folds. C: amber to gray with dark brown or apricot blotches or zigzags. Interior purple. H: d1; sublittoral. W: INDP. R: 1.

Oliva carneola

(GMELIN, 1791)
carnelian olive

D: 23mm. S: solid, slender shell. Spire fairly low with a deep suture between whorls. O: smooth, fine columellar folds. C: variable: often pale pink and yellow bands. H: d1; shallow water. W: INDP. R: 1.

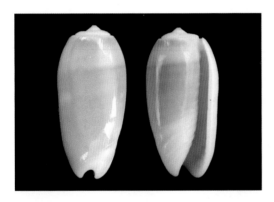

Oliva hirasei

KIRA, 1959
Hirase's olive

D: 45mm. S: robust, cylindrical shell. Pointed apex. Callused inner lip with a great many fine folds. O: smooth. C: olive-brown with a dark brown pattern of lines and flecks. H: d2; deep water. W: INDP. R: 2.

Oliva incrassata

(LIGHTFOOT, 1786)
angled olive

D: 55mm. S: thick, wide shell. Small spire. Widest just above center of body whorl. O: keel at top of whorls. C: gray-green with dark brown dashes and spots. H: d1; littoral, on sand. W: PAN, PER. R: 1.

Oliva polpasta

DUCLOS, 1833
Panamanian olive

D: 40mm. S: thick, elongated oval shell. Widest above the center. Level whorls. Relatively pointed apex. Several folds on inner lip. O: smooth. C: olive-brown with dark brown dots and flecks. Inner and outer lips white. H: d1; sublittoral. W: PAN. R: 1.

Oliva porphyria

(LINNAEUS, 1758)
tent olive

D: 100mm. S: large, elongated shell. Rounded at top and bottom (like an olive). Pointed apex.

O: smooth. Early whorls sometimes with a slight keel around the shoulder. C: pale pinkish-violet with reddish-brown triangular markings and lines. Dark violet base. Sometimes a violet blotch above the aperture too. H: d1; sublittoral to approx. 25m. W: PAN. R: 2. NB: the largest olive shell. The name refers to the pattern – just like successive rows of tents.

Oliva reticulata

(RÖDING, 1798)
blood olive

D: 45mm. S: thick, cylindrical shell. Quite a sharp apex. Slightly thickened outer lip and a small anal notch at the top. Thick columellar callus with 3–4 folds. O: smooth apart from the folds. C: grayish-brown with a pattern of russet, net-like lines. Usually 2 dark spiral bands as well. Columellar callus apricot to blood-red. H: d1; littoral and sublittoral. W: INDP. R: 1.

Oliva rubrolabiata

H. FISCHER, 1903
red-lipped olive

D: 45mm. S: thick, slender, cylindrical shell. Thick inner and outer lips. Inner lip heavily callused. O: several folds on inner lip. C: glossy grayish-brown with dark brown bands and stripes. Inner and outer lips bright orange. H: d1; sublittoral. W: AUS, INDP; New Caledonia. R: 3.

Oliva rufula

DUCLOS, 1840
rufula or reddish olive

D: 30mm. S: solid, cylindrical shell. Fairly pointed spire. O: smooth, only a few columellar folds and teeth on the inner lip. C: apricot horizontal bands and zigzags on a paler background. H: d1–2; sublittoral and slightly deeper water. W: INDP; the Philippines, Indonesia. R: 2.

Olivancillaria urceus

RÖDING, 1798
bear ancilla

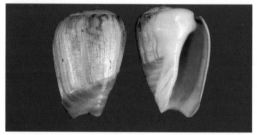

D: 25mm. S: thick shell. Wide aperture. Low, callused spire. Very thick, parietal shield callus extending over body whorl. O: slight radial ribs, columellar spirals. C: grayish-brown, orange callus. H: d1; sublittoral. W: PAT. R: 2.

Olivancillaria vesica

(GMELIN, 1791)
rotund olive

D: 40mm. S: thick, rotund shell with a truncated to flattened spire. Shouldered whorls with a deep suture in between, often covered by callus. Relatively wide aperture, with callused columellar folds. Callus often extends over a large part of the body whorl. O: broad callused band on lowest part of body whorl. C: grayish-white, brown callused band. Aperture brown. H: d1; sublittoral. W: CAR, PAT; Brazil, Uruguay. R: 1. NB: often considerably "plumper" than the specimen shown.

Pleioptygmatidae

QUINN, 1989
A very small family. These shells look like those from Mitridae. There are mainly anatomical distinctions between them. Only one genus: *Pleioptygma* Conrad, 1863, occurring in Honduras.

Pseudolividae

P. FISCHER, 1884
pseudo-olives

Rounded, fusiform shells with low spires. The final whorl accounts for approximately two thirds of the shell's total height. The upper part has spiral ribs. There is an anal canal at the top of the mouth. The columella is smooth, often has folds, and ends in a siphonal canal. A pari-etal shield (callus) is present around the aperture. These shells differ in particular from some forms of Olividae (olive shells) by the presence of a deep spiral groove in the body whorl that terminates in a tooth on the apertural margin ("pseudolivid groove"). Several genera, including: *Benthobia, Fulmentum, Fusopsis, Luizia, Macron, Pseudoliva, Sulcoliva, Zemira.*

Strepsiduridae

COSSMANN, 1901
A family of fossil species in which the genus *Melapium* must also be included according to some taxonomists. A few modern-day, living species from South Africa occur in this genus. Closely related to Olividae (olive shells).

Turbinellidae

SWAINSON, 1840
chank and vase shells

Robust, thick shells with spiral ribs, spines, blunt tubercles, or smooth. Siphonal canal either short or extended. Spire either short or long. Usually two to three columellar folds. Corneous, clawlike operculum. The Australian genus Syrinx, containing the largest gastropod shell on earth: *S. aruanus* (Linnaeus, 1758)— the Australian trumpet—is now also classified under Turbinellidae. Turbinellidae live in the warmer maritime regions on sand in the sublittoral. They are carnivores, feeding, for example, on worms and bivalves. Subdivided into four subfamilies. The subfamily Columbariinae Tomlin, 1928—pagoda shells—contains fusiform shells, keeled whorls, and a long siphonal canal. Only a few species in deeper waters, including some around Japan. The subfamily Ptychatractinae Stimpson, 1865 contains high-spired, deepwater snails with a slender aperture and slight columellar folds. The subfamily Turbinellinae Swainson, 1840—chanks—contains thick, fusiform shells with an extended siphonal canal and three or four columellar folds. Indian Ocean and Caribbean regions. The subfamily Vasinae H. & A. Adams, 1853—vase shells—has shells that are thick with conical-shaped tops and bottoms, and nodulose or spiny ribs, two to four columellar folds, and a short siphonal canal. Found in tropical seas, coral reefs, and deeper water. In total, the family contains only a few dozen species classified within several genera, including: *Benthovoluta, Columbarium, Coluzea, Cyomesus, Fulgurofusus, Latiromitra, Ptychatractus, Surculina, Syrinx, Tudicla, Tudivasum, Turbinella, Vasum.*

Syrinx aruanus

(LINNAEUS, 1758)
Australian trumpet

D: 800mm. S: extremely large, thick, heavy shell. Pointed spire, long siphonal canal. O: irregular, prominent and finer spirals. C: creamy white to pale yellow. H: d1; sublittoral to 10m. W: AUS. R: 2–3. NB: the largest gastropod shell on earth.

Turbinella angulata

LIGHTFOOT, 1786
West Indian chank

D: 200mm. S: thick, heavy shell. Angular whorls with sloping shoulders. Angular aperture, narrows toward the base, ending in a fairly long siphonal canal. O: large shoulder tubercles and irregular spirals. C: creamy white. H: d2; deep water. W: CAR; Cuba, West Indies, the Bahamas. R: 1. NB: sometimes blown as a horn.

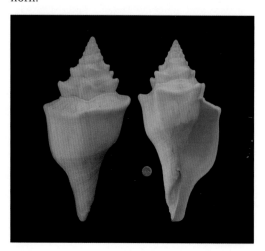

Turbinella pyrum

(LINNAEUS, 1767)
Indian or sacred chank

D: 150mm. S: very thick, heavy shell. O: slight spirals, particularly at base. Immature specimens sometimes have shoulder nodules. C: white to grayish-white, aperture apricot or white. Dark brown, fibrous periostracum. H: d1; mostly in fairly deep water. W: INDP; India, Sri Lanka. R: 1. NB: normally wound clockwise. Counterclockwise specimens are extremely rare and considered sacred (see Chapter 3).

Volutidae

RAFINESQUE, 1815
volutes

Fusiform or ovoid shells, usually with short spires and a large body whorl. The apex is domed or bud-like and somewhat inflated. The surface is smooth or has radial ribs and, in rare instances, spirals. Wide, elongated aperture with a generally deep siphonal notch at the base. The siphonal canal hardly extends at all. Inner lip smooth or has three to five columellar folds. Only a few species with a thin, corneous operculum. They are carnivorous scavengers with an extendable proboscis that paralyzes prey with poison.

Mostly occurring on sand and in mud in warmer seas, especially around Australia, Africa, and the West Indies. However, they also occur in colder regions (Antarctica). Most species live in deeper water between 10 and 3000m. Some species live in the intertidal zone. These are relatively large, colorful species, much sought-after by collectors. Various subfamilies: Athletinae Pilsbry & Olsson, 1954; Calliotectinae Pilsbry & Olsson, 1954; Cymbiolinae Bondarev, 1995; Fulgorariinae Pilsbry & Olsson, 1954; Plicolivinae Bouchet, 1989; Scaphellinae H. & A. Adams, 1858; Volutinae Rafinesque, 1815; Zidoninae H. & A. Adams, 1853.

Over 200 species in dozens of genera, including: *Adelomelon, Alcithoe, Amoria, Ampulla, Athleta, Callipara, Cymbiola, Cymbium, Enaeta, Ericusa, Festilyria, Fulgoraria, Fusivoluta, Harpulina, Livonia, Lyria, Melo, Miomelon, Nannamoria, Nanomelon, Neptuneopsis, Notopeplum, Notovoluta, Odontocymbiola, Provocator, Saotomea, Scaphella, Voluta, Volutoconus, Zidona.*
(Photograph: *Melo amphora* (Lightfoot, 1786) – the Australian baler – creeping over an exposed sandbar. Its siphon is clearly visible. Photograph: P.L. van Pel.)

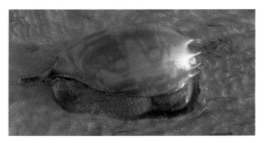

Amoria ellioti

(SOWERBY, 1864)
Elliot's volute

D: 85mm. S: solid, slender shell. Slightly curved whorls. O: 4 columellar folds. Un-thickened outer lip. C: smooth with thin, russet, radial stripes. H: d1; shallow water on sand. W: AUS. R: 2.

Amoria maculata

(SWAINSON, 1822)
Carol's volute

D: 65mm. S: robust, slender shell. Slightly curved whorls. Clear suture, albeit shallow. O: smooth. C: amber with three or four rows of russet to purplish-brown, radial stripes. H:

d1–2; sublittoral and deeper to 80m. W: AUS, INDP. R: 1.

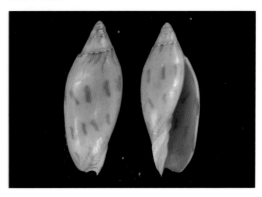

Amoria zebra

(LEACH, 1814)
zebra volute

D: 55mm. S: solid, wide shell with relatively convex whorls. Quite a wide aperture with 4 columellar folds. O: slight ornament on earlier whorls. Body whorl smooth. C: amber with russet radial lines and bands. Apricot aperture. H: d1; sublittoral. W: AUS; northern part. R: 1.

Ampulla priamus

(GMELIN, 1791)
spotted flask

193

D: 65mm. S: a quite thin, inflated shell. Convex whorls, very blunt spire. Wide aperture, siphonal canal absent or slight. O: smooth. C: glossy apricot with 4–6 rows of russet spots. H: d1–2; deep water. W: LUS (the Algarve, Portugal), WAFR. R: 3. NB: sought-after European species.

Cymbiola aulica

(SOWERBY I, 1825)
princely volute

D: 100mm. S: solid to thick shell. Reasonably slender, shouldered whorls. Strong, blunt apex. O: sharp shoulder nodules. C: amber with irregular, orange markings. Aperture margin orange. H: d1–2; sublittoral and slightly deeper water to 50m. W: INDP; the Philippines. R: 3.

Cymbiola imperialis

(LIGHTFOOT, 1789)
imperial volute

D: 200mm. S: robust shell with straight-sided, shouldered whorls. Strong, bud-like apex. O: smooth. C: variable: cream, amber to orange, with brown blotches or zigzags. H: d1; shallow water on sand. W: INDP; the Philippines. R: 3. NB: below the form *robinsona* Burch, 1954.

Cymbiola pulchra

(SOWERBY, 1825)
beautiful volute

D: 75mm. S: solid, fairly slender shell. Straight-sided whorls with sloping shoulders. O: clear shoulder tubercles. C: variable: orange with both pale, triangular patterns and bands of russet speckles, often circled in white. Russet stripes often at top. H: d1–2; sublittoral to 60m. W: AUS. R: 3. NB: variously colored forms.

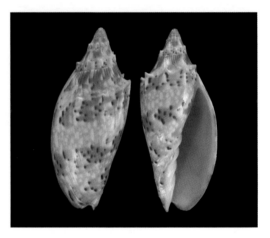

Cymbiola vespertilio

(LINNAEUS, 1758)
bat volute

D: 80mm. S: thick, wide shell. Very blunt, bud-like apex. Whorls with sloping shoulders. O: strong, spiny shoulder tubercles. C: grayish-brown to greenish-yellow with patterned lines of russet V-shapes or triangles. H: d1; sublittoral, muddy substrate. W: AUS, INDP. R: 1. NB: often bought from tourist shops.

Cymbium glans

(GMELIN, 1791)
elephant's snout

D: 320mm. S: a relatively solid, large shell in a stretched, cylindrical shape. O: the body whorl envelops all earlier ones. A sharp "collar" at the top. Middle of aperture enlarged. C: olive-green to grayish-brown, interior apricot. H: d1; littoral and sublittoral to 15m. W: WAFR. R: 1.

Cymbium olla

(LINNAEUS, 1758)
olla volute

D: 120mm. S: an inflated, cylindrical shell. Fairly thin-shelled. Defined, bud-like apex. Very wide body whorl. Middle of aperture enlarged. O: smooth or with very low spirals. C: apricot. H: d1–2; deeper water. W: LUS, the Algarve (Portugal), southern Spain; WAFR. R: 2.

Ericusa fulgetrum

(SOWERBY I, 1825)
lightning volute

D: 100mm. S: large, solid shell with a very truncated, bud-like apex. Rather convex whorls, in-flated body whorl. O: smooth. C: apricot with russet, zigzag, radial bands (like lightning). H: d1; littoral and sublittoral in shallow water. W: AUS; southern part. R: 2.

Lyria kurodai

(KAWAMURAI, 1964)
Kuroda's lyria

D: 90mm. S: solid, slender shell. Pointed spire. Slightly thickened outer lip. O: close succession of axial and fine spiral ribs. C: cream and amber with chocolate-brown blotches and spirals. H: d2–3; deep water. W: INDP, JAP; Taiwan. R: 4.

Melo amphora

(LIGHTFOOT, 1786)
Australian baler

D: up to 500mm. S: a very large, relatively thin, oval shell. The body whorl envelops earlier whorls. However, the apex remains visible. Wide aperture. Callus extends from inner lip over part of body whorl. O: smooth, very slight axial ribs. Long, hollow shoulder spines. In older shells, these are less pronounced toward the aperture or entirely absent. Spine color and development vary. C: variable: gray-green with slight brown blotching or garish red-brown coloration on a pale background. H: d1. W: AUS, INDP. R: 2.

Melo melo

(LIGHTFOOT, 1786)
Indian volute

D: 230mm. S: fairly thin, oval shell. Body whorl envelops all earlier whorls. Apex not visible. Wide aperture. O: smooth or with strong growth lines. C: greenish-yellow or olive-green. Aperture usually apricot. H: d1; sublittoral, shallow water. W: INDP, JAP; Malaysia, South China Sea. R: 2.

Provocator mirabilis

(FINLAY, 1926)
astonishing volute

D: 110mm. S: thin, slender shell with a very pointed spire and apex. O: smooth, spirals around the columella only. C: apricot. H: d2–3; deep water to 800m. W: AUS; New Zealand. R:

4–5. NB: a species that is much sought-after by collectors.

Scaphella junonia

(LAMARCK, 1804)
the junonia or Juno's volute

D: 100mm. S: solid, slender shell. Defined, bud-like apex. Curved whorls. O: very slight spirals. C: cream to white with red-brown spots. H: d1–2; in fairly deep water. W: CAR; Gulf of Mexico. R: 3–4.

Voluta musica

LINNAEUS, 1758
common music volute

D: 75mm. S: quite a rotund, thick shell. Angular, clearly shouldered whorls. Thickened outer lip. Callused inner lip with several columellar folds. O: clear shoulder tubercles. C: creamy white to pale yellow with variable patterning, reminiscent of staves used for musical notation. H: d1; sublittoral on sand to 20m. W: CAR. R: 1.

Volutoconus bednalli

(BRAZIER, 1878)
Bednall's volute

D: 100mm. S: solid shell with a strong, bud-like apex. O: very low axial ribs. C: white with a pattern of chocolate-brown lines like a trellis. H: d1–2; sublittoral and deeper, 10–40m. W: AUS; northern part. R: 3–4.

Volutomitridae

J.E. GRAY, 1854
The species in this family have fusiform shells, similar in appearance to those in Mitridae. The radula is different, however, and has more in common with Volutidae. The shell surface is smooth or has radial ribs. The siphonal canal does not include a basal notch. They occur in temperate and cold seas. Only a few genera: *Conomitra, Microvoluta, Peculator, Proximitra, Volutomitra, Waimatea*.

CANCELLARIOIDEA

FORBES & HANLEY, 1851
A superfamily of specialized, carnivorous scavenger snails. They occur on sandy and muddy substrates from the sublittoral to the deep sea in tropical and subtropical maritime regions.

Cancellariidae

FORBES & HANLEY, 1851
nutmeg shells

Relatively robust, compact, or elongated shells with radial ribs and narrow spirals that intersect to produce a lattice sculpture. The aperture is ovate or in the form of a rounded triangle with an anal groove at the top. The inner lip has folds, as does the columella, which is callused. The siphonal canal is often beak-like and extended. Either with or without an umbilicus. No operculum. The animals have a long proboscis and live on micro-organisms and other mollusks that live buried in the substrate. They occur from the sublittoral to deeper water in all warmer and tropical maritime regions. Divided into three subfamilies: Admetinae Troschel, 1866; Cancellariinae Forbes & Hanley, 1851; Plesiotritoninae Beu & Maxwell, 1987. The first of these principally contains deep-sea species resembling *Colubraria*, while the latter subfamily mostly contains small deep-sea species. Various genera, including: *Admete, Agatrix, Aphera, Axelella, Bonellitia, Cancellaria, Fusiaphera, Gergovia, Hertleinia, Inglisella, Iphinopsis, Narona, Pepta, Plesiotriton, Scalptia, Solatia, Sveltia, Trigonostoma, Zeadmete*.

Cancellaria reticulata

(LINNAEUS, 1767)
common nutmeg

D: 30mm. S: thick shell with a pointed spire. Convex whorls. Slightly thickened outer lip, clear apertural folds. Thick pleats on the columella. O: lattice sculpture. C: amber with dark brown bands and blotches. H: d1; sublittoral to 30m. W: CAR, VIR. R: 1.

Scalptia mercadoi

(OLD, 1968)
Mercado's nutmeg

D: 30mm. S: solid shell with very convex whorls. Thickened outer lip. Callus-strengthened inner lip. Columellar folds. Aperture folds (lirae). O: very wide axial ribs, deeply interspaced. Finer spirals. C: amber with russet spirals. H: d1–2; deeper water. W: INDP; the Philippines. R: 3.

Scalptia textilis

(KIENER, 1841)
textured nutmeg

D: 25mm. S: solid shell with convex, stepped whorls. Wide aperture with strong folds within thickened outer lip. Clear umbilicus. O: wide axial ribs with slight spirals. C: dark brown with paler dashes. H: d1; sublittoral, shallow water. W: INDP. R: 2.

Trigonostoma antiquata

(HINDS, 1843)
antique nutmeg

D: 18mm. S: solid shell with quite defined, stepped whorls. Very wide umbilicus. Folds within outer lip. Flattened shoulders. O: granulose spirals and very spiny shoulder nodules. C: creamy white to pale yellow. H: d1–2; deeper water. W: AUS, INDP, JAP. R: 4.

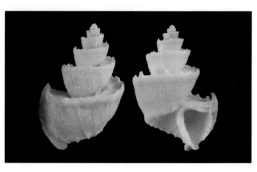

Trigonostoma goniostoma

(SOWERBY, 1832)
angle-mouth nutmeg

D: 25mm. S: thick shell with angular, stepped shoulders on whorls. Angular aperture. O: wide axial ribs crossed by irregular spirals. C: creamy white to light brown. H: d1; sublittoral, shallow water to 10m. W: PAN. R: 1.

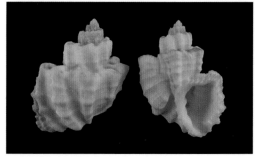

CONOIDEA

RAFINESQUE, 1815
All of the groups in this superfamily possess a venomous gland used in association with a radula containing dagger-like teeth.

Conidae

RAFINESQUE, 1815
cones

An extremely wide-ranging and well-known family with upturned, cone-shaped (obconical) shells. The spire is generally low or flat. The aperture is narrow and stretched. The operculum is extremely small. The outer lip is sharp and rarely thickened. There is a great variety of form and coloration within the family. These animals are widely distributed throughout all tropical and warmer maritime regions. They occur from the intertidal zone to deeper water on sand and hard substrates such as coral reefs and rocks. They are actively predacious, their prey consisting of worms, mollusks, and fish. These are paralyzed with an injection of venom from sharp, harpoon-like teeth. These venomous teeth are not fixed to the radula and consist of a hollow, barbed shaft. They remain lodged in the victim after the initial "bite." An extremely poisonous substance is injected into the prey through the tooth from a venom gland. The venomous tooth can also be used in defense. A sting from a cone can also have serious consequences for humans and result in paralysis or even death. The species most dangerous to man are: *Conus aulicus, C. geographus, C. marmoreus, C. striatus, C. textile* and *C. tulipa.* The family contains hundreds of species, almost all of which are classified within one genus. Cones are very popular among collectors and considerable sums of money are often paid for rare species. (Photograph: as is the case with many species, the shells of living cones are often covered with algae and other accretions. Only once they have been cleaned are the often beautiful colors and patterns revealed. *Conus dorreensis* Péron, 1807—the pontifical cone. Photograph P.L. van Pel.)

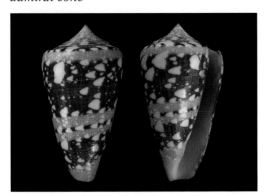

Conus ammiralis

LINNAEUS, 1758
admiral cone

D: 60mm. S: solid shell with flat sides. Fairly pointed spire. O: almost smooth, only very slight ornament. C: milky white with coffee-colored and light brown spirals and white markings, often triangular. The amount of white varies. H: d1; sublittoral. W: INDP. R: 2.

Conus arenatus

HWASS, 1792
sand-dusted cone

D: 40mm. S: solid shell with convex sides. Truncated spire, often with slight shoulder nodules. Curved columella. O: virtually smooth. Granulose texture in rare cases. C: cream or white with fine, russet to brownish-black speckles and often wider bands. H: d1; sublittoral. W: INDP. R: 1.

Conus augur

(LIGHTFOOT, 1786)
augur cone

D: 60mm. S: solid shell with flat sides. Low spire, pointed protoconch. O: virtually smooth. C: creamy white to pale yellow with very fine coffee-colored speckling. Also 2 broad bands. H: d1; sublittoral. W: INDP. R: 2.

Conus barthelemyi

BERNARDI, 1861
Barthelemy's cone

D: 60mm. S: solid shell with flat sides. Fairly low spire. O: fairly clear spirals, especially at base. C: matt orange-brown with dark brown bands and markings broken by white spots. Aperture white. H: d2; fairly deep water. W: INDP. R: 3–4.

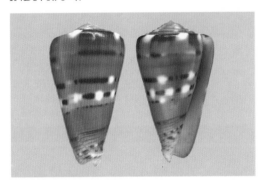

Conus bengalensis

(OKUTANI, 1968)
Bengal cone

D: 90mm. S: tall, slender shell with straight sides and a very pointed spire. Sharply angled shoulders. O: virtually smooth. C: orange-brown with a pattern of large and small triangles. Usually dark brown around the shoulder. H: d2–3; deep water. W: INDP; Bay of Bengal, Myanmar, Thailand. R: 3.

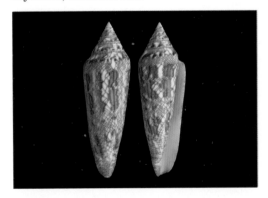

Conus bullatus

LINNAEUS, 1758
bubble cone

D: 60mm. S: solid shell with convex sides. Low spire, rounded shoulders, blunt apex. O: fine spi-

rals. C: orange-brown with paler blotches. H: d1–2; deep water. W: INDP. R: 2.

Conus cedonulli mappa

LIGHTFOOT, 1786
West Indian spiral cone

D: 50mm. S: solid shell with straight to gently curved sides. Fairly pointed spire. O: slight spirals over the whole surface. C: variable: orange, light to dark brown with irregular blotches of paler colors. Fine, broken lines often mark spirals. H: d1–2; sublittoral and deeper water, mostly under rocks. W: CAR; the Antilles. R: 2. NB: superficially resembles *C. aurantius* Hwass, 1792 – the golden cone – from the same area (see Foreword).

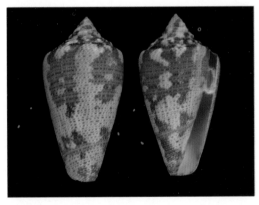

Conus chaldeus

(RÖDING, 1798)
vermiculate cone

D: 30mm. S: thick, rotund shell with slightly convex sides. Truncated spire, fairly convex whorls with vague shoulder nodules. O: spirals clearest at base. C: yellowish-white with dark brown, wavy axial stripes. H: d1; sublittoral.

W: INDP; including the Galapagos and Clipperton Islands. R: 2.

Conus coccineus

GMELIN, 1791
scarlet cone

D: 40mm. S: solid shell with slightly curved sides. Fairly convex whorls and slight shoulders. O: fine spirals. C: apricot to dark brown. Usually a band of color in the center with a distinctive pattern. H: d1; shallow water. W: INDP. R: 2.

Conus coffeae

GMELIN, 1791
leaden cone

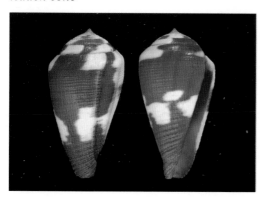

D: 30mm. S: solid shell with straight or slightly curved sides. Convex whorls with sloping shoulders. Pointed apex. O: granulose spirals over the whole surface. C: coffee-colored with white, irregular blotches. Purple sheen in aperture and on base. H: d1; sublittoral on sand and reefs. W: INDP, JAP. R: 2.

Conus coronatus

GMELIN, 1791
crowned cone

D: 30mm. S: thick shell with gently curving sides and a rounded spire. Clear shoulder nodules. O: granulose spirals over the whole surface. C: grayish-white with pale gray bands. Spirals with brown and white dashes. Sometimes orange-brown coloration. H: d1; sublittoral, on reefs. W: INDP. R: 1.

Conus cylindraceus

BRODERIP & SOWERBY, 1830
cylindrical cone

D: 35mm. S: very slender, solid shell. Curved sides. Tall, pointed spire with shallow suture between whorls. O: slight spirals. C: glossy russet with irregular, white vertical bands. H: d1–2; mostly in deep water. W: INDP. R: 2.

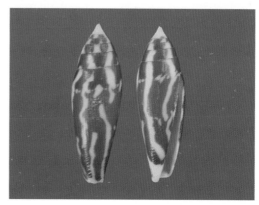

Conus dalli

STEARNS, 1873
Dall's cone

D: 40mm. S: solid shell with straight sides. Apical whorls slightly curved. O: vague spirals. C: orange-brown with a pattern of white, triangular markings. H: d1; sublittoral. W: PAN. R: 2–3.

Conus delessertii

RÉCLUZ, 1843
Sozon's cone

D: 75mm. S: quite thin-shelled. Flat sides. Very pointed spire. Flat-sided whorls with sloping shoulders. O: shoulders sometimes very slightly nodulose. Strongest spirals on columella. C: creamy white with apricot spiral bands and rows of russet dashes and spots. H: d1; reefs in deep water. W: CAR. R: 3.

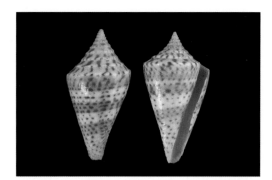

Conus diadema

SOWERBY, 1834
diadem cone

D: 40mm. S: solid shell with a very flattened spire and slightly curved sides. O: irregular spirals and very strong shoulder tubercles. C: brown, tubercles often paler. H: d1; sublittoral

rocky coasts. W: CAL, PAN; including the Galapagos Islands. R: 2.

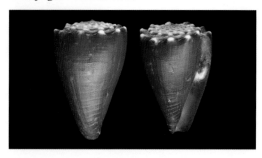

Conus dorreensis

PÉRON, 1807
pontifical cone

D: 30mm. S: solid, compact shell with convex whorls, an elongated spire, and a blunt apex. O: very delicate lattice sculpture. Strong shoulder tubercles. C: new specimens amber. White band edged in brown around shoulder tubercles. Another band at the base. Shell can even appear creamy white on removal of periostracum. H: d1; sublittoral. W: AUS; western part. R: 1.

Conus ebraeus

LINNAEUS, 1758
Hebrew cone

D: 40mm. S: solid shell with moderately curved sides. Fairly flat spire. O: slight spirals. C: chalky white with dark, brownish-black vertical blotches. Sometimes with a hint of purple. H: d1; sublittoral. W: INDP; including west coast of Central America. R: 1.

Conus eburneus

HWASS, 1792
ivory cone

D: 50mm. S: solid shell with flat sides. Relatively pointed to flattened spire. O: slight spirals at base. C: ivory with fairly widely interspaced dark brown spots and often 2 light brown spiral bands. H: d1; sandy substrate in sublittoral. W: INDP. R: 1.

Conus genuanus

LINNAEUS, 1758
garter cone

D: 50mm. S: solid to thick shell with flat sides. Apical whorls evenly raised. Suture scarcely visible. O: very slight spirals. C: creamy white background with pink to orange spiral bands covered by spiral rows of alternate dark brown and white dashes and' dots. Also some spiral bands of very fine, light brown dots higher up. H: d1; shallow water. W: WAFR. R: 2. NB: also known as the "Morse-code cone."

Conus generalis

LINNAEUS, 1767
general cone

D: 75mm. S: solid shell with very straight sides. Very sharp spire. Angular, sharp shoulders. O: virtually smooth, very slight spirals only. C: variable coloration, often with wide amber to orange bands and wavy vertical stripes. H: d1; littoral and sublittoral. W: INDP. R: 1.

Conus geographus

LINNAEUS, 1758
geography cone

D: 100mm. S: relatively thin-shelled. Convex sides. Relatively wide aperture. Strong shoulder tubercles. O: smooth. C: pale pink, cream to white, with irregular brown bands and blotches and a more delicate pattern of (often) small triangular markings. H: d1; shallow water in sublittoral. W: INDP. R: 1.

203

Conus glaucus

LINNAEUS, 1758
glaucous cone

D: 50mm. S: solid shell with slightly convex whorls. Low spire with a pointed apex. O: smooth. C: dirty gray, often with an ashen to gray-green sheen. Dark blotches on spire. Fine, broken, russet spiral lines on body whorl. H: d1–2; mostly in fairly deep water. W: INDP; western part. R: 3.

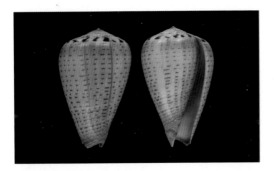

Conus gubernator

HWASS, 1792
governor cone

D: 60mm. S: solid, tall, slender shell. Spire slightly raised, whorls relatively curved with a narrow shoulder. O: wide, separated, low spirals, especially around the columella. C: grayish-white with a pattern of brown, orange, or pale pink half-erased markings. H: d1; shallow water. W: INDP; Indian Ocean. R: 1.

Conus gloriamaris

CHEMNITZ, 1777
glory-of-the-sea

D: 100mm. S: a solid, tall, and slender shell with straight sides. Convex apical whorls, elevated spire. O: extremely flat spirals. C: pale yellow with a complex pattern of small triangles, orange-red and brown lines, dots, and stripes. H: d1–2; shallow and deep water. W: INDP. R: 3. NB: once one of the most valuable of all species, for which astronomical sums of money were paid. Nowadays, its habitat is well known and specimens appear on the market quite regularly.

Conus guinaicus

HWASS, 1792
Canaries cone

D: 30mm. S: solid to thick, squat shell. Spire either flattened or more pointed. Gently curved sides. Somewhat inflated body whorl. O: fine spirals. C: variable: usually gray-green to brown markings on a paler background. H: d1; rocky coasts to 25m. W: WAFR; Canary Islands. R: 1. NB: closely resembles *C. ventricosus* Gmelin, 1791—known as the Mediterranean cone, as it lives in the Mediterranean Sea. The latter is a little smaller, and often has broken, colored spirals.

Conus imperialis

LINNAEUS, 1758
imperial cone

D: 75mm. S: thick shell with straight sides. Low spire with strong shoulder tubercles. O: slight spiral ribs or smooth. C: grayish-white with a large number of fine, broken spiral bands of long and short dashes. In places these coalesce to make broad bands. H: d1; sublittoral, on reefs. W: INDP. R: 1. NB: a variable species with a variety of forms and extremely wide distribution.

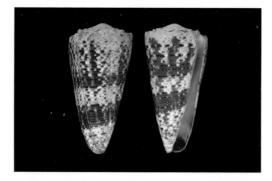

Conus jickelii

WEINKAUFF, 1873
Jickeli's cone

D: 35mm. S: thin shell with flat sides and a low spire. Pointed apex. O: granulose spirals around columella. C: creamy white with brown streaks and smudges. H: d2–3; deep water. W: INDP; Indian Ocean, western part. R: 4.

Conus kuroharai

(HABE, 1965)
Kurohara's cone

D: 65mm. S: solid with flat sides and a fairly pointed spire. O: low spirals over the whole shell. C: cream with russet radial lines. H: d2–3; deep water. W: INDP, JAP; Taiwan. R: 3–4.

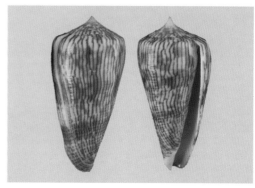

Conus literatus

LINNAEUS, 1758
lettered cone

D: 120mm. S: very thick, heavy shell. Spire usually low. O: smooth. C: creamy white and pale yellow with rows of dark brown to black dashes and dots. Dark brown columella. H: d1–2; sublittoral and deeper. W: INDP, JAP. R: 1.

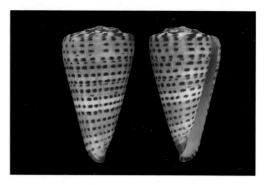

Conus litoglyphus

HWASS, 1792
lithograph cone

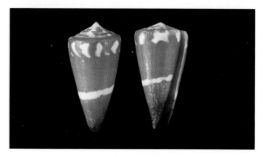

D: 50mm. S: solid shell with flat sides. Flattened spire, pointed apex. O: some slight spirals. C: orange dominates with creamy white blotches. Base dark brown. H: d1; shallow water in sublittoral. W: INDP. R: 1.

Conus marmoreus

LINNAEUS, 1758
marble cone

D: 100mm. S: fairly flat-sided. Spire fairly low. Slight to strong shoulder nodules. O: vague spirals. C: pattern of white, rounded, triangular markings on a dark brown to black background. H: d1; sandy substrate in sublittoral. W: INDP. R: 1. NB: once painted by Rembrandt (a counterclockwise example). Extremely toxic sting.

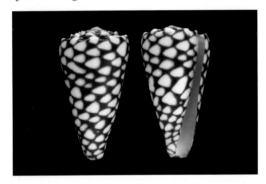

Conus mercator

LINNAEUS, 1758
trader cone

D: 30mm. S: solid shell with a rather blunt spire. Flat sides, sometimes slightly curved. O: slight spirals. C: creamy white with patterned chocolate-brown bands reminiscent of basket weaving. Pale yellow periostracum. H: d1; sublittoral. W: WAFR; Cape Verde Islands. R: 2.

Conus milneedwardsi

JOUSSEAUME, 1894
glory-of-India

D: 125mm. S: slender and fairly thin-shelled with a much elevated spire. Flat sides. Whorls with sloping shoulders. O: very fine spirals, especially on earlier whorls. C: white or cream with a pattern of russet lines, chocolate-brown bands, and white triangles. H: d1–2; deep water. W: INDP; Indian Ocean. R: 3–4. NB: sought-after by collectors.

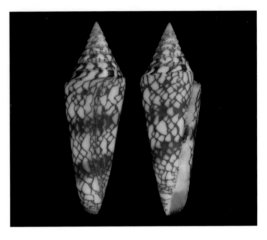

Conus nobilis

LINNAEUS, 1758
noble cone

D: 50mm. S: solid shell with flat sides. Low spire or slightly raised. O: smooth, very low spirals only. C: pale yellow to golden orange with a distinctive pattern of blurred triangular shapes. H: d1–2; sublittoral and deeper. W: INDP; eastern part of the Indian Ocean, Indonesia. R: 3. NB: on the right in the photograph is the subspecies *C. nobilis victor* Broderip, 1842 – the victor cone.

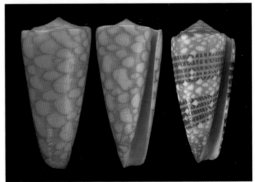

Conus nussatella

LINNAEUS, 1758
nussatella cone

D: 30mm. S: cylindrical and fairly thin-shelled with slightly convex sides. Raised spire, moderately convex whorls. O: strong spirals over the whole shell. C: creamy white with neat spiral lines of chocolate-brown dots. Sometimes golden orange background blotches. H: d1; sublittoral, shallow water. W: INDP. R: 1.

Conus princeps

LINNAEUS, 1758
prince cone

D: 90mm. S: solid shell with straight sides. Flattened spire. Slight shoulder nodules. O: low spirals, especially around columella. C: bright orange with chocolate-brown lines creating a zebra pattern. H: d1; sublittoral, shallow water. W: CAL, PAN. R: 3.

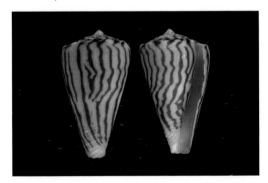

Conus pulcher

LIGHTFOOT, 1786
butterfly cone

D: 260mm. S: very thick, heavy shell. Spire slightly raised or lower. O: slight spirals. Shoul-

der nodules in rare instances. C: variable: grayish-yellow with brown markings or brighter coloration. H: d1; shallow. W: WAFR, ZAFR. R: 2. NB: the world's largest species of *Conus*.

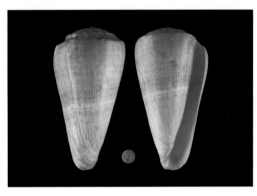

Conus textile

LINNAEUS, 1758
textile cone

D: 75mm. S: solid shell with slightly convex sides. Pointed spire. O: virtually smooth. C: pattern of white triangles on an amber, densely interlaced background. H: d1; shallow water. W: INDP. R: 1. NB: has a venomous sting.

Terebridae

MÖRCH, 1852
auger shells

Distinctively slender shells, ranging from robust to thick-shelled, most often with a large number of whorls that gradually increase in size. The aperture is relatively small with a sharp outer lip that is rarely thickened. The siphonal canal is short and the operculum corneous. Ornament comprises radial ribs, spiral grooves, or beading below the suture in rows. Species from the genus *Terebra* have no radula. Some species (subgenus *Impages*) are equipped with venom in a similar way to Conidae. The animals live in shallow water on sand. They usually burrow within the substrate, their long siphons poking above the sand in the search for food. There are numerous species in warm and tropical maritime regions. Only a few genera, including *Duplicaria*, *Hastula*, *Terebra*, *Terenolla*.

Duplicaria duplicata

(LINNAEUS, 1758)
duplicate auger

D: 50mm. S: a solid shell with virtually straight-sided whorls. O: slightly wavy axial grooves. A deep subsutural spiral groove in the upper half of each whorl. C: often a uniform light to deep, dark brown. Sometimes speckled light and dark. H: d1; sublittoral. W: INDP. R: 1.

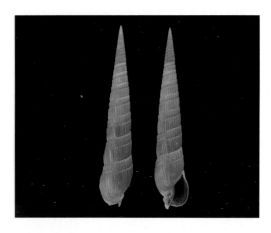

Duplicaria dussumierii

(KIENER, 1839)
Dussumier's auger

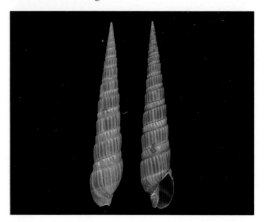

D: 50mm. S: solid, pointed shell with flat to slightly convex whorls. O: axial ribs and a deep, subsutural spiral groove. C: brown, ribs paler. A pale spiral line below the center of the whorls. H: d1; shallow water. W: INDP; Korea to China. R: 2.

Hastula lanceata

(LINNAEUS, 1767)
lance auger

D: 65mm. S: solid, pointed shell. Gently shouldered whorls with flat sides. O: fine axial ribs. C: creamy white to pale yellow with thin, wavy, russet vertical lines. H: d1; sublittoral on sandy substrate. W: INDP. R: 1.

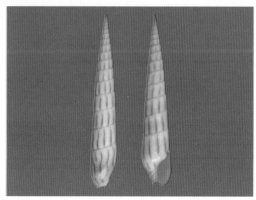

Terebra areolata

(LINK, 1807)
fly-spotted auger

D: 130mm. S: thick shell. Whorls slightly convex. Shallow suture. O: very fine, slight axial ribs. C: amber with red- to dark brown spots arranged in wide bands. H: d1; shallow water in sublittoral. W: INDP. R: 2.

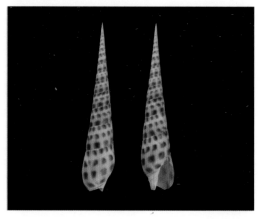

Terebra commaculata

(GMELIN, 1791)
many-spotted auger

D: 130mm. S: solid, exceptionally slender shell. Up to 22 angular, shouldered whorls. Narrow aperture. Short siphonal canal. O: 2 thick, beaded spirals below the suture. Narrower spirals otherwise. C: amber with dark brown, oblong blotches. H: d1; sublittoral. W: INDP. R: 2.

Terebra dimidiata

(LINNAEUS, 1758)
divided auger

D: 130mm. S: very pointed, solid shell. Flat-sided, non-shouldered whorls. O: a strong spiral groove a short distance below the suture. C: orange-red with yellowish-white to white wavy, radial lines that run down from the spiral groove. H: d1; shallow water on sand. W: INDP. R: 2.

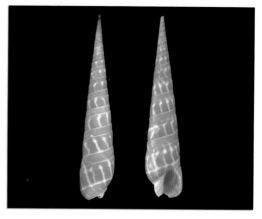

Terebra felina

(DILLWYN, 1817)
tiger auger

D: 70mm. S: solid, pointed shell with flat-sided, non-shouldered whorls. O: a single spiral groove in the center of the whorls. This is strongest on the first few whorls and almost obsolete on the final ones. Sometimes slight radial ribs on first few whorls. C: creamy white with a row of russet spots. H: d1; sublittoral on sand. W: INDP, JAP. R: 2.

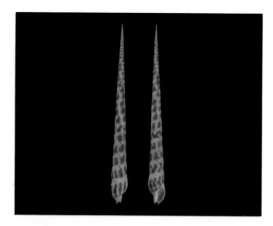

Terebra crenulata

(LINNAEUS, 1758)
crenulate auger

D: 120mm. S: moderately thick-shelled. 18–20 fairly flat-sided, shouldered whorls. O: strong shoulder nodules. C: amber with russet blotches and spots, jointly creating 3–4 spiral bands. H: d1; sublittoral. W: INDP; Indian Ocean. R: 2.

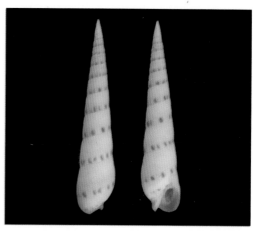

Terebra maculata

(LINNAEUS, 1758)
marlinspike

D: 150mm. S: relatively wide, thick shell. O: smooth. C: glossy, pale amber with 2 rows of successive dark brown markings. Some bands with light brown markings at the base. H: d1; shallow water on sand. W: INDP. R: 1.

Terebra ornata

GRAY, 1834
ornate auger

D: 85mm. S: a solid, very pointed shell. Gently shouldered whorls. Curved columella and siphonal canal. O: strong spiral groove a short distance below the suture. Very subtle axial ribs or beads at top of whorls. C: creamy white to pale yellow with roughly circular, dark brown spots, often with a russet outline. H: d1–2; sublittoral and deeper water. W: CAL, PAN; the Galapagos Islands. R: 2.

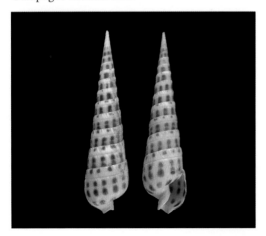

Terebra triseriata

GRAY, 1834
triseriate auger

D: 100mm. S: quite a solid, exceptionally long, slim shell with a record number of 50 whorls. Shouldered whorls, bent columella and siphonal canal. O: 2 beaded spirals below the suture. Finer spirals below this, similarly beaded. C: grayish-yellow. H: d1–2; sublittoral and deeper water to 100m. W: INDP, JAP. R: 3–4. NB: much sought-after collector's item. Flawless mature specimens are hard to obtain.

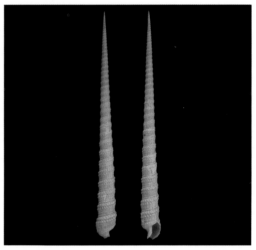

Turridae

SWAINSON, 1840
turrids

The family Turridae is generally considered to be the world's largest family of gastropods. They are mostly smaller species, measuring below 20mm in length. However, several larger species exist. Usually, the shells are roughly fusiform with an anal siphonal notch at the edge of the upper lip. Whorls are angular or rounded. Although almost every conceivable type of ornament occurs, it is often the axial ribs that predominate. Quite often, however, there are also spiral ribs or a lattice sculpture, or a granulose, nodulose, or grooved surface. The siphonal canal is usually open and can be long and slender or short and squat. The columella is mostly smooth and only rarely has folds or nodules. The operculum is corneous. Distinct anatomical differences occur, such as in the shape of the proboscis and radula. All species have a venom gland and often a toxoglossate radula, comparable to the venomous equipment seen in Conidae. Venom is injected by means of a "venomous tooth." Found in all maritime regions at all temperatures, both in shallow water and in the deep sea at depths of some thousands of meters. Placed in various subfamilies, together accounting for many hundreds of separate genera and many thousands of species. This encyclopedia includes only a few select examples.

Clavus enna

(DALL, 1918)
enna turrid

D: 25mm. S: fairly pointed, thick shell. Full whorls with angled shoulders. Moderately wide siphonal canal, clear anal siphon. O: finer spirals and strong, rounded axial ribs diminishing toward the base. C: creamy white. A touch of orange on lower part of whorls. H: d1–3; deep water. W: INDP, JAP. R: 3.

Cochlespira elegans

(DALL, 1889)
elegant star turrid

D: 45mm. S: solid, slender shell with pointed apex and flat, stepped whorls with wide shoulders. Very long, narrow siphonal canal. Clear anal siphon. O: fine spirals, sharp thorn-like

projections on shoulders. C: amber. H: d2–3; deep water. W: CAR; Florida, Cuba. R: 4.

Cochlespira pulchella pulcherrissima

KURODA, 1959
Japanese coronate turrid

D: 30mm. S: slender, quite thin-shelled turrid. Wide, angled shoulder on whorls. Clear anal siphon. O: fine, subtly nodulose spirals. Sharp, thorn-like shoulder tubercles. C: milky white to light brown. H: d2; deep water to 200m. W: INDP, JAP; China, Japan, Taiwan. R: 3–4.

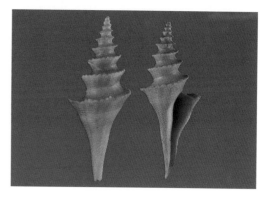

Comitas kaderlyi

(LISCHKE, 1872)
Kaderly's turrid

D: 80mm. S: quite thick-shelled and pointed. Long, siphonal canal. Shallow, angular anal siphon. Whorls have sharply angled shoulders. O: slight spiral ribs. Wide axial ribs, diminishing below. C: creamy white to white with amber spiral bands on the shoulder and below the ribs. H: d2–3; deep water. W: INDP, JAP. R: 3.

Gemmula kieneri

(DOUMET, 1840)
Kiener's turrid

D: 55mm. S: thin-shelled with a long siphonal canal. Clear anal notch. Whorls not stepped but with rounded shoulders. O: strong and subtler, nodulose spirals. A very wide, keel-shaped spiral rib below the shoulder with oblong beading. C: creamy white with brownish-orange dashes and spiral lines. H: d2–3. W: INDP, JAP. R: 3.

Genota mitraeformis

(WOOD, 1828)
miter-shaped turrid

D: 30mm. S: solid, slender shell. Slightly stepped whorls with sloping shoulders. Long, narrow aperture. Recurved inner lip, callus extends over body whorl. Thickened outer lip. O: fine spirals and thin axial ribs. Rounded shoulder tubercles. C: amber with dark brown blotches. H: d2–3. W: WAFR. R: 3.

Lophiotoma indica

(RÖDING, 1798)
Indian turrid

D: 90mm. S: fairly solid, slender shell with a very long siphonal canal. Deep, cleft-like anal

notch. Flat-sided whorls, angled shoulder. O: combined fine and strong, nodulose spirals. One stronger, nodulose spiral below the shoulder. C: creamy white to amber with russet markings and radial, zebra-like stripes. H: d2–3. W: AUS, INDP; Sri Lanka to Australia. R: 1.

Oenopota turricula

(MONTAGU, 1803)
common Atlantic turrid

D: 20mm. S: solid shell with strongly shouldered whorls. Pointed apex. Narrow aperture ending in a straight siphonal canal. No umbilicus. O: 12–16, almost perpendicular, axial ribs and fine spirals in between. C: cream to milky white. H: d1–4; silty substrates. Sublittoral to depths of some hundreds of meters. W: ARC, KEL, VIR. R: 2.

Thatcheria mirabilis

(ANGAS, 1877)
Japanese wonder shell

D: 90mm. S: thin-shelled yet quite robust. Pagoda-shaped. Flat-sided whorls. Slightly sloping shoulder. O: extremely fine spirals and radial lines. Strong, rounded spiral keel around the shoulder. C: yellowish-white to beige. H: d2–4; 150–400m. W: AUS, INDP, JAP. R: 3. NB: an exceptionally sought-after shell.

wide (and narrow), nodulose spirals. C: milky white with dark brown and pale russet spots on the nodules. H: d1–2; sublittoral and deeper to 50m. W: INDP, JAP. R: 2.

Turricula javana

(LINNAEUS, 1767)
Java turrid

D: 75mm. S: solid, pointed shell. Long, slightly curved, siphonal canal. Short, but clear, anal siphon. O: strong and subtler spirals. A wide, strongly nodulose spiral across center of whorls. A further 2 stronger spirals below the center. C: matt reddish-brown to dark brown. H: d1–3; sublittoral and deeper water, on muddy substrates. W: INDP, JAP. R: 2.

Turris grandis

(GRAY IN GRIFFITH & PIDGEON, 1834)
supreme turrid

D: 150mm. S: solid, very slim shell. Extremely pointed with a very long, narrow, and straight siphonal canal. O: strong spirals with many narrower, finely beaded spirals in between. Cleft-like anal siphon. C: Cream with reddish-brown to brown square-shaped blotches. H: d2–4. W: INDP. R: 4. NB: world's largest turrid.

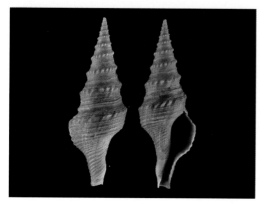

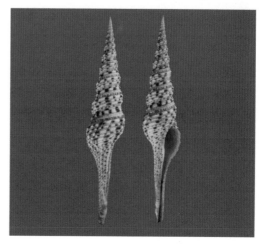

Turris babylonia

(LINNAEUS, 1758)
Babylonia turrid

D: 75mm. S: slender, thin-shelled. Very pointed. Very long siphonal canal. O: quite low,

SUPERORDER HETEROBRANCHIA

J.E. GRAY, 1840
irregularly gilled snails

213

ARCHITECTONICOIDEA

J.E. GRAY, 1840

Species from this superfamily change the direction of their growth as they mature. Embryonic whorls are counterclockwise with a depressed apex. Subsequent whorls are clockwise in orientation (heterostrophy).

Architectonicidae

J.E. GRAY, 1840
sundials

Flat, circular or conical shells with a distinctive shape. The umbilicus gapes open to the top of the shell. In fact, the whorls barely touch. Whorls often have keels, usually have spiral ribs, and are sometimes smooth or granulose. Coloration follows the spirals. The umbilicus often has a thick margin. The operculum is corneous and thick and pustular in the center. The family occurs in all tropical and subtropical maritime regions, usually in shallow water, but found in deeper water as well. The animals live on corals and sea anemones, which are their food. Several genera, the most familiar of which is *Architectonica*.

Architectonica nobilis

RÖDING, 1798
American sundial

D: 50mm. S: robust, much flattened, circular shell with a relatively narrow umbilicus. O: beaded spirals on the base. Strongly pleated spiral around the umbilicus. C: cream with russet dashes, especially on top of the whorls. H: d1; sublittoral to a depth of several tens of meters. W: CAR. R: 1.

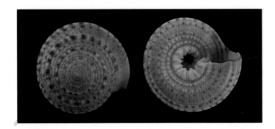

Architectonica perdix

(HINDS, 1844)
partridge sundial

D: 35mm. S: robust, much compressed shell. Quite narrow umbilicus. O: a strongly beaded spiral around the umbilicus. Apical whorls more strongly beaded. C: yellowish-white with brown dashes. H: d1–2; sublittoral and deeper. W: INDP, JAP. R: 1.

Architectonica perspectiva

(LINNAEUS, 1758)
clear sundial

D: 40mm. S: much compressed, circular, and thick shelled. Relatively wide umbilicus. O: deep spiral groove below suture. Various beaded spirals. C: beige with a touch of blue-gray. Beading and spirals with alternately light and darker coloration. H: d1; sublittoral and deeper

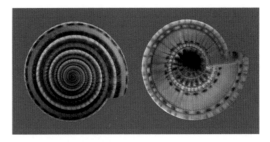

water. W: INDP. R: 1.

Mathildidae

DALL, 1889

Spire-shaped or ovate conical shells. Lattice sculpture. The umbilicus is narrow or absent. Operculum without interior thickening. Embryonic whorls in some species first run counterclockwise only to bend back subsequently. Deep suture. Worldwide distribution in shallow and deep water, mostly in temperate maritime regions. Only a few species and genera, including *Brookesena, Fimbriatella, Gegania, Granulicharilda, Mathilda, Mathildona, Opimilda*.

OMALOGYROIDEA

G.O. SARS, 1878

Micro-mollusks with a flat, planospiral shell.

Omalogyridae

G. O. SARS, 1878
ammonite-like snails

Shells virtually or entirely wound in a spiral on one plane (planospiral). Less than 2mm in diameter with some species reaching only 0.5mm at maturity. The surface is smooth or has radial ribs and grooves. The protoconch is wound normally and is not heterostrophic. Occur in all warmer maritime regions. The animals live in the littoral and sublittoral and feed on the cellular contents of algae. Only few genera, including: *Adeuomphalus, Ammonicera, Omalogyra*.

Ammonicera rota

(FORBES & HANLEY, 1850)
ribbed ammonite snail

D: 1.2mm. S: minuscule, flat shell. The whorls increase in size evenly and are wound in a spiral, flat plane. The apex is completely sunken. The aperture is almost circular. O: axial ribs perpendicular to the suture. Some specimens have a slight keel. C: amber to russet, sometimes with a dark spiral band that may be interrupted. H: d1; sublittoral of rocky coasts amid red seaweed. W: KEL, LUS. R: 2. NB: on the right in the photograph is the species *Omalogyra japonica* (Habe, 1972). (SEM image of a specimen found off the coast of Oman.)

PYRAMIDELLOIDEA

J.E. GRAY, 1840
Many species from this superfamily, largely composed of micro-mollusks, live parasitically on polychaete worms and other mollusks. Several groups have a long proboscis and a pointed suction organ instead of a radula.

Amathinidae

PONDER, 1987
amathina shells and others

Principally, these differ anatomically from Pyramidellidae. They are ectoparasites with a preference for large bivalves and come in all kinds of guises, from virtual limpets to gastropod-type shells with either large or small apertures. Only a few genera, including: *Amathina, Clathrella, Leucotina* en *Phasianema*.

Amathina tricarinata

(LINNAEUS, 1767)
common or three-ridged amathina

D: 25mm. S: limpet-like shell with furled up, laterally twisted apical (heterostrophic) whorls. O: 3 strong, radial ribs, running from the apex to the posterior of the shell. Also coarse, wavy concentric ribs. C: creamy white with a membranous, dark brown periostracum that is soon abraded. H: d1; sublittoral, attached to hard substrates. W: INDP. R: 2.

Clathrella clathrata

(PHILIPPI, 1844)
lattice clathrella

D: 4mm. S: thick-shelled and rotund. Convex whorls with wide shoulder. Large aperture. O: strong lattice sculpture. C: creamy white to pale yellow. H: d1–2; sublittoral and deeper water. W: KEL, LUS. R: 2; regularly wash ashore.

Anisocyclidae

VAN AARTSEN, 1995
A few millimeters long, these are slender, spire-shaped shells with numerous whorls. A few genera: *Anisocycla, Henrya*.

Pyramidellidae

J.E. GRAY, 1840
pyrams and other pyramidellids

Micro-mollusks with spire-shaped or conical shells. The embryonic apical whorls are often heterostrophic, blunt, and bent to one side, but can also be coiled, or take other shapes. Usually one, sometimes up to three strong, columellar folds. Sometimes also folds in the aperture. Divided into subfamilies: Odostomiinae Pelseneer, 1928; Pyramidellinae J.E. Gray, 1840; Turbonillinae Bronn, 1849. All together, there are a great many species and genera, including *Chrysallida, Eulimella, Folinella, Kleinella, Noemiamea, Odostomia, Ondina, Pyramidella, Syrnola, Tragula, Turbonilla*. Some compilation photographs of European species have been included as examples (KEL, LUS, WAFR). The following species can be seen in the top photograph (from left to right): *Chrysallida sarsi* Nordsieck, 1972 – blunt pyramidellid; *Folinella excavata* (Philippi, 1836) – rasper pyramidellid; *Chrysallida spiralis* (Montagu, 1803) – small pyramidellid.

The following species can be seen in the bottom photograph (from left to right): *Turbonilla crenata* (Brown, 1827) – striped turbonille; *Odostomia scalaris* (MacGillivray, 1843) – musselnibbler pyramidellid (a parasite on common, edible mussels); *Odostomia acuta* (Jeffreys, 1848) – stepped pyramidellid.

Tjaernoeidae

WARÉN, 1991
Only one genus: *Tjaernoeia*

Cimidae

WARÉN, 1993
Micro-mollusks. The shells have several whorls that very gradually increase in size. In many cases there is no ornament and no coloration. Some species show similarities with Rissoidae. Found in colder and temperate maritime regions. Genera include: *Cima, Graphis, Murchisonella*.

Graphis albida

(KANMACHER, 1798)
checked cimid

D: 4mm. S: awl-shaped, thin shell. Up to 10 quite convex whorls. Quite robust, blunt apex. Oval aperture with a subtle umbilical groove alongside. O: lattice sculpture of clear axial ribs curved in an S-shape and somewhat finer spiral ribs in between. C: glossy white or vitreous. H: d1–2; sublittoral to a depth of some tens of meters. W: KEL, LUS, WAFR. R: 3.

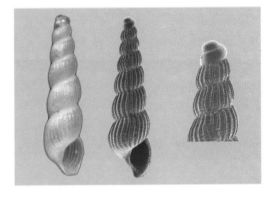

VALVATOIDEA

J.E. GRAY, 1840
This superfamily principally contains freshwater mollusks, but also contains a few marine groups with a worldwide distribution. They are thin-shelled, small, top-shaped or planospiral, with an open umbilicus, and only a few whorls. The animals contain both sexes.

Cornirostridae

PONDER, 1990
Micro-mollusks with a top-shaped, smooth, compressed shell. Few whorls. Intertidal zones

of Australia and Florida. Genera: *Cornirostra, Noerrevangia, Tomura*.

Hyalogyrinidae

WARÉN & BOUCHET, 1993
Micro-mollusks. Deep sea to a depth of 2000m. Genera: *Hyalogyra, Hyalogyrina, Xenoskenea*.

Xylodisculidae

WARÉN, 1992
Micro-mollusks with planospiral, smooth shells and a hyperstrophic (inverted) protoconch. Found at greater depths, including in the Mediterranean Sea and around Australia on sunken driftwood. One genus: *Xylodiscula*.

Orbitestellidae

IREDALE, 1917
micro-planospiral snails

Micro-mollusks. Incredibly small, thin-shelled, and planospiral (often under a millimeter in size). With some strongly ribbed keels around the periphery of the whorls. Found worldwide in the sublittoral under rocks and on seaweed.

Boschitestella donaldi

MOOLENBEEK, 1994
Omani micro-planospiral shell

D: 0.86mm. S: thin-shelled, planospiral. Very wide umbilicus. O: sharp keel around periphery. Also regular axial ribs and very fine spiral sculpture. C: glossy white or vitreous. H: d1; littoral, in tidal pools. W: INDP; Oman. R: 4.

RISSOELLOIDEA

M.E. GRAY, 1850

Rissoellidae

M.E. GRAY, 1850
Micro-mollusks with thin, oval to conical shells. The apex is generally prominent. Whorls are convex. Large body whorl. Wide, oval aperture. Un-thickened outer lip. The animals live amid seaweed in the littoral and sublittoral. Genus: *Rissoella*.

SUBCLASS OPISTHOBRANCHIA

MILNE-EDWARDS, 1848
The gills in most members of this subclass are moved over to the right, ending up behind the heart due to detorsion (untwisting) of the spirally wound gastropod body. In many groups the shell is diminished or else wholly absent. In those species that do have a shell, it is often thin and, in many cases, entirely enveloped by the mantle. Only a few species are able to withdraw fully into their shells. This encyclopedia includes only a few of the shell-bearing opisthobranch sea slugs. The slugs found in Nudibranchia and Gymnosomata will not be discussed further.

ORDER CEPHALASPIDEA

P. FISCHER, 1883
These animals have a characteristic headshield: an expansion at the head that is of use to the animal when plowing through sand. The foot sometimes has laterally extended lobes (parapodia), which are present in Gastropteridae and aid swimming. Acteonidae alone have an operculum, although some species from the families Bullinidae, Cylichnidae, and Retusidae still have the remnants of one in a much-diminished form. They are carnivorous hunters that live on and in the ocean floor in the proximity of their prey: sedentary mollusks, polychaete worms, and foraminifers. The shell is usually not enveloped by the mantle, although in some cases it is.

ACTEONOIDEA

(D'ORBIGNY, 1842)
Three families with diminished shells (sometimes greatly, sometimes less so). Acteonidae can withdraw completely into the shell and have an operculum. While Bullinidae are able to withdraw, they cannot seal off the aperture as the operculum is too small. Hydatinidae have no operculum, and highly colored bodies that are too large to withdraw fully into the shell.

Acteonidae

(D'ORBIGNY, 1842)
acteons, and others

Ovoid or fusiform shells, usually with a short or sunken spire. Heterostrophic apex (coiled contrary to the normal direction). The aperture is elongated, narrowing at the top and widening at the base. The columella is somewhat twisted and usually carries a fold. Wide distribution. Carnivorous hunters that prey on polychaete worms. Several genera, including: *Acteon, Crenilabium, Japonacteon, Punctacteon, Pupa*.

Acteon tornatilis

(LINNAEUS, 1758)
lathe acteon

D: 25mm. S: sturdy shell with a very large body whorl. Quite a pointed apex. Elongated aperture about 2/3 of the total height. A clear fold or nodule within inner lip. O: spiral grooves, especially below the final whorl. C: grayish-white with 2–3 pink bands. H: d1–3; sublittoral to great depths, on sand. W: KEL, LUS. R: 1.

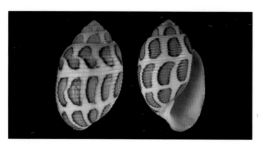

D: 25mm. S: a solid, inflated shell. Convex whorls with a flat shoulder. O: strong spirals. C: creamy white with large, russet spots with a dark brown to black outline. H: d1; sublittoral. W: INDP; Oman. R: 4.

Punctacteon variegatus

(BRUGUIÈRE, 1789)
pink-speckled acteon

D: 20mm. S: solid, rotund shell. Slight shoulder on whorls. O: strong spirals. C: creamy white with pink markings, never with a dark outline. H: d1; sublittoral on sand. W: INDP. R: 1.

Punctacteon virgatus

(REEVE, 1842)
striped acteon

D: 25mm. S: solid, fairly slender shell. Rounded whorls, sharp apex. O: even spirals. C: creamy white with wide, wavy, dark brown vertical bands. H: d1; shallow water. W: INDP; western part. R: 4.

Bullinidae

LAMARCK, 1801
grooved bubble shells

Ovoid shells with a short or compressed apex. Similar in form to Acteonidae but with delicately pitted spirals. Found in the sublittoral of tropical and subtropical maritime regions. Genus: *Bullina*.

Bullina nobilis

(HABE, 1950)
noble bubble

D: 25mm. S: ovoid shell with a rather squat spire. Final whorl accounts for over 9/10 of the total height. Elongated aperture narrowing at the top. Columella has a curve or slight fold. O: pitted spirals. C: creamy white with dark spiral bands and wavy radial lines. H: d1–2; sublittoral and deeper. W: INDP. R: 1.

Hydatinidae

PILSBRY, 1895
paper-bubble shells

Thin, ovoid, convex, or cylindrical shells. Sunken spire. Cream-colored with colored bands. Wide aperture. Curved columella with a callused inner lip. Found in warmer maritime regions on sandy substrates in the intertidal zone and sublittoral, on and under rocks, and in sea grass. The animals hunt polychaete worms. Genera include: *Hydatina*, *Micromelo*.

Hydatina albocincta

(VAN DER HOEVEN, 1839)
white-banded paper-bubble

D: 40mm. S: inflated, extremely thin-shelled. Sunken spire. The body whorl encloses earlier whorls. Very wide aperture. O: smooth, only growth lines. C: milky white to amber with dark brown bands. H: d1; littoral and sublittoral. W: INDP. R: 1.

Hydatina amplustre

(LINNAEUS, 1758)
royal paper-bubble

D: 25mm. S: extremely thin-shelled. Spire bluntly flattened, inflated whorls with a clear suture in between. O: smooth, only growth lines. C: cream to white with 2 very wide orange-brown bands lined in black. H: d1; sublittoral. W: INDP. R: 3.

Hydatina physis

(LINNAEUS, 1758)
green-lined paper-bubble

D: 50mm. S: thin-shelled, inflated. Sunken spire. Body whorl encloses earlier whorls. Wide aperture. O: smooth. C: gray-green with greenish-brown stripes. White aperture. Callus extends over body whorl from inner lip. H: d1; littoral and sublittoral. W: INDP. R: 1.

Hydatina zonata

(LIGHTFOOT, 1786)
zoned paper-bubble

D: 40mm. S: extremely thin-shelled. Sunken spire. Body whorl encloses earlier whorls.

Very wide aperture. O: smooth with coarse growth lines. C: amber to pinkish with a broad, white stripe bordered in black at the center of the whorl. A second white band at the base of the whorl. H: d1–2; sublittoral and deeper to 50m. W: INDP. R: 2.

BULLOIDEA

LAMARCK, 1801
Large, ovoid, robust shells within which the animal is able to withdraw entirely. No operculum. Herbivorous.

Bullidae

LAMARCK, 1801
bubble shells

Ovoid, inflated shells with a sunken or involute top. Aperture as high as the rest of the shell. Columella bent. Line of callus runs along the margin of the inner lip without folds. Smooth surface with brown dots and dashes. Found on sand and mud in shallow water in warmer maritime regions. Genus: *Bulla*.

CYLINDROBULLOIDEA

THIELE, 1931
Very thin shells into which the small animals are able to withdraw entirely.

Cylindrobullidae

THIELE, 1931
Small, cylindrical shells with sunken spires. No operculum. The Mediterranean Sea, Atlantic Ocean, and Indo-Pacific region. Genus: *Cylindrobulla*.

DIAPHANOIDEA

ODHNER, 1914

Diaphanidae

ODHNER, 1914
miniature glassy bubble shells

Micro-mollusks (smaller than 5mm). Thin-shelled, convex, ovate, or pear-shaped with a barely projecting or sunken apex. Cold maritime regions. From the sublittoral to the abyssal zone. Genera include: *Colpodaspis, Diaphana, Toledonia*.

Diaphana minuta

BROWN, 1827
European miniature glassy bubble

D: 4mm. S: very thin-shelled and cylindrical. Fairly convex whorls. Body whorl encloses earlier whorls almost completely, making the apex virtually invisible. Deep suture between whorls. An umbilical cleft alongside the aperture. O: smooth, growth lines only. C: translucent to pale white. H: d2–3. W: KEL, LUS. R: 3.

Notodiaphanidae

THIELE, 1931
These shells closely resemble those of Haminoeidae. Indian Ocean. One genus: *Notodiaphana*.

HAMINOEIDEA

PILSBRY, 1895
Thin, ovoid, or oval to squat shells within which the animal is able to withdraw either wholly or partially. Principally herbivorous.

Bullactidae

THIELE, 1926
Thin-shelled and translucent with a very wide aperture. Delicate ornament. Known only from river mouths along the coast of China. Genus: *Bullacta*.

Haminoeidae

PILSBRY, 1895

glassy bubble shells

Thin-shelled and translucent. Ovoid with sunken or enclosed apical whorls. Large body whorl with fine spiral grooves. Outer lip projects far above the rest of the shell. Found in all warmer and temperate maritime zones. Herbivorous – feeds on green seaweed. Several genera, including: *Atys, Cylichnium, Haminoea*.

Atys naucum

(LINNAEUS, 1758)

white Pacific atys

D: 40mm. S: very thin-shelled, ovoid, and inflated. Body whorl encloses all earlier whorls. Apertural margin projects above the apex. Bent columella. O: fine spiral grooves. C: milky white, brownish-gray periostracum. H: d1–2; sublittoral and deeper water. W: INDP; tropical parts including the Philippines. R: 1.

Haminoea navicula

(DA COSTA, 1778)

Atlantic glassy bubble

D: 32mm. S: very thin-shelled and inflated. O: strong growth lines and very fine spiral ribbing. C: amber, reddish-brown periostracum. H: d1; shallow water, sheltered bays. W: KEL, LUS. R: 2.

Smaragdinellidae

THIELE, 1925

Oval, yellowish-green shells with sunken and covered apical whorls. Very wide aperture with a spoon-like projection on the edge of the columella. Indo-Pacific region, Mediterranean Sea. Genera: *Phanerophthalmus, Smaragdinella*.

PHILINOIDEA

J.E. GRAY, 1850

Shells greatly diminished and surrounded by the whole body. Only *Scaphander* species are able to fully withdraw into their shells. Predators or scavengers with a large head-shield and internal gizzard plates for crushing and grinding.

Aglajidae

PILSBRY, 1895

Micro-mollusks with shells that only partly contain calcium. Small apex and a wide, gaping aperture. Entirely surrounded by the mantle. Active predators, preying on polychaete worms and small sea snails and slugs. Genera include: *Aglaja, Philinopsis*.

Cylichnidae

H. & A. ADAMS, 1854

canoe bubbles

Elongated, pear-shaped or cylindrical shells. The top is either raised or sunken. Narrow aperture, as high as the rest of the shell, rounded at the base. Habitats include muddy substrates and sea-grass meadows. From the intertidal zone to the deep sea, including the Indo-Pacific region, the Atlantic Ocean, and the Mediterranean Sea. Several genera, including *Acteocina, Cylichna, Roxania, Scaphander, Tornatina*.

Cylichna cylindracea

(PENNANT, 1777)

cylindrical canoe-bubble

D: 15mm. S: quite a solid, cylindrical shell. Resembles Retusidae. The final whorl completely envelops all earlier whorls. The aperture narrows slightly at the top. O: irregular growth lines and very fine spiral grooves. C: creamy white with dark yellow periostracum. H: d1–4;

sublittoral to great depths, on sand and mud. W: ARC, KEL, LUS. R: 1.

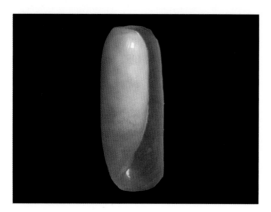

Scaphander lignarius

(LINNAEUS, 1758)
woody canoe-bubble

D: 70mm. S: solid, pear-shaped shell. The final whorl is convex and envelops previous whorls. The shell has no apex. O: fine spiral grooves crossed by growth lines. C: fresh specimens are grayish-white or cream, often with dark brown stripes parallel to the spiral ribs. The periostracum is reddish- to rust-brown. H: d2–3; sublittoral and deeper water, on sand and mud. W: KEL, LUS. R: 1. NB: these carnivorous sea slugs grind their prey (mollusks, foraminifers, worms, and crustaceans) between thick, calcareous gizzard plates.

Gastropteridae

SWAINSON, 1840
The shells look like very small species from the Haliotidae family but are only thinly calcified and are entirely covered by the mantle. Genus: *Gastropteron*.

Philinidae

J.E. GRAY, 1850
philinid sea slugs

Very thin-shelled. A broad, expanded body whorl in the shape of an ear or scoop. The mantle entirely covers the shell. Internal gizzard plates.

Philine aperta

(LINNAEUS, 1767)
great-shelled philinid

D: 20mm. S: very thin-shelled and fragile. 2–3 whorls, quickly increasing in size. The final whorl is expanded into a great "ear." O: smooth, slight growth lines only. C: milky white or translucent and vitreous. H: d1–3. W: INDP, KEL, LUS. R: 2. NB: a cosmopolitan sea slug. Apart from Europe, where it is locally commonplace (Normandy, France), it is also known in the Indo-Pacific region.

Philine punctata

(J. ADAMS, 1800)
dotted philinid

D: 2.5mm. S: very thin-shelled and fragile. In shape it resembles *P. aperta* but the shell is much smaller, is more angular and rounded, and has a different ornament. O: clear, longitudinally pitted grooves. C: vitreous white. H: d1–3. W: KEL, LUS. R: 3. NB: occasionally found washed ashore in very fine sand.

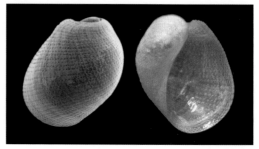

Retusidae

THIELE, 1926
retusid bubble shells

Cylindrical or fusiform shells with a sunken or slightly prominent apex. Narrow aperture, nearly as high as the shell itself and widening out at the base. Found in all maritime regions on sand and mud substrates, from the upper part of the intertidal zone to the deep sea. Most species measure only a few millimeters. Several genera, including *Cylichnina, Retusa, Volvulella*.

Retusa obtusa

(MONTAGU, 1803)
European retusid

D: 8mm. S: fairly thin-shelled and cylindrical. 5–6 straight-sided whorls. Body whorl partly encloses earlier whorls. Spire only barely projects above the shell. Elongated aperture, narrower above than below. No umbilicus. O: smooth, growth lines only. C: creamy white or white. H: d1; littoral, mud flats. W: KEL, LUS. R: 1. NB: the animals burrow into soft mud in places that do not dry out completely at low tide. They are predatory, their prey consisting of diatoms and (in particular) the laver spire shell *Peringia ulvae*.

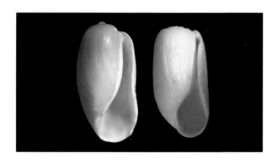

RINGICULOIDEA

PHILIPPI, 1853
Shells that differ from those of other members of Cephalaspidea: ovoid or conical, squat, with short to fairly high apical whorls, and thick-shelled. The animal is able to withdraw fully into its shell. No operculum.

Ringiculidae

PHILIPPI, 1853
ringiculid bubble shells

Thick-shelled and glossy white with a narrowed aperture due to thick, columellar folds and a strong parietal callus. Outer lip greatly thickened, occasionally with one or more folds within. Siphonal canal present. Smooth surface with fine spiral grooves or lattice sculpture. Found in warmer seas on sandy ground and in the proximity of seaweed forests and sea-grass meadows. Sublittoral to deep sea. Genus: *Ringicula*.

ORDER SACCOGLOSSA

VON IHERING, 1876
Distinctly herbivorous. The radula is contained in a kind of sack (saccus), which also contains the worn-down teeth. The animals tear seaweed open and suck out the contents with the help of the radula. Mostly found in seaweed beds in warm and tropical seas.

OXYNOOIDEA

H. & A. ADAMS, 1854
Herbivorous sea slugs with shells in a variety of shapes that can contain the entire animal. Otherwise, flat, diminished, shield-like shells that only cover part of the animal. Furthermore, this superfamily contains what are known as the "bivalve gastropods" from the family Juliidae. All species feed on green weed.

Juliidae

E.A. SMITH, 1885
bivalve snails

Micro-mollusks. In terms of their bodies, these mollusks belong among Gastropoda. However, they possess bivalve shells into which the animals are able to withdraw entirely. Found in all tropical and temperate maritime regions. Their food consists of green weed. Several genera, including: *Berthelinia* and *Julia*.

Oxynoidae

H. & A. ADAMS, 1854
Thin shells that protect only the visceral hump. Wide, with an outer lip that projects above the final whorl (genus *Oxynoe*), or an elongated oval, with a very wide aperture (genus *Lobiger*). A few genera, including: *Artessa, Lobiger, Oxynoe*.

Volvatellidae

PILSBRY, 1893
Thin, elastic shells with sunken spires. The animals are able to withdraw fully into their shells.

A narrow aperture, widened at the base, is present in the genus *Volvatella*, while the outer lip tapers into a beak-like point and projects above the final whorl. Shallow water in warmer seas. Found amid green weed. Genera: *Ascobulla*, *Volvatella*.

ORDER ANASPIDEA

P. FISCHER, 1883
The shells are small in comparison to the body and are covered by the mantle, or reduced. No head-shield. An extremely diverse range of forms. Found in warmer coastal regions rich in plant life. Eat seaweed.

AKEROIDEA

PILSBRY 1893

Akeridae

PILSBRY, 1893
akeras

Paper-thin, cylindrical shells. Sunken protoconch, truncated apical whorls. Aperture as high as the body whorl, narrowing at the top, and somewhat distanced from earlier whorls. The animal is unable to withdraw fully into its shell. This sea slug is able to swim by squeezing out water held in the funnel created by its folded parapodia. Occurrence on soft mud and coral sand in all maritime regions. One genus: *Akera*.

Akera soluta

(GMELIN, 1791)
solute akera

D: 35mm. S: paper-thin, flexible shell. Angular whorls with a narrow shoulder at the top. O: strong growth lines. C: amber. H: d1; shallow, sheltered bays. W: AUS, INDP. R: 1.

APLYSIOIDEA

LAMARCK, 1809

Aplysiidae

LAMARCK, 1809
sea hares

Extremely large, herbivorous sea slugs (up to 600mm in size) with paper-thin, shield-like shells, partly covered by the mantle. These animals' parapodial lobes fold upward and they have long, ear-shaped tentacles. They occur in shallow water near the coast. Their food consists of seaweed. Found in all warmer and temperate maritime regions. Several subfamilies, including completely shell-less groups, such as: Aplysiinae Lamarck, 1809; Dolabellinae MacFarland, 1918. Genera include: *Aplysia, Dolabella, Dolabrifera, Notarchus, Syphonata*.

Aplysia depilans

GMELIN, 1791
European sea hare

D: 300mm. S: an extremely large sea slug with an internal, rudimentary, and exceptionally thin shell that is triangular in shape. O: growth lines and indistinct ribs. C: amber (on the inner side grayish-white with paler blotches). H: d1; shallow water, often in sea-grass meadows. W: KEL, LUS, WAFR. R: 1. NB: the photograph shows 2 mating sea slugs. The "ears" are clearly visible and account for the animal's name. Insert photograph: the shell (frontal view).

ORDER NOTASPIDEA

P. FISCHER, 1883

TYLODINOIDEA

J.E. GRAY 1847
This superfamily contains all members of No-taspidea with external shells. Found in warm and temperate maritime regions.

Tylodinidae

J.E. GRAY, 1847
parasol sea slugs

Flat, oval, cap-shaped shells with an asymmetric protoconch of one and a half whorls. The margin is not calcified and paper-thin. White with dark bands radiating from the apex. Genera: *Anidolyta, Tylodina.*

Umbraculidae

DALL, 1889
umbrella sea slugs

Oval, cap-shaped shells. Large animals, up to 300mm, only partially covered by the shell. Genera: *Spiricella, Umbraculum.*

Umbraculum umbraculum

(LIGHTFOOT, 1786)
great umbrella sea slug

D: animal up to 100mm, shell up to approx. 60mm. S: low, cap-shaped, covering only part of the animal. O: large growth lines and slight, radiating ribs. C: creamy white with radiating, tawny markings and bands. H: d1; sublittoral and slightly deeper water. W: CAR, INDP. R: 4.

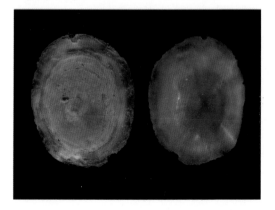

PLEUROBRANCHOIDEA

DE FÉRUSSAC, 1822
If present, the shells are completely internal. Carnivorous predators, preying on sea squirts, worms, and other mollusks. Some species have venom glands.

Pleurobranchidae

DE FÉRUSSAC, 1822
Small shells shaped like ears and covered by the mantle. One shell-bearing genus: *Pleuro-branchus.*

ORDER THECOSOMATA

DE BLAINVILLE, 1824
shell-bearing pteropod sea slugs

These are planktonic sea slugs that feed on micro-plankton and are often found in large groups in the open sea. The shell is either reduced, absent, or replaced by a secondary shell-like structure (a pseudoconch). The foot's parapodial lobes are fin-like, reminiscent to some of butterfly wings. Worldwide distribution.

Cavoliniidae

J.E. GRAY, 1850
thecosome pteropods, cavolines, clios, etc.

The shell is not spirally wound but bilaterally symmetrical, often funnel-shaped. Several subfamilies: Cavoliniinae J.E. Gray, 1850; Clioniinae Van der Spoel, 1967; Cuvierininae Van der Spoel, 1967. Only a few genera: *Cavolinia, Clio, Creseis, Cuvierina, Diacria, Hyalocyclis, Styliola.*

Cymbuliidae

CANTRAINE, 1841
A pseudoconch made of conchiolin is present instead of a calcareous shell. Two subfamilies: Cymbuliinae Cantraine, 1841; Glebinae Van der Spoel, 1967. Genera: *Corolla, Cymbulia, Gleba.*

Limacinidae

DE BLAINVILLE, 1823
counterclockwise pteropods

Counterclockwise, paper-thin, top-shaped shells. Genus: *Limacina.*

Peraclididae

TESCH, 1913
Counterclockwise shells with approximately five whorls and a distinctive, beak-like projection at the base of the aperture. Genera: *Peracle, Procymbulia*.

ORDER PULMONATA

CUVIER & DE BLAINVILLE, 1814
pulmonate gastropods

Principally land and freshwater snails with many dozens of superfamilies. Only a few of these have representatives in coastal habitats. The mantle cavity is transformed into a primitive lung containing a network of blood vessels. In aquatic species this is partly replaced by secondary gills.

SUBORDER SYSTELLOMMATOPHORA

PILSBRY, 1948
A mollusk group with retractable tentacles, or feelers, at the ends of which are eyes.

OTINOIDEA

H. & A. ADAMS 1855

Otinidae

H. & A. ADAMS, 1855
otinas

Micro-mollusks with very small, ear-shaped shells. The final whorl is a very wide, rounded oval and contains virtually the whole shell. The columella is curved, merging with the apertural margin. These snails live in the intertidal zone on rocks, weed, and amid acorn barnacles. One genus: *Otina*, occurring on the southwest coast of Great Britain and along the northern coast of France.

SUBORDER BASOMMATOPHORA

KEFERSTEIN, 1864
Eyes at the base of the tentacles, or feelers, and not at the ends. Shells are spire-shaped, dish-shaped, or discoid. Brackish and freshwater habitats.

AMPHIBOLOIDEA

J.E. GRAY, 1840
The snails in this superfamily breathe through the walls of the water-filled pulmonary cavity lined with blood vessels. Conical shells with convex, slightly raised apical whorls. Umbilicus present. Corneous operculum. No jaws. No gills.

Amphibolidae

J.E. GRAY, 1840
Rounded shells with a large final whorl. Some species found in brackish water at river mouths. Indo-Pacific region. Genera: *Amphibola, Salinator*.

SIPHONARIOIDEA

J.E. GRAY, 1840
Diminished gills found at the back of the pulmonary cavity. The animals live in the littoral and can withstand being out of water. Found in tropical and temperate maritime regions.

Siphonariidae

J.E. GRAY, 1840
marine false limpets

Cap-shaped (limpet-like) shells with radial ribs. Colored interior. The muscle scar is horseshoe-shaped and interrupted on the right by a siphonal groove. The animals live just like the limpets that they resemble in the intertidal zone, attached to rocks. Only a few genera, including *Siphonaria, Williamia*.

SUBORDER EUPULMONATA

(SENSU HASZPRUNAR & HUBER, 1990)
Snails with shells wound normally or shell-less. Eyes at the base of the tentacles. A contractible respiratory aperture is present. The animals are mostly terrestrial.

INFRAORDER ACTOPHILA

DALL, 1885

ELLOBIOIDEA

L. PFEIFFER, 1854
Resident in coastal areas and estuarine water. Some species are wholly marine, living on mud flats or under rocks. Mostly in warmer maritime regions.

Ellobiidae

L. PFEIFFER, 1854
coffee beans and others

Elongated cone-shaped to fusiform shells. Aperture usually contains folds and teeth, especially on the columella (inner lip). Several subfamilies: Ellobiinae H. & A. Adams, 1854; Pedipedinae P. Fischer & Crosse, 1880; Pythiinae Odhner, 1925. Various genera, including: *Auriculinella, Cassidula, Creedonia, Ellobium, Laemodonta, Melampus, Myosotella, Ovatella, Pedipes, Pythia, Tralia.*

Ovatella myosotis

(DRAPARNAUD, 1801)
European coffee bean

10mm. S: thin-shelled with relatively convex whorls. Pointed apex. Oval aperture. 3 toothed folds on inner lip. No umbilicus. O: smooth, growth lines only. C: amber to purple. H: d1; on mud flats, salt marshes, waterside plants, under driftwood and seaweed washed ashore, etc. W: KEL, LUS. R: 1. NB: the species *O. denticulate* (Montagu, 1803) is beige and has a number of teeth on either side of the aperture (photograph, right).

INFRAORDER
TRIMUSCULIFORMES

MINICHEV & STAROBOGATOV, 1975

TRIMUSCULOIDEA

ZILCH, 1959
Cap-shaped (limpet-like) shells with radial ribs.

Trimusculidae

ZILCH, 1959
Solid, low, circular to oval, cap-shaped shells with the apex away from the center. The apex is often eroded. A siphonal groove within to the right. Warm maritime regions, intertidal zone, attached to rocks. One genus: *Trimusculus*.

11. Class Bivalvia

LINNAEUS, 1758
bivalves

The bivalves or Bivalvia, formerly also referred to by the names Lamellibranchia De Blainville, 1824, and Pelecypoda Goldfuss, 1820, constitute the second largest group of mollusks after slugs and snails (Gastropoda). All of its species are aquatic. The shells are mostly bilaterally symmetrical (equivalved), being composed of two valves that contain the entire animal. The shape of the shells varies considerably and can be circular, ovoid, oval, wedge-shaped (sphenoid), beaked, or scabbard-like. The shell anterior and posterior often differ and may range from rounded (truncated) to tapered. In most cases, the valves fit exactly together. However, species occur with gaping valves or valves that are differently shaped (inequivalved) where one valve may be extended, gripping the edge of the other. Furthermore, the valves may have different degrees of curvature. The latter depends on the way the animals live: lying on one side (Pectinidae) or growing on one side attached to the substrate (Chamidae, Ostreidae, Spondylidae). The ligament that binds the valves is made up of layers that exert different degrees of force when closing the valves. Externally they pull, internally they push. Respiration is performed by gills. There is no radula. Food is filtered from the water. This is often through short or (very) long inhalant siphons.

Recent practice has been to divide Bivalvia into five subclasses: Anomalodesmata Dall, 1889; Heterodonta Neumayr, 1884; Palaeoheterodonta Newell, 1965; Protobranchia Pelseneer, 1889; Pteriomorphia Beurlen, 1944.

Just as for Gastropoda, the superfamilies have been arranged taxonomically and the families alphabetically.

SUBCLASS PROTOBRANCHIA

PELSENEER, 1889

ORDER NUCULOIDA

DALL, 1889
All species have a taxodont hinge, meaning many short, evenly sized, chevron-shaped teeth that radiate outward in a row either side of the umbo. Equivalved. The interior is nacreous or porcelain-like and glossy. There are two equal adductor muscle scars.

NUCULOIDEA

J.E. GRAY, 1824
The shell valves are usually triangular and rounded. The umbones project quite far back. No siphons. Nacreous interior. Two muscle scars, no embayment in the pallial line. Locomotory foot. Food collection (micro-organisms and particles) by means of labial palps (paired ciliated flaps on either side of the mouth).

Nuculidae

J.E. GRAY, 1824
nut clams

Oval to slanted, triangular shells. Smooth surface or concentric sculpture. Buried in mud or sand (fine or coarse) below the surface of the substrate. Using their strong foot, the animals plow through the substrate in their search for food. Worldwide occurrence, with most species found in fairly to extremely deep water. Two subfamilies: Nuculinae J.E. Gray, 1824 and Nuculominae Maxwell, 1988. Various genera, including: *Acila, Austronucula, Condylonucula, Ennucula, Lamellinucula, Leionucula, Linucula, Nucula, Nuculoma, Pronucula.*

Acila divaricata

(HINDS, 1843)
northern divaricated nut clam

D: 25mm. S: thick-shelled and triangular. Does not gape. The umbones curve over. Taxodont hinge with a row of teeth to the anterior and posterior of the triangular ligament cleft. No pallial sinus. O: exterior has a herringbone ornament of V-shaped, radial ribs and grooves (chevron sculpture). Finely crenulated shell margin. C: grayish-white with an amber periostracum that partly abrades following the surface relief of the shell. Very glossy nacreous interior. H: d2–3; in somewhat deeper water between 50 and over 150m. W: INDP, JAP; China, Japan. R: 3. NB: all species from the genus *Acila* have chevron sculpture.

Ennucula superba

(HEDLEY, 1902)
superb nut clam

D: 20mm. S: solid, oval shell. Not gaping. Umbones curve over. Taxodont hinge with relatively defined teeth and an internal ligament. No pallial sinus. O: smooth. Crenulated shell margin. C: tawny with a very glossy, beige periostracum. Very glossy, nacreous interior. H: d1–2; sublittoral and deeper, buried in sandy substrate. W: AUS. R: 2.

Ennucula tenuis

(MONTAGU, 1808)
thin nut clam

D: 10mm. S: thin-shelled, oval. The umbones are relatively convex and clearly project beyond the shell. Taxodont hinge but with fewer teeth than the previous species. O: exterior virtually smooth, slight growth lines only. Shell margin not crenulated. C: yellowish-white with a very glossy, golden yellow to olive-green periostracum. H: d2–3; sublittoral and deeper, 25m and below. W: ALE, ARC, CAL, KEL, LUS. R: 2.

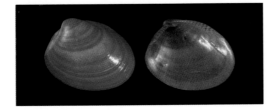

Nucula nitidosa

WINCKWORTH, 1930
triangular nut clam

D: 13mm. S: solid, triangular shell. Not gaping. Umbones bent over. Taxodont hinge with a row of teeth to the anterior and posterior of the umbones. Internal ligament in a triangular ligament cleft. No pallial sinus. O: smooth or has slight, radial grooves and concentric growth lines. Finely crenulated shell margin. C: greenish-yellow, usually in radial bands. Very glossy, nacreous interior. H: d1–2; in fine sand or muddy substrate just under the surface. From sublittoral to deeper water. W: KEL, LUS, WAFR. R: 1.

Nucula nucleus

(LINNAEUS, 1758)
oval nut clam

D: 14mm. S: solid, oval shell. Not gaping. Umbones bent over. Taxodont hinge with internal ligament. No pallial sinus. O: slight radial grooves, shell margin crenulated. C: cream to grayish-white. Periostracum brown to russet and matt (very slight sheen). No radial colored bands. Glossy nacreous interior. H: d1–2; sublittoral and deeper to over 150m. W: KEL, LUS, WAFR. R: 2.

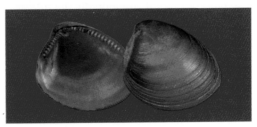

Pristiglomidae

SANDERS & ALLEN, 1973
miniature nut clams

Micro-mollusks (1–3mm). Circular. Deep sea between 2000 and 5000m (Baltic Sea and northern Atlantic Ocean). Two genera: *Microgloma* and *Pristigloma*.

NUCULANOIDEA

H. & A. ADAMS, 1858
Elongated oval shells, extending posteriorly into a "beak." No nacre within. With siphons and a pallial sinus. Worldwide distribution, especially in deep water.

Lametilidae

ALLEN & SANDERS, 1973

Micro-mollusks from the deep sea. Internal ligament. Hinge has two long hinge plates. Atlantic Ocean. Genera: *Lametila, Prelametila*.

Malletiidae

H. & A. ADAMS, 1858

Oval or elongated shells, posteriorly truncated. No nacre. Exterior ligament. Expanded hinge margins. With siphons. Distributed throughout deep water in the northeastern Atlantic Ocean. Genera include: *Malletia, Malletiella*.

Neilonellidae

SCHILEYKO, 1989

Thick shells, oval and inflated, slightly beaked posteriorly. Ligament external or internal. With siphons. Found in deep water of the Pacific and Atlantic Ocean. Genera include *Neilonella, Protonucula*.

Nuculanidae

H. & A. ADAMS, 1858
beaked nut clams

The posterior of the shell valves are elongated or rounded off into a "beak." Curved hinge teeth. Found worldwide in warm and cold maritime regions. The animals live partly buried in sandy substrates with the narrow side of the sell protruding just above the surface. Unlike ordinary nut clams, these animals have two short merged siphons that are used to suck in water and food particles. Unusual labial palps with long, extended feelers also help in the collection of food. Divided into subfamilies: Ledellinae Allen, 1978; Nuculaninae H. & A. Adams, 1858; Spinulae Allen & Sanders, 1982. Only a few genera, including: *Leda, Ledella, Nuculana, Spinula*.

Nuculana illepida

IREDALE, 1929
coarse nut clam

D: 25mm. S: elongated shell. Upper shell angular. Lower shell rounded. Posterior pointed like a beak. Umbones almost in the center. Pallial line with a clear pallial sinus. O: dense concentric ribs, sometimes diminishing slightly at the margins. Lower margin not crenulated. C: grayish-white or white with glossy, olive-green to beige periostracum. Interior white without

nacre. H: d1–2; sublittoral and deeper in sandy substrates. W: AUS. R: 1.

Nuculana minuta

(MÜLLER, 1776)
ribbed nut clam

D: 19mm. S: elongated, rounded shell. Posteriorly pointed. The umbones are centered. Clear pallial sinus. O: strong concentric ribs. Lower margin not crenulated. C: chalky white with an amber to pale green periostracum. Interior white with a slight nacreous sheen. H: d2–3; sublittoral to deeper water. W: ARC, KEL, LUS. R: 2–3.

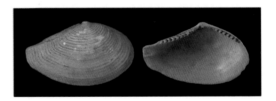

Phaseolidae

SCARLATO & STAROBOGATOV, 1971

Micro-mollusks (1mm). Valves are obliquely oval and smooth. Hinge has a few evenly interspaced teeth. Found in the Mediterranean Sea, North Sea, and Atlantic Ocean. Genus: *Phaseolus*.

Sareptidae

A. ADAMS, 1860

Elongated oval shells, posterior extended into a "beak." Slightly gaping. A row of hinge teeth broken by the ligamental pad. Deep pallial sinus. With siphons. Wide distribution in both warm and cold maritime regions. Several subfamilies: Sareptinae A. Adams, 1860; Yoldiellinae Allen, 1978; Yoldiinae Habe, 1977. Includes the genera: *Adranella, Megayoldia, Portlandia, Yoldia, Yoldiella*.

Siliculidae

ALLEN & SANDERS, 1973

Micro-mollusks. Elongated oval, compressed on one side, posteriorly truncated, and gaping. Small umbo, barely projecting. Internal ligament. Long teeth on both sides of the hinge plate. With siphons. Found in the Atlantic Ocean in deep water. Includes the genera: *Propeleda, Silicula*.

Tindariidae

VERRILL & BUSH, 1897

Rounded, triangular valves, smooth or with concentric ribs. Elevated umbones, centrally positioned and pointing slightly forward. No siphons. Found in deep water in the western part of the Atlantic Ocean, Caribbean, eastern Pacific Ocean. Genus: *Tindaria*.

ORDER SOLEMYOIDA

DALL, 1889

Large gills, diminished labial palps, and an extended foot. Live symbiotically with chemo-autotrophic (sulfur-oxidizing) bacteria.

SUBORDER SOLEMYINA

DALL, 1889

SOLEMYOIDEA

J.E. GRAY, 1840

Solemyidae

J.E. GRAY, 1840
awning clams

Thin-shelled, cigar-shaped clams with rounded extremities. Umbo located quite far to the rear. Very glossy periostracum, extending beyond the shell margin, and usually frayed. Ligament far to the rear. Hinge plate without teeth. No nacre. Shallow to deep water, buried in sand. Found in both warm and cold maritime regions. Few genera: *Acharax, Solemya*.

Solemya australis

LAMARCK, 1818
Australian awning clam

D: 50mm. S: thin-shelled, extremely fragile, cigar-shaped clam. O: surface has quite low, radiating ribs. Lower margin smooth and not crenulated. C: yellowish-white below the periostracum, sometimes with dark bands. Extremely glossy periostracum, red to chestnut brown, extending well beyond the margin (but often frayed). H: d1; sublittoral, in sandy substrates to a depth of approx 10m. W: AUS. R: 1.

Solemya togata

(POLI, 1795)
toga awning clam

D: 55mm. S: thin-shelled, fragile, cigar-shaped clam. O: quite low, radiating ribs. Lower margin not crenulated. C: yellowish-gray below periostracum with dark bands. Extremely glossy periostracum, amber to dark brown, sometimes almost black. H: d1–2; sublittoral and deeper. W: LUS, ZAFR. R: 3.

SUBORDER NUCINELLINA

SCARLATO & STAROBOGATOV, 1971

231

MANZANELLOIDEA

CHRONIC, 1952

Nucinellidae

H.E. VOKES, 1956
Micro-mollusks from the deep sea. Oblique oval valves. Smooth or with concentric grooves. Exterior ligament. Wide, short hinge plate with 4–8 thick cardinal (central) teeth and a long lateral tooth posteriorly. Worldwide. Only a few genera: *Huxleyia, Nucinella*.

SUBCLASS PTERIOMORPHIA

BEURLEN, 1944
Bivalves that can be attached to the substrate (byssate), burrowed into a substrate, or free-swimming. Often inequivalved. Byssate species do not use the foot for burrowing and, instead, have a byssus gland that produces byssus threads for anchorage. Poorly developed siphons. Worldwide distribution.

ORDER ARCOIDA

STOLICZKA, 1871
Has a taxodont hinge containing a large number of roughly even teeth. Interior not nacreous. No pallial sinus due to the absence of siphons. Often byssate, although some groups are not.

ARCOIDEA

LAMARCK, 1809
Usually equivalved and thick-shelled. Oval to trapezoid, often with radial ribs. A flat ligament shelf lies between the widely separated umbones. The hinge plate is straight. Muscle scars are roughly equal. Periostracum often fibrous or hairy.

Arcidae

LAMARCK, 1809
ark shells

Inequilateral with a wide ligamental area between the umbones. Wide distribution, occurring especially in the intertidal zone and upper parts of the sublittoral. Divided into subfamilies. Species from the subfamily Anadarinae Reinhart, 1935 mostly burrow into sand or sediment. Species from the subfamily Arcinae Lamarck, 1809 live attached to a hard substrate by byssus threads. Occasionally this pertains exclusively to their juvenile stage. Various genera, including *Anadara, Arca, Barbatia, Bathyarca, Senilia, Trisidos.*

Anadara floridana

CONRAD, 1869
cut-ribbed ark

D: 12mm. S: thick-shelled, inflated shell. O: many narrow, evenly spaced radial ribs. C: amber with a velvety, brownish-black periostracum. Interior white. H: d1–2; sublittoral and slightly deeper water. W: CAR, VIR; southeastern United States and the Antilles. R: 3.

Anadara grandis

(BRODERIP & SOWERBY, 1829)
grand ark

D: 100mm. S: very thick-shelled and heavy. Inflated umbones. O: wide, low ribs. C: grayish-white, interior white. Thick, brownish-black periostracum. H: d1; mangroves, buried in black mud. W: PAN; Mexico to Peru. R: 2.

Arca imbricata

BRUGUIÈRE, 1789
mossy ark

D: 75mm. S: oblong, gaping shell. Very inflated. A very wide ligamental area between the umbones. O: a clear keel runs from the umbo to the posterior lower margin. Fine, closely packed, granulose ribs. C: russet with white. Tawny, fibrous periostracum. H: d1. W: CAR. R: 1.

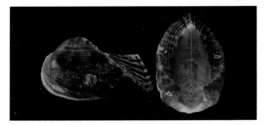

Arca zebra

SWAINSON, 1833
Atlantic turkey wing

D: 70mm. S: thick-shelled, elongated, gaping. Relatively inflated. Long, dead-straight hinge line. O: slight keel toward lower rear. Rounded radial ribs, often diminishing somewhat. C: white with a zebra pattern of reddish-orange stripes and markings. H: d1; sublittoral on reefs and along rocky coasts. W: CAR; also Bermuda. R: 1. NB: *A. noae* Linnaeus, 1758 – Noah's ark – is similar but its zebra striping is less defined and the species is limited to the Celtic and Lusitanian regions.

Barbatia amygdalumtostum

(RÖDING, 1798)
almond ark

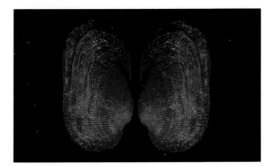

D: 35mm. S: solid, oval shell. Not particularly inflated. O: fine radial ribs crossed by concentric ribs. C: amber with a dark brown, tough, fibrous, and hairy periostracum. H: d1; sublittoral, reefs and rocky coasts. W: INDP. R: 2.

Barbatia barbata

(LINNAEUS, 1758)
European bearded ark

D: 60mm. S: elongated oval shell, irregular outline. Quite flattened. O: fine radial and concentric ribs create a lattice sculpture. C: orange-brown with white. Dark brown periostracum with fibrous hairs. H: d1; littoral, rocky coasts. W: LUS. R: 1.

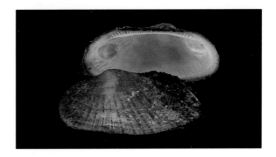

Trisidos semitorta

(LAMARCK, 1819)
half-propellor ark

D: 75mm. S: a rounded, triangular shell, twisted to one side in the center. O: a slight keel runs from the umbo to the posterior lower margin. Fine radial and concentric ribs create lattice sculpture. C: chalky white to yellow, interior apricot. Dark brown, fibrous periostracum. H: d1; sublittoral. W: AUS, INDP, JAP. R: 2. NB: the sideways torsion shown is also present in *Trisodos tortuosa*.

Trisidos tortuosa

(LINNAEUS, 1758)
propellor ark

D: 100mm. S: a distinctively shaped, triangular shell, twisted in the center. O: a strong keel from the umbo to the posterior lower margin. Fine radial ribs crossed by even finer, concentric ribs, creating lattice sculpture. C: chalky white to grayish-yellow. Brownish-black, fibrous periostracum. H: d1; shallow water in the sublittoral. W: AUS, INDP, JAP. R: 3.

Cucullaeidae

STEWART, 1930

Thick-shelled and trapezoid with dense ribs. Left valve overhangs slightly. Straight hinge plate with short cardinal (central) teeth and longer, oblique lateral teeth. Indo-Pacific region. One genus: *Cucullaea*.

Noetiidae

STEWART, 1930
ark shells

Trapezoid shells with a straight hinge plate. Usually have densely radiating ribs. Shortened ligament found in a narrow area between the umbones. Found in the Indo-Pacific and Caribbean regions, the Mediterranean Sea, and the North Sea. Divided into the subfamilies: Noetiinae Stewart, 1930 and Striarcinae Mac-Neil, 1938. Several genera, including: *Arcopsis*, *Noetia*, *Striarca*.

Striarca lactea

(LINNAEUS, 1758)
milk-white ark

D: 18mm. S: solid, oval to rectangular shell. Umbones out of central alignment. Ligament in exterior ligament cleft just under the umbones. O: fine, even lattice sculpture. C: creamy white or white. Dark brown, coarse, and fibrous periostracum. H: d1–2; sublittoral and deeper, attached within rock crevices. W: KEL, LUS. R: 1.

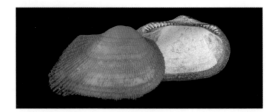

Parallelodontidae

DALL, 1898
Oval or trapezoid. Slanted hinge teeth. Mostly fossil species with a few modern-day species in the western Atlantic Ocean and in the Pacific Ocean. Genera: *Paragrammatodon, Porterius*.

LIMOPSOIDEA

DALL, 1895
Circular to oblique oval shells, sometimes with radiating ribs. A curved taxodont hinge. Equally sized muscle scars. Periostracum often fibrous and hairy. No siphons.

Glycymerididae

NEWTON, 1916
bittersweet clams

Thick-shelled, usually circular or oval, and sometimes slightly oblique. Smooth or with radial ribs. Creamy white or brown, several species having marbled, russet coloration and a glossy porcelaneous layer on the interior. Internal ligament. Curved hinge plate with strong teeth on either side. Found in the sublittoral of warm seas. The animals live buried in sediment or sand just below the surface. Some species are edible. Only a few genera, including: *Axinola, Glycymeris, Melaxinaea, Tucetona*.

Glycymeris albolineata

(LISCHKE, 1872)
white-lined bittersweet

D: 75mm. S: thick-shelled and round. Inflated, prominent umbo in the center. O: very low radial ribs, actually composed of several finer ribs. Concentric growth lines cross these to create a delicate lattice effect. C: yellowish-gray with a hint of purple. Sometimes paler, or white, bands. H: d1; to 20m. W: JAP. R: 1.

Glycymeris bimaculata

(POLI, 1795)
two-spotted bittersweet

D: 115mm. S: very thick-shelled, heavy, and round. Wide hinge plate. O: very low, radial sculpture. C: light brown, often with dark brown, concentric bands. H: d1; coarse and fine sand. W: LUS, WAFR. R: 3.

Glycymeris glycymeris

(LINNAEUS, 1758)
common European bittersweet

D: 75mm. S: thick-shelled and circular. Umbo is central. Taxodont hinge. Crenulated lower margin. 2 muscle scars, no pallial sinus. O: very narrow radial riblets crossed by concentric growth lines create an exceptionally delicate lattice. C: cream, yellow, or orange with a marbled pattern of orange-red to purple dashes. Dark brown, velvety periostracum. H: d1–2; burrow in substrate of coarse shell fragments close to surface. W: KEL, LUS. R: 1. NB: often eaten.

Glycymeris undata

(LINNAEUS, 1758)
Atlantic bittersweet

D: 50mm. S: a round shell, dorsally slightly angular. O: fine radial ribs strongest toward the lower margin. C: white with russet, marble coloration. Brownish-black, fibrous periostracum. H: d1; sublittoral. W: CAR, VIR; southeastern United States to Brazil. R: 1.

Tucetona pectunculus

(LINNAEUS, 1758)
comb bittersweet

D: 50mm. S: thick-shelled, almost circular shell. Wide hinge plate with clear, if relatively few, teeth. O: up to 16 broadly radiating, low ribs. C: creamy white with purplish-brown and golden orange bands. H: d1; shallow water. W: INDP. R: 1.

Limopsidae

DALL, 1895

Circular to oblique oval shells, often with radial ribs. Internal ligament. Hinge plate in the center with a triangular resilifer. The anterior muscle scar is slightly smaller. The periostracum is often fibrous and hairy. Found in cold and temperate seas. Only a few genera, including: *Crenulilimopsis, Limopsis*.

235

Philobryidae

F. BERNARD, 1897

Oval to oblong shells. Ligament lies in a ligament cleft in the hinge plate between two raised areas. Without teeth (genera *Cosa* and *Philobrya*) or with additional taxodont teeth (*Cratis* and *Lissarca*). Found in warm seas from the intertidal zone to the deep sea.

ORDER MYTILIDA

DE FÉRUSSAC, 1822

Equivalved shells without hinge teeth. Muscle scars vary in size. Exterior ligament along the anterior half of the dorsal side. No siphons. Filamentous gills. The animals live either attached to a substrate by byssus threads or are unattached.

Mytilidae

RAFINESQUE, 1815

mussels

Elongated or oblique, triangular shells with a pointed anterior and an expanded, rounded posterior. Equivalved. Umbones often found far forward. Smooth or with concentric stripes. Some species have radial ribs. Brown or black periostracum, often flaky or hairy. Interior may be nacreous. Only a small anterior muscle scar, or it may even be absent. An enlarged foot with a byssus gland that produces its anchorage threads. Found in all maritime regions from the intertidal zone and sublittoral to the deep sea next to hydrothermal vents (genus *Bathymodiolus*). The genus *Lithophaga* lives in crevices in soft limestone that it creates through acidic secretions. Various species are edible. Divided into subfamilies: Bathymodiolinae Kenk & Wilson, 1985; Crenellinae J.E. Gray, 1840; Lithophaginae H. & A. Adams, 1857; Modiolinae Keen, 1958; Mytilinae Rafinesque, 1815. Various genera, including: *Adula, Amygdalum, Brachydontes, Crenella, Gregariella, Idasola, Lithophaga, Modiolarca, Modiolula, Modiolus, Musculus, Myoforceps, Mytilaster, Mytilus, Perna, Rhomboidella*.

Modiolarca subpicta

(CANTRAINE, 1835)

marbled mussel

D: 20mm. S: thin-shelled and very inflated. O: radial grooves radiating from the umbo to the front and back with a smooth area in the center. Finely crenulated hinge plate. C: yellowish-white or orange, often with marbled coloration.

Glossy pale green periostracum. Interior has a faint sheen. H: d1; attached to rocks in the sublittoral. The animals frequently nestle in the mantle cavity of tunicates (sea squirts). W: KEL, LUS. R: 2.

Modiolus barbatus

(LINNAEUS, 1758)

bearded horse mussel

D: 65mm. S: elongated, triangular shell. The dorsal margin makes a clear angle with the lower (ventral) margin. The umbo side is more convex than the posterior side. The brownish-gray periostracum has long, fibrous hairs even in mature specimens. O: strong growth lines, otherwise smooth. C: russet. Glossy mauve interior. H: d1–2; sublittoral and deeper, attached to rocks. W: KEL, LUS, WAFR. R: 1.

Modiolus micropterus

(DESHAYES, 1836)

winged horse mussel

D: 59mm. S: thin-shelled, elongated, and angular with a clear, rounded keel toward the posterior, creating a wing-like area that projects

above the umbo. O: strong growth lines. C: either white with a purple winged section or entirely orange-red. Densely hairy periostracum, although usually abraded. H: d1; sublittoral to 22m. W: INDP; Thailand. R: 3.

Modiolus modiolus

(LINNAEUS, 1758)
northern horse mussel

D: 170mm. S: a solid shell. Blunt umbones slightly distanced from the anterior margin. The shell is raised from the umbo to the posterior margin. External ligament. The tawny to black periostracum has short, fibrous hairs in juvenile specimens. O: irregular growth lines, otherwise smooth. C: violet, interior white or mauve. H: d1–2; sublittoral to a depth of a few hundred meters. On coarse sand or gravel where there is a strong current. W: ARC, CAL, KEL, LUS, JAP. R: 1.

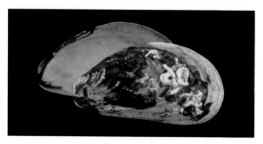

Musculus niger

(J.E. GRAY, 1824)
little black mussel

D: 55mm. S: elongated oval and fairly thin-shelled. The umbo projects just beyond the anterior margin. O: radiating grooves on the anterior and posterior sides of the shell, smooth in the center. C: immature specimens have a yellowish-green to dark brown periostracum. Underlying shell is pale lilac. Interior glossy white. H: d1–2; sublittoral to deep water, often byssate on sediment, sand, or rock. W: ARC, KEL, LUS. R: 3.

Mytilus edulis

LINNAEUS, 1758
common blue mussel

D: 95mm. S: an elongated triangle and fairly thin-shelled. The posterior margin is rounded, the lower margin is almost straight. The umbo is fully anterior. Hinge has small cardinal (central) teeth. Long, exterior ligament. One large and one small muscle scar within. O: smooth with strong growth lines. C: violet, amber to green, often with dark purple bands radiating from the umbo. Black periostracum. H: d1; attached to rocks and shells by byssus in the littoral and sublittoral. Forming great mussel beds in muddy locations. W: worldwide distribution in more temperate regions: ARC, CAL, JAP, KEL, LUS. R: 1. NB: well known and very widely eaten.

Mytilus galloprovincialis

LAMARCK, 1819
Mediterranean blue mussel

D: 100mm. S: looks like the common blue mussel but is squatter and triangular with a higher posterior. O: regular growth lines only. C: violet with a greenish-brown to black periostracum. H: d1; on rocks and shells in the littoral and sublittoral. W: KEL, LUS. R: 1.

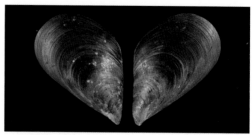

Perna picta

(VON BORN, 1780)
African mussel

D: 90mm. S: an elongated triangle and thin-shelled, yet robust. Umbo right at the front. O:

strong growth lines. C: russet, often in a V-shaped pattern below a pale to dark green periostracum. H: d1; littoral and sublittoral, attached to rocks. W: LUS, western Mediterranean Sea; WAFR. R: 1.

Perna viridis

(LINNAEUS, 1758)
green mussel

D: 50mm. S: elongated oval shell with rather blunt umbones. O: quite strong, regular growth lines. C: glossy with a bright greenish-yellow periostracum. H: d1; littoral and sublittoral, attached to various substrates. W: INDP. R: 1.

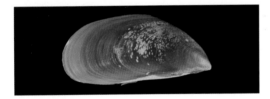

Septifer bilocularis

(LINNAEUS, 1758)
box mussel

D: 25mm. S: fairly thin-shelled and triangular. O: clearly checkered sculpture. C: orange to brown with a green to brown periostracum. H: d1; littoral, on rocks in muddy regions. W: INDP. R: 1.

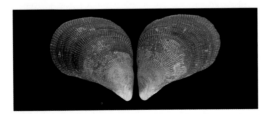

ORDER PTERIOIDA

NEWELL 1965

SUBORDER PTERIINA

NEWELL, 1965
The shell valves are often inequivalved and inequilateral. The hinge is without teeth and has an external ligament. There are no siphons.

PTERIOIDEA

J.E. GRAY, 1847
Usually inequivalved shells. The flat right valve often rests against a hard substrate attached by the byssus. The interior is nacreous, or shiny and porcelaneous. The hinge is essentially toothless (dysodont) with an external ligament. The anterior adductor muscle is diminished and sometimes entirely absent. There is a pallial line without a pallial sinus. Either byssate or unattached.

Isognomonidae

WOODRING, 1925
tree oyster

Inequivalved shells. Hinge line has ligament clefts. Shell margin has a notch for the byssus. Nacreous interior. Most familiar genus: *Isognomon*. Some species attach themselves to the aerial roots of mangroves.

Isognomon isognomon

(LINNAEUS, 1758)
Pacific tree oyster

D: 100mm. S: a very irregularly shaped shell. Quite flat, round, oval, or roughly hook-shaped. Hinge has very clear, strong grooves. O: flaky surface. C: purplish brown. Interior has silver-white nacre. H: d1; littoral and sublittoral attached to wood (trees), rocks, and any other hard substrate. W: INDP. R: 1.

Isognomon legumen

(GMELIN, 1791)
elongate tree oyster

D: 90mm. S: irregular shape, often oblong or curved. O: flaky surface. C: pale, yellowish-white. Up to half the interior has silver-gray nacre. H: d1; sublittoral. W: INDP. R: 1.

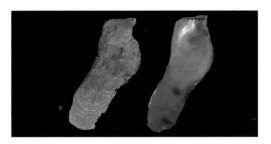

Isognomon perna

(LINNAEUS, 1767)
rayed tree oyster

D: 75mm. S: oval to round, flat or slightly domed shell. O: vague to defined, irregular ribs. C: amber, interior often paler. H: d1; shallow water of reefs. W: INDP. R: 1.

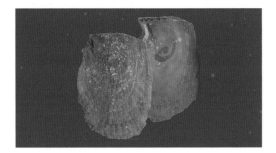

Malleidae

LAMARCK, 1819
hammer oysters

Bivalves with extraordinary shells, hammer or T-shaped, either with or without a bent "handle." The hinge plate is extended either side of the umbo and is without teeth. The roughly equivalved shells usually gape. Triangular ligamental pad. Found in warmer maritime regions. Only a few genera: *Malleus, Vulsella.*

Malleus albus

LAMARCK, 1819
white hammer oyster

D: 200mm. S: a robust, hammer-shaped shell. The valves of the "hammer" are often unequal. O: flaky surface. C: exterior pale yellow to white. Interior is dark blue to purple under the

umbo. The rest of the shell remains pale. H: d1–2; sublittoral and deeper. W: INDP. R: 1.

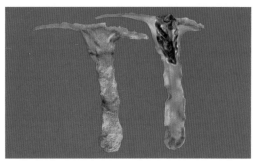

Malleus malleus

(LINNAEUS, 1758)
common hammer oyster

D: 200mm. S: thick-shelled and hammer-shaped. "Handle" may be bent to one side. O: flaky surface. C: violet or mauve. Interior is equally dark, often with a strong nacreous sheen. H: d1; shallow water in the sublittoral. W: INDP. R: 1.

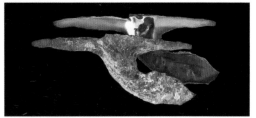

Vulsella vulsella

(LINNAEUS, 1758)
sponge finger oyster

D: 60mm. S: thin-shelled to robust. Usually elongated and rounded. A few hammer- or ear-like projections alongside the umbo, but sometimes these are absent. Ligament occupies a deep recess. O: very fine, dense scales, usually arranged in longitudinal ribs. Also has strong concentric ribbing. C: beige with violet markings and stripes. Interior partly nacreous (silver-gray). H: d1; shallow water, lives in sponges. W: INDP. R: 3.

Pteriidae

J.E. GRAY, 1847
pearl oysters, wing oysters

Oblique oval to semicircular shells. Wing-like projections on one or both sides of the straight hinge line (genus *Pteria*). Hinge plate has tooth-like calluses. The ligament is quite long and slightly depressed. The umbo is displaced toward the anterior. Interior has a thickly nacreous surface. One adductor muscle scar in the center. The genus *Pinctada* is particularly famous for its often extremely valuable pearls. Found in warmer maritime regions. A few genera: *Electroma, Pinctada, Pteria*.

Pinctada fucata

(GOULD, 1850)
Japanese pearl oyster or *Akoya*

D: 60mm. S: a solid, fairly flat, oval to round shell. The left valve is more convex. O: strong, flat scales that may be on radiating ribs. C: amber to russet, sometimes with a claret-colored sheen. Thickly nacreous interior. H: d1; sublittoral to 20m. W: INDP, JAP. R: 1. NB: produces valuable pearls.

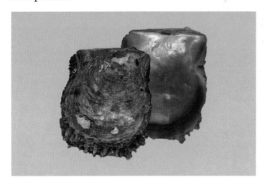

Pinctada margaritifera

(LINNAEUS, 1758)
black-lipped pearl oyster

D: 20mm. S: robust to thick-shelled. Round to oval shell, angular on one side. O: extremely flaky ribs that may bear low projections. C: exterior grayish-yellow with greenish-yellow stripes and markings around the umbo area. A rich, lustrous, silvery-white nacreous interior edged with a wide dark brown to black band. H: d1; to 30m. W: INDP. R: 1. NB: the most famous of the pearl oysters with the most beautiful, and most expensive, natural pearls.

Pteria colymbus

(RÖDING, 1798)
Atlantic wing oyster

D: 75mm. S: a solid, elongated oval shell with a long, wing-like projection from one side of the umbo. O: very low, flaky, concentric radial ribs and very slight, irregular longitudinal ribs. C: purplish-black, longitudinal ribs yellowish-white to apricot. H: d1; sublittoral. W: CAR, VIR; southeastern United States to Brazil. R: 2.

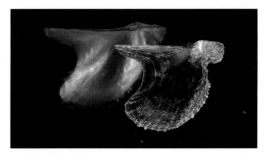

Pteria peasei

(DUNKER, 1872)
black wing oyster

D: 95mm. S: fairly thin-shelled. A convex, oval shell with a wing-like projection, ending in a very long point, that is longer than the shell itself. O: only strong, irregular, flaky growth lines. C: purplish-brown with amber and violet radial stripes. Interior has rich, lustrous, silvery-white nacre. H: d1. W: INDP. R: 1.

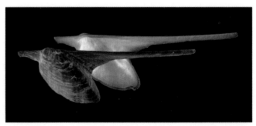

Pteria penguin

(RÖDING, 1798)
penguin wing oyster

D: 70mm. S: oblique oval shell with a long, wing-like projection from one side of the umbo. Projection on the other side is very small. O: very coarse, irregular growth lines. C: purplish-brown, markings sometimes mauve. Rich, lustrous nacre within. A very wide band around lower margin without nacre. H: d1–2; sublittoral and somewhat deeper water. W: INDP. R: 2.

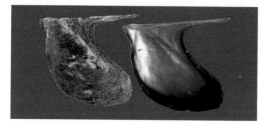

Pulvinitidae

STEPHENSON, 1941

Rounded, triangular shells without teeth but with long ligament clefts. Scaled shell surface. Right valve almost flat with a round notch below the ligament for the byssus. Found only around Australia. One genus: *Foramelina*.

SUBORDER PINNINA

WALLER, 1978

PINNOIDEA

LEACH, 1819

Pinnidae

LEACH, 1819
pen shells

Triangular, gaping shells ending in a long point. Nacreous interior. Ligament lies alongside the straight hinge line. Hinge without teeth. Has a byssal notch in the lower margin. Large shells up to approximately 800mm in size. The shells stand in the substrate with the point uppermost and are found in sheltered bays or are anchored by very tough byssus threads to a hard substrate. In warmer maritime regions from the shallows to slightly deeper water. Only a few genera, including: *Atrina, Pinna, Streptopinna*.

Pinna muricata

LINNAEUS, 1758
prickly pen shell

D: 150mm. S: thin-shelled. Elongated, triangular shell. Rounded or angular posterior end. O: low, radial ribs bearing hollow, scaly spines. A deeper groove in the center. C: purplish-brown (the point is often paler) to silvery-gray. H: d1; sublittoral. W: INDP, JAP; East Africa to Polynesia. R: 1.

Pinna nobilis

LINNAEUS, 1758
noble pen shell

D: 600mm. S: very elongated. Posterior end usually rounded. O: surface covered in fine or coarse scales (often abraded). No distinctive ribs. Interior has one horizontal groove. C: orange to claret. Amber scales. Yellowish-gray periostracum. H: d1; sublittoral to 25m. W: KEL, LUS, WAFR. R: 2. NB: items such as gloves were once woven from the strong byssus threads.

ORDER LIMOIDA

WALLER, 1978

Only one adductor muscle. The animals do not anchor to a substrate. Only contains the family Limidae.

LIMOIDEA

RAFINESQUE, 1815

Limidae

RAFINESQUE, 1815
file clams, lima shells

Equivalved, obliquely oval shells. The shell valves are generally convex, usually, but not always, gaping at the sides. Small, ear-shaped appendages (auricles) either side of the umbo on the hinge line. Smooth or toothed hinge line. Exterior generally coarse with radiating ribs or scaled. The shells are not colored: cream or white. The mantle margin has tentacles and some species have eyes. File clams can swim. Some species make nests on the ocean floor of stones and shell fragments, which are glued together with an adhesive substance secreted by the byssus gland. The animals are usually orange-red in color and are luminous in the dark. Found in both cold and warmer maritime regions. Several genera, including: *Acesta, Ctenoides, Lima, Limaria, Limatula, Limea*.

Acesta excavata

(FABRICIUS, 1779)
European giant lima

D: 100mm. S: a robust, oval shell. Auricles very asymmetrical, the smallest is barely visible. O: a great many very fine, low ribs. Indistinct in the center. C: white. H: d1–2; to greater depths. W: KEL, LUS; Norway to the Azores. R: 4.

Acesta rathbuni

(BARTSCH, 1913)
Rathbun's giant lima

D: 150mm. S: thin-shelled yet still quite robust. Oval. Auricles very asymmetrical, the smallest is barely visible. O: smooth surface, concentric growth lines only. C: yellowish-white to lemon yellow. Glossy, silvery-white interior with a yellow sheen. H: d2–3; deep water. W: INDP; the Philippines. R: 3. NB: fished in large numbers around Bohol in the Philippines.

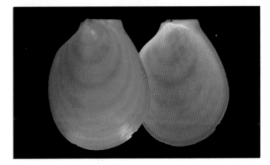

Ctenoides scabra

VON BORN, 1778
flame or fire scallop

D: 55mm. S: solid and oval with rounded sides. O: a great many fine, dense radial ribs covered in short, scaly spicules. C: its brown coloration is due to its strong, tawny periostracum. Below this it is white. H: d1; sublittoral under rocks. W: CAR. R: 2.

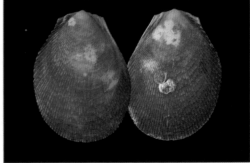

Lima lima

(LINNAEUS, 1758)
spiny lima

D: 40mm. S: thin-shelled and obliquely oval. Asymmetrical, small auricles. O: strong, wide ribs with narrower grooves in between. Ribs covered in scaly spicules. C: white. H: d1–2; sublittoral and deeper water. W: CAR. R: 2.

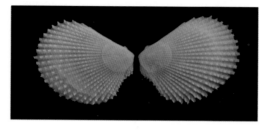

Lima zealandica

SOWERBY, 1876
New Zealand lima

D: 50mm. S: thick-shelled and obliquely oval. Asymmetrical auricles. O: up to 18 wide, low ribs with narrower grooves in between. Occasional scaly projections on the ribs. C: off-white, often with a hint of brownish-gray. H: d1–2; deep water to 150m. W: AUS; New Zealand. R: 4.

Limaria fragilis

(GMELIN, 1791)
fragile lima

D: 25mm. S: thin-shelled and very slanted. Auricles almost symmetrical. O: wavy, uneven, narrow ribs. C: white. Beige periostracum. H: d1; sublittoral. W: INDP, JAP. R: 1.

Limaria tuberculata

(OLIVI, 1792)
inflated lima

D: 20mm. S: thin-shelled, elongated, and slanted with a short, wing-like projection on either side of the umbo. Strongly gaping valves. Ligament is half external, half internal in a triangular ligament pit. O: narrow ribs radiate from the umbo covered in subtle scales. C: white with an amber periostracum. H: d1–2; at depths of between 10 and 200m on sandy sediment with gravel or shell fragments. W: LUS, WAFR. R: 2.

ORDER OSTREOIDA

DE FÉRUSSAC, 1822

SUBORDER OSTREINA

DE FÉRUSSAC, 1822
Extremely varied, inequivalved shells (pleurothetic—one valve is less convex than the other). A valve is usually cemented to the substrate by a calcareous secretion. The foot and byssus are diminished. The valves have scales, ribs, ridges, and nodules made up of calcite lamellae. The anterior adductor muscle is reduced or entirely absent. The posterior adductor muscle is located centrally and creates a comma-shaped scar on the shell.

OSTREOIDEA

RAFINESQUE, 1815
Essentially toothless hinge (dysodont). Triangular ligamental pad below the umbo in a special pit. Lower margin of the shell often has locking nodules (right valve) and pits (left valve). Unlike Pterioidea, Ostreoidea shells are usually cemented by the left valve.

Gryphaeidae

VYALOV, 1936
Oval shells. The hinge of both valves contains short, tubular locking nodules (chomata). These are anterior and posterior to the ligament. One circular muscle scar lying just off-center. A few genera: *Hyotissa, Neopycnodonte, Parahyotissa, Pycnodonte.*

Hyotissa hyotis

(LINNAEUS, 1758)
honeycomb oyster

D: 150mm. S: a solid, oval shell. Both valves are quite convex. O: up to 12 rounded, pleated ribs bearing hollow scales in the form of spicules. C: magenta to violet-brown. Interior yellowish-white to brown. H: d1; sublittoral, attached to hard substrates. W: CAR, INDP. R: 2.

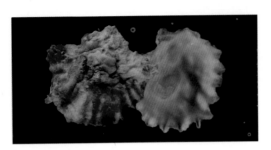

Ostreidae

RAFINESOUE, 1815
true oysters

Irregular shell valves. Oval, pear-shaped, or oblong. The more convex left valve, on which the animals lie attached, often has several rather more strongly pleated ribs, while the flatter right valve has more scaly, lamellose structures. Occasionally, both sides exhibit roughly the same ornament. One muscle scar in the center of the valve, usually comma-shaped. The foot is reduced in size. Found in temperate and warmer maritime regions in the littoral and sublittoral. Also sometimes found in slightly deeper water. Divided into three subfamilies: Crassostreinae Scarluto & Starobogatov, 1979; Lophinae Vyalov, 1936; Ostreinae Rafinesque, 1815. Several genera, including: *Alectryonella, Crassostrea, Dendostrea, Lopha, Ostrea, Saccostrea, Striostrea.*

Crassostrea gigas

(THUNBERG, 1793)
Pacific king or *Japanese oyster*

D: 230mm. S: thick-shelled, irregular shape. Usually oblong. Left valve fuller than the right. Ligament has a thick, internal ligamental pad and a short, external ligament. No hinge teeth. Slight beading on either side of the umbo. O: irregular, scabrous ribs on the fuller valve. Flat valve has flaky lamellae. C: amber to magenta with lilac markings and stripes. Muscle scar lilac or brown. H: d1–2; littoral and deeper with

one or both valves cemented to a hard substrate. W: ARC, ALE, AUS, CAL, JAP, KEL, LUS, WAFR; cosmopolitan. Not originally a European species, it was introduced from the British Isles to Portugal and the Mediterranean. Farmed in many places together with *Ostrea edulis*. R: 1. NB: the species *C. angulata* (Lamarck, 1819)—the Portuguese oyster—is considered to be a synonym for the Japanese oyster, *C. gigas*. Genetically, these species cannot be distinguished from one another.

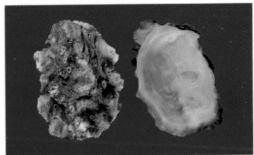

Dendostrea frons

(LINNAEUS, 1758)
frond oyster

D: 50mm. S: a solid, irregular shell. Usually oblong and slanted. O: various angular V-shaped pleats. C: yellowish-white, purplish-brown to dark brown. H: d1; sublittoral attached to rocks, tree trunks, etc. W: CAR, VIR; from the United States to Brazil. R: 2.

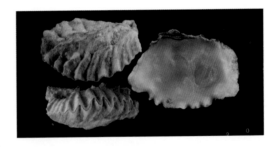

Lopha cristagalli

(LINNAEUS, 1758)
cock's-comb oyster

D: 100mm. S: a solid shell with a most unusual sculpture. O: about 6 very defined, V-shaped, sharply angular pleats with deep channels in between. Finely granulose surface. Irregular spines project near the umbo with which the oysters attach themselves to the substrate. C: violet-brown. Iridescent, nacreous interior with a violet shell margin. H: d1; sublittoral. W: INDP. R: 1.

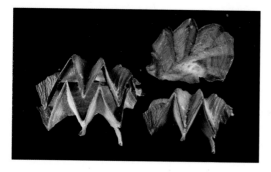

Ostrea edulis

LINNAEUS, 1758
common European oyster

D: 220mm. Oysters used for consumption are usually 100mm. S: thick-shelled and variable in shape. The left valve is more convex than the right. Ligament has an internal ligamental pad and a short, external ligament. No hinge teeth but slight beading on either side of the umbo. O: both valves are heavily ornamented with scabrous lamellae, often with wavy ribs on the convex valve. C: grayish-white to brownish-purple with irregular markings. Glossy white interior. H: d1–2; attached to a hard substrate by one or both valves, from the littoral to greater depths. W: ARC, KEL, LUS. R: 1. NB: In Europe, this species has been widely replaced by the Japanese oyster.

DIMYOIDEA

P. FISCHER, 1886
Irregularly shaped, inequivalved shells with two adductor muscle scars. The anterior scar is small, while the posterior scar is larger. A small, external ligament. A triangular resilium pad lies in a pit below the umbo. Reduced foot. Lies on its right valve. A small superfamily with one family.

Dimyidae

P. FISCHER, 1886
Round and very thin-shelled. The left valve is flatter than the right. The exterior is nacreous, while the interior is more porcelaneous. The hinge to the right valve occasionally has fine teeth along the margin. There are no wing-shaped projections next to the umbones. Small species no larger than 20mm. Found in the Caribbean and Indo-Pacific regions, as well as in the western Atlantic Ocean. A few genera: *Basiliomya, Dimya, Dimyella*.

PLICATULOIDEA

WATSON, 1930
A small superfamily with only one family. Attached to the surface by the right valve. Only one adductor muscle.

Plicatulidae

WATSON, 1930
kitten paws

Roughly triangular shells with a few, quite low, but large, radial ribs. A short hinge plate with a deep resilium pit flanked by two long teeth in the right valve or deep sockets in the opposing left valve. The exterior often has a reddish-brown coloration with a porcelaneous interior. Found in the sublittoral in shallow water. Usually attached to a hard substrate by one or both valves. Occurrence in the Caribbean and Indo-Pacific regions. Only one known (modern-day) genus: *Plicatula*.

Plicatula gibbosa

LAMARCK, 1801
Atlantic kitten's paw

D: 25mm. S: thick-shelled, umbo curled over. O: 8–10 irregular, wavy pleats. C: creamy white to magenta. H: d1; sublittoral to 20m. W: CAR, VIR; United States to Brazil. R: 2.

Plicatula muricata

SOWERBY, 1873
scaled kitten's paw

D: 30mm. S: pear-shaped shell with wide, rounded ribs. O: ribs covered in scabrous projections. C: amber to orange, sometimes white. H: d1–3; 20–200m. W: JAP. R: 2.

SUBORDER PECTININA

WALLER, 1978
Sometimes inequivalved with one convex and one flatter valve (pleurothetic). Unattached or with one of its valves attached to the substrate. Usually an opening or notch for the byssus in the right valve. One adductor muscle scar. The interior is not nacreous but white and porcelaneous.

PECTINOIDEA

WILKES, 1810
Triangular or somewhat circular shells, usually with radial ribs and wing-like projections either side of the umbones ("ears" or auricles). Toothless hinge, the upper shell margins having shelves and grooves. The family Spondylidae has an isodont hinge (a symmetrical arrangement of teeth and sockets). The ligament has a triangular resilium pad. Some species have tentacles and eyes on the mantle margin.

Entoliidae

KOROBKOV, 1960
Micro-mollusks from deeper water. Asymmetrical auricles either side of the umbones. Either a smooth exterior or the finest ornament. The interior is finely granulose. Occurrence includes Hawaii and the Fiji Islands. Only a few genera, including *Pectinella*.

Pectinidae

WILKES, 1810
scallops

Pleurothetic valves (i.e., one valve is usually more convex than the other). Ornament may also differ depending on the valve concerned. Their coloration and patterning is often exuberant and distinctive. Ornament usually comprises rays of radial ribs emanating from the umbones with wing-like projections on either side of these—the "ears" or auricles. Immature scallops are often attached to a substrate by a byssus. On reaching maturity, they become unattached with many species being able to swim by vigorously flapping their valves open and shut. Some groups lie peacefully with their convex right valve buried into the ocean floor with the flat valve parallel to the substrate (*Annachlamys, Patinopecten, Pecten*). Only one muscle scar is visible on the inside. Hinge teeth are absent. The ligament is small and lies in an internal, triangular ligament pit. They are very popular collector's items. Several subfamilies: Camptonectinae Habe, 1977; Chlamydinae Von Teppner, 1922; Patinopectininae Hertlein, 1969; Pectininae Wilkes, 1810. Found worldwide with several hundred species divided among dozens of genera, including: *Aequipecten, Amusium, Anguipecten, Annachlamys, Bractechlamys, Caribachlamys, Chlamys, Crassadoma, Decatopecten, Delectopecten, Excellichlamys, Flexopecten, Gloripallium, Hemipecten, Hinnites, Hyalopecten, Lyropecten, Mimachlamys, Minnivola, Mirapecten, Palliolum, Patinopecten, Pecten, Pedum, Placopecten, Pseudamussium*.
(Below: some scallops attach themselves by byssus threads within rock crevices. *Mimachlamys varia* (Linnaeus, 1758)—the variable scallop. Photograph: P.L. van Pel.)

Aequipecten opercularis

(LINNAEUS, 1758)
queen scallop

D: 100mm. S: quite a solid, round shell. Left valve slightly more convex than the right. O: up to 25 ribs with finer ones in between. Channels between ribs as wide as the ribs themselves. C: yellowish-white to magenta, often with irregular blotches or stripes. H: d1–2; sandy or muddy substrates. Immature specimens byssate on all kinds of substrate. W: ARC, KEL, LUS, WAFR. R: 1. NB: edible. The form *lineata* (Da Costa, 1778) is pale white with russet ribs.

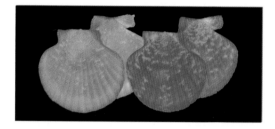

Amusium japonicum

(GMELIN, 1791)
Japanese moon scallop

D: 100mm. S: thin-shelled and very flat. Auricles almost symmetrical. O: exterior smooth, interior has increasingly pronounced, rib-like ridges. C: right valve white, left valve wine-red. H: d1–2; between 10 and 100m. W: INDP, JAP. R: 1.

Amusium pleuronectes

(LINNAEUS, 1758)
Asian moon scallop

D: 75mm. S: thin-shelled and flat. Symmetrical auricles. O: exterior has vague, radial ribs, interior has increasingly pronounced, rib-like ridges. C: right valve white, left valve dark pink, radial ribs purplish-brown. H: d1–2. W: INDP, JAP. R: 1.

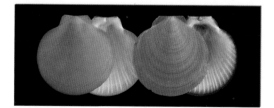

Annachlamys reevei

(A. ADAMS & REEVE, 1850)
Reeve's scallop

D: 50mm. S: quite a robust shell. Auricles almost symmetrical. O: over 20 wide ribs, narrowly interspaced. C: amber with wine-red blotches or entirely russet. Interior often bright rose-red. H: d1; fairly deep water. W: INDP. R: 2.

Argopecten gibbus

(LINNAEUS, 1758)
calico scallop

D: 60mm. S: a robust to thick-shelled scallop, almost circular in outline. Asymmetric auricles. Equally convex valves. O: up to 20 rounded ribs. Often smooth, sometimes with finer intermediate ribs. C: very variable: yellowish-white to russet. Often with magenta dashes and bands. H: d1; sublittoral to approx. 30m. W: CAR. R: 2.

Argopecten purpuratus

(LAMARCK, 1819)
purple scallop

D: 130mm. S: a solid shell. Asymmetric auricles. O: over 22 narrowly interspaced ribs. C: lilac to purple. Interior often partly covered in magenta markings. H: d1; sublittoral on sandy substrates to approx. 30m. W: PER. R: 1. NB:

fished commercially for consumption.

Chlamys islandica

(MÜLLER, 1776)
Iceland scallop

D: 100mm. S: a thin-shelled to robust, oval scallop. Very asymmetric auricles. O: a great many uneven ribs, often with slight concentric ribs as well. Slight scales often on the ribs. C: creamy white, yellow, orange, pink to deep purple, or speckled. Valves often differ in coloration. H: d1–2; down to deep water. W: ALE, ARC, CAL, KEL. R: 1. NB: fished for consumption.

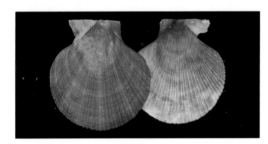

Crassadoma gigantea

(GRAY, 1825)
giant rock scallop

D: 150mm. S: a solid, irregularly shaped shell. Asymmetric auricles. Left valve slightly more convex than the right. Initially has a normal shape, later developing a more asymmetrical growth pattern. The left (more convex) valve often has a particularly "humpbacked" appear-

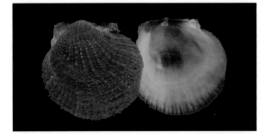

ance. O: irregular radial ribs covered in scoop-like projections and scales. C: light to dark brown. Valves differ in color. H: d1; sublittoral, attached to rocks. W: ALE, CAL, PAN. R: 2.

Crassadoma pusio

(LINNAEUS, 1758)
humpback scallop

D: 40mm. S: a fairly thin-shelled, irregularly shaped scallop. Asymmetric auricles. Left valve slightly more convex than the right. The left valve is often particularly misshapen. O: a great many radiating ribs of variable width following the growth orientation of the shell. C: variable: amber to magenta or orange. Sometimes speckled. H: d1–2; sublittoral and deeper attached to rocks. W: KEL, LUS. R: 2.

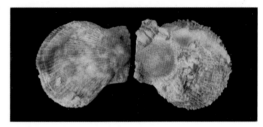

Decatopecten plica

(LINNAEUS, 1758)
plicate scallop

D: 40mm. S: a solid, elongated shell. Rounded sides, often somewhat curved over at the margins. Small, asymmetric auricles. O: a few wide, subtle, pleated ribs. Otherwise very fine ribs across the whole shell. C: variable: yellowish-white, pink, orange, purple in a variety of patterns. H: d1–2; mostly in deep water. W: INDP, JAP. R: 1.

Flexopecten flexuosus

(POLI, 1795)
arched scallop

D: 60mm. S: thin-shelled. Valves are equally convex. Quite large, slightly asymmetric auricles. O: up to 6 wide, vaulted ribs. Various narrower ribs in addition to these. C: variable: creamy white to pink, often in an irregular pattern of dark brown and white, magenta, or yellow markings. H: d1. W: KEL, LUS. R: 2.

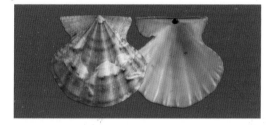

Gloripallium speciosum

(REEVE, 1853)
specious scallop

D: 40mm. S: a solid to thick-shelled, oval scallop. Asymmetric auricles. O: approximately 12 ribs densely covered in very coarse, scabrous projections. C: yellowish-white to pink, often with alternate purple, orange, and brown scales and blotches. H: d1; sublittoral. W: INDP, JAP. R: 3. NB: *G. pallium* (Linnaeus, 1758) – the royal cloak scallop – is similar but not as heavily scaled.

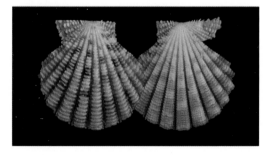

Manupecten pesfelis

(LINNAEUS, 1758)
cat's-paw scallop

D: 60mm. S: thin-shelled and elongated oval. Very asymmetric auricles. O: up to 8 wide, wavy ribs with wide, deep channels in between. Whole surface additionally covered in many fine riblets. C: valves differ in color. Cream, yellow, orange to red; often mottled a claret color.

H: d1–2; especially in deep water. W: LUS, WAFR. R: 2.

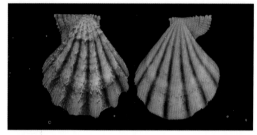

Mimachlamys asperrima

(LAMARCK, 1819)
prickly scallop

D: 70mm. S: thin-shelled and oval. Asymmetric auricles. O: up to 30 ribs covered in scabrous spicules. Finer ribs in between. C: yellow, orange, russet to purple. H: d1–2; sublittoral to deeper water. W: AUS. R: 1.

Mimachlamys varia

(LINNAEUS, 1758)
variable scallop

D: 70mm. S: a robust, flat shell. Slightly inequivalved. Asymmetric auricles. O: up to 35 ribs, wider than the interspacing channels. Fresh shells have pointed projections or spines on the ribs. These soon erode. C: very variable: yellow-

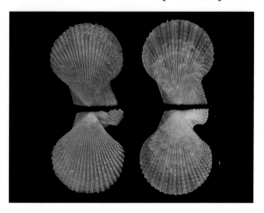

ish-white to magenta, sometimes mottled. Left and right valves have the same coloration. H: d1–3; byssate along rocky coasts. W: KEL, LUS, WAFR. R: 1.

Nodipecten nodosus

(LINNAEUS, 1758)
lion's paw

D: 110mm. S: a robust, broadly ovate shell. Asymmetric auricles. O: up to 9 wide, pleated ribs, various fine ribs and concentric grooves. Broad nodules on the ribs. C: apricot, pink to russet. H: d1–2; sublittoral to 50m. W: CAR. R: 1.

Nodipecten subnodosus

(G.B. SOWERBY I, 1835)
Pacific lion's paw

D: 120mm. S: a solid, oval shell. Asymmetric auricles. O: up to 10 wide, deeply interspaced

ribs. Also finer ribs and concentric ribs. Hollow thick scales, especially at intersections, particularly on the left valve. C: pink to purple. Interior also magenta or white. H: d1–2; in fairly deep water. W: PAN, PER. R: 2.

Palliolum tigerinum

(MÜLLER, 1776)
tiger scallop

D: 30mm. S: quite thin-shelled and flat. The left valve is only slightly more convex than the right. Asymmetric auricles. O: surface appears smooth but on magnification shows 50–60 fine, radial grooves branching out. Some specimens have 3–5 wide, wavy ridges. C: yellowish-white, light brown, pink to purple with irregular, round or angular, paler patches. H: d1–3; sometimes attached by byssus to a hard substrate at depths of up to 400m. W: KEL, LUS. R: 3.

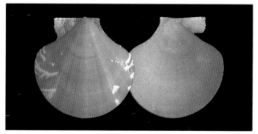

Pecten jacobaeus

(LINNAEUS, 1758)
St. James' scallop

D: 130mm. S: a solid shell in a broad fan shape. Left valve flat, right valve very convex. Auricles almost symmetrical. O: sharply declining ribs, almost angular, with deep grooves in between. Ribs and grooves also crossed by many very fine lines. C: left valve colored, usually a pinkish-red. Right valve yellowish-white. H: d1. W: KEL, LUS. R: 1. NB: see Chapter 3.

Pecten maximus

(LINNAEUS, 1758)
great scallop

D: 180mm. S: a robust shell. Right valve far more convex than the left. Auricles virtually symmetrical. O: up to 17 wide ribs radiate from the umbones. Many much finer riblets run across and between these. Immature specimens are relatively flat, while the ribs are absent on the first part of the shell. C: yellowish-white to russet, often slightly mottled. Convex valve usually much paler. H: d1–2; lies flat on the ocean floor to depths of over 100m. W: KEL, LUS, WAFR. R: 1. NB: widely eaten (sometimes referred to on menus as "coquilles St. Jacques"). See Chapter 3.

Pseudamussium peslutrae

(LINNAEUS, 1771)
seven-rayed scallop

D: 50mm. S: fairly thin-shelled and almost circular. Both valves almost equally convex. Auricles almost symmetrical. O: 3 to 10 relatively low, radial ribs that quickly widen. Much finer, radial grooves on and between the ribs, crossed by concentric lines. C: the left valve is usually a uniform orange-red or brown, sometimes marbled. The right valve is much paler: white or cream. H: d1–3; on soft sandy or muddy substrates to over 200m. W: ARC, KEL, LUS, WAFR. R: 4.

Propeamussiidae

ABBOTT, 1954
glass scallops

Thin-shelled, flat, and often circular, these shells are mostly quite small in scale. The right valve is frequently the flattest. They are smooth or else have concentric ribs, sometimes with radial ribs or lattice sculpture as well (left valve). The interior has radial folds. They have a toothless hinge and a ligament with a ligamental pad. Found in the Caribbean and Indo-Pacific regions as well as the eastern Atlantic Ocean from the sublittoral to the deep sea. Only a few genera, including: *Parvamussium, Propeamussium.*

Spondylidae

J.E. GRAY, 1826
thorny oysters

Inequivalved with thick shells. Usually have irregular, radial ribs bearing generally long, often scabrous, spines. The umbones are widely separated. The right valve is usually attached to a hard substrate. The upper (left) valve has two auricles on either side of the umbo. On one valve there are two large hinge teeth, while the other valve has sockets (an isodont hinge). The mantle margin has eyes. Found on rocks and coral in warm maritime regions. The shells are often heavily encrusted with sponges and other organisms. One genus: *Spondylus.*

Spondylus americanus

HERMANN, 1781
American thorny oyster

D: 100mm. S: a fairly solid, obliquely oval to round shell. Quite convex. O: both fine and defined ribs, partly covered in round, robust spines. C: white, colored apricot to claret at the top. H: d1–2; sublittoral and deeper water on a hard substrate. W: CAR, VIR; US to Brazil. R: 2.

Spondylus foliaceus

SCHREIBERS, 1793
Chinese thorny oyster

D: 70mm. S: a solid, oval shell. Fairly flat valves. O: irregular, wide ribs with finer ones in between. A small number of spines on the ribs, widening at the ends into fin-like projections. C: orange to brownish-purple, interior white with margin the same color as the exterior. Creamy white spines. H: d1; sublittoral on hard substrate. W: JAP. R: 2–3.

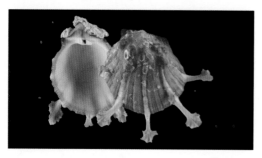

Spondylus princeps

BRODERIP, 1833
Pacific thorny oyster

D: 130mm. S: thick-shelled and often rather round. O: irregular ribs, 6–10 of which bear large spines. Finer ribs in between that may also bear spines. The large spines are coarse, wide, often flattened or hollow. C: often orange-red to claret-colored. Interior white with margin the same color as the exterior. H: d1–2; often in rather deep water on hard substrates. W: CAL, PAN. R: 3.

Spondylus regius

LINNAEUS, 1758
regal thorny oyster

D: 100mm. S: oval and thick-shelled. O: up to 10 wide, spiny ribs with various irregular, finer ribs in between also covered in finer scales and spicules. The spines on the wide ribs can grow extremely long. C: magenta to purple, the wide ribs often differ slightly in color. Interior white, pink margin. Muscle scar grayish-green. H: d1; sublittoral attached to hard substrate. W: INDP. R: 3. NB: much sought-after by collectors.

Spondylus wrightianus

CROSSE, 1872
Wright's thorny oyster

D: 120mm. S: thin-shelled. O: irregular ribs, some of which bear very long, wide, and straight spines. Finer, flatter, hook-shaped spines in between. C: milky white, sometimes with vague, brownish-purple stripes. Apricot spines. H: d1; sublittoral on hard substrate. W: AUS. R: 3.

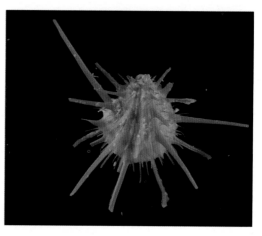

ANOMIOIDEA

RAFINESQUE, 1815
Relatively thin-shelled, these animals live attached to a substrate. They are irregular in shape, being molded to the substrate beneath. There is a notch or round hole in the right valve through which the calcified byssus projects, attaching the shell to the substrate. No hinge teeth.

Anomiidae

RAFINESQUE, 1815
jingle shells

Thin-shelled and inequivalved, these shells are irregular in shape: triangular, rounded, or often saddle-shaped. In terms of shape, they mold themselves to the substrate on which they lie. For example, specimens attached to scallops often have a corresponding rib sculpture on their own shells, while other specimens may be entirely smooth or flaky. The flat valve in some species has a hole from which a number of byssus threads protrude that have been calcified into a "stalk" that the animal uses to attach itself to rocks and shells. The valve interior is glossily nacreous. Several empty shells shaken together make a jingling sound, hence the name. Found worldwide in both cold and warm maritime regions from the sublittoral to deeper water. Two subfamilies: Anomiinae Rafinesque, 1815 and Placunanomiinae Beu, 1967. A few genera: *Anomia, Heteranomia, Isonomia, Monia, Placunanomia, Pododesmus.*

Anomia ephippium

LINNAEUS, 1758
European jingle shell

D: 60mm. S: thin-shelled and irregularly shaped. Molded according to the underlying substrate. Convex left valve, very flat right valve with an oval hole in the center. 3 round, shiny muscle scars within the convex valve embedded in a matt white background. Internal ligament, no hinge teeth. O: flaky surface that may be covered in irregular, wavy ridges. C: pale yellow to deep purple. Interior often very glossy. H: d1–2; sublittoral of rocky coasts and deeper to over 100m. W: KEL, LUS. R: 1.

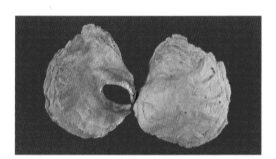

Heteranomia squamula

(LINNAEUS, 1758)
prickly jingle

D: 25mm. S: very thin-shelled and irregular. Usually roughly circular. 2 muscle scars within the convex left valve. Internal ligament, no hinge teeth. O: very flaky surface, sometimes covered in spiky ribs. C: pale white or yellow

and roughly translucent. Nacreous interior. H: d1–2; littoral to deeper water, attached by calcified byssus to rocks, shells, and other substrates. W: ARC, KEL, LUS, VIR, WAFR. R: 1. NB: often washed ashore attached to driftwood.

Pododesmus squama

(GMELIN, 1791)
green jingle

D: 35mm. S: a robust, irregularly shaped shell, often somewhat triangular or round. 2 finely striped muscle scars lie alongside each other within the convex valve. Internal ligament, no hinge teeth. A relatively large hole in the flat valve. O: very scabrous lamellae, often with many scaled radial ribs. C: yellowish-white to bottle-green. Often a glossy dark green within. H: d1–2; mostly in deep water. W: ARC, KEL. R: 4.

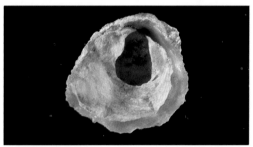

Placunidae

J.E. GRAY, 1842
saddle and windowpane oysters

Circular or less evenly shaped shells, thin-shelled and flat. Flaky or smooth surface, interior glossily nacreous. Some species are translucent. One adductor muscle. Found on soft sediment in lagoons and in the sublittoral. Indo-Pacific region. One known genus: *Placuna.*

Placuna ephippium

(PHILIPSSON IN RETZIUS, 1788)
saddle oyster

D: 20mm. S: a solid, irregularly shaped shell. O: flaky lamellae and occasionally subtle, pleated ribs. C: yellowish-gray with vague purplish-brown blotches and stripes. Sometimes translucent. Older specimens are thicker, calcareous, and not translucent. H: d1; littoral and sublittoral, shallow water. W: INDP. R: 1.

Placuna placenta

(LINNAEUS, 1758)
windowpane oyster

D: 10mm. S: very thin-shelled, almost circular. 2 roof-shaped cardinal (central) teeth. One central, circular muscle scar. O: fine concentric ribs. C: vitreous, translucent. H: d1; shallow water in lagoons and calm bays. W: INDP. R: 1. NB: much used in the tourist trade for making lanterns and such.

SUBCLASS PALAEOHETERODONTA

NEWELL, 1965
This subclass, which also contains large freshwater mussels or unionids, is sometimes considered a superorder.

ORDER TRIGONIIDA

DALL, 1889

TRIGONIOIDEA

LAMARCK, 1819
Triangular to oval shells with umbones pointing to the rear. The hinge teeth are roughly at right angles to the umbones.

Trigoniidae

LAMARCK, 1819
brooch clams

Equivalved, thick-shelled, and roughly triangular. Their ornament is that of oblique radial ribs, sometimes beaded or covered in scales. The interior has a thick, nacreous luster (and is used in the jewelry industry). They have robust hinges with a thick, triangular central tooth in the left valve. The cardinal (central) teeth have strong ridges. Two adductor muscles located close to the hinge. It was long considered to be extinct until living specimens were dredged up in the nineteenth century off Australia. Found exclusively in Australian waters in the sublittoral to deeper water. One known genus: *Neotrigonia*.

Neotrigonia gemma

IREDALE, 1924
coarse-ribbed brooch clam

D: 35mm. S: thick-shelled, almost rectangular. Very thick hinge plate with coarse hinge teeth. O: quite strong, angular ribs covered in nodules. C: grayish-white to pale pink. Silvery-white, nacreous interior. H: d1; sublittoral. W: AUS. R: 3.

Neotrigonia margaritacea

(LAMARCK, 1804)
Australian brooch clam

D: 50mm. S: thick-shelled and obliquely triangular. Very thick hinge plate. O: thick, rounded ribs covered in dense, scabrous nodules. C: amber. Interior with silvery-white to claret-colored nacre. H: d1; to 50m. W: AUS. R: 1. NB:

widely used to make spoons, brooches, and such like.

SUBCLASS HETERODONTA

NEUMAYR, 1884
The vast majority of bivalves come under this subclass. All species have a heterodont hinge with cardinal (central) and lateral teeth found in both valves. Furthermore, far and away the majority of its representatives have well-developed siphons that are either unified or separate. Many species burrow into the substrate. The siphons take in oxygenated water as well as all the food particles this contains, which are filtered out by large, leaf-like gills. These are then transported to the mouth cavity by means of mucus threads.

ORDER VENEROIDA

H. & A. ADAMS, 1856
An extremely large order containing several smaller superfamilies. All together the order comprises over one third of the bivalves found in the world today.

VENEROIDEA

RAFINESQUE, 1815
Equivalved shells. Heterodont hinges. Two roughly equal adductor muscle scars. The mantle lobes are often fused. Either with or without siphons. Several small families and one that is very extensive: Veneridae (Venus clams).

Cooperellidae

DALL, 1900
A small family with thin shells. A narrow hinge plate with two cardinal right teeth and three cloven left teeth. No lateral teeth. Deep pallial sinus. 6–12mm. Found in the Caribbean region and in the eastern Pacific Ocean. One genus: *Cooperella*.

Glauconomidae

J.E. GRAY, 1853
Small family. Thin-shelled, in the shape of an elongated ellipse. Equivalved. Truncated posterior. A narrow hinge plate with three cardinal (central) teeth. Wide ligament. Strong, rib-like growth lines. Periostracum is greenish-brown or greenish-yellow. 20–45mm. Tropical parts of the Indo-Pacific region. One genus: *Glauconome*.

Petricolidae

D'ORBIGNY, 1837
false piddocks

Elongated or round clam shells. The genus *Mysia* is circular without any exterior ornament. Some species from the genus *Petricola* have similarities with "true" piddocks (family Pholadidae). These shells range from oval to oblong, gaping slightly at the posterior end, with umbones projecting well forward and radial ribs bearing scabrous nodules. External ligament. Ribbed species burrow into soft substrates, such as intertidal peat, clay, wood, or soft rock, by making twisting motions with their shell valves. Found in shallow water in, for example, the Atlantic Ocean, North Sea, Caribbean, and Indo-Pacific. Only a few genera, including *Choristodon*, *Mysia*, *Petricola*, *Petricolaria*, *Rupellaria*.

Mysia undata

(PENNANT, 1777)
circular mysia

D: 35mm. S: thin-shelled, quite convex, and circular. The umbones are centrally positioned. Three cardinal hinge teeth in the left valve and two in the right valve. No lateral teeth. Pallial line has a deep embayment unlike clams from the families Lucinidae and Ungulinidae, which the shell resembles in terms of shape. O: smooth, growth lines only. C: yellowish-white or cream, grayish-white periostracum. H: d1; burrows into sand or mud at depths of up to 50m. W: KEL, LUS, WAFR. R: 2.

Petricolaria pholadiformis

LAMARCK, 1818
false angel wing

D: 80mm. S: quite a robust, elongated shell. The upper margin is not curved over as in many "true" piddocks. The umbones are located at a fifth of the shell width from the anterior margin. O: fine and coarse ribs radiate from the umbones. Ribs just below the umbones bear clear, scaly projections. C: chalky white or yellowish-white. H: d1; found in self-bored holes in medium-hard to hard substrates. Common in coastal areas with intertidal peat and in driftwood. On occasion also found in heavy clay. W: CAL, CAR, VIR, KEL, LUS, WAFR. R: 1. NB: originally solely an American species. Around 1890 it was introduced accidentally to Great Britain with oysters and spread out from there southward along the Atlantic coast of Europe.

Rupellaria lithophaga

(PHILIPSSON IN RETZIUS, 1788)
Mediterranean rupellaria

D: 20mm. S: an oval, irregularly shaped, often somewhat compact shell. Gaping habit at the posterior end. The umbones project well forward. External ligament. O: concentric ribs and growth lines, as well as fine and coarser radial ribs, sometimes bearing subtle, scabrous nodules. C: yellowish-gray, chalky white, sometimes with russet stripes and markings. H: d1; sublittoral, bores into hard limestone. W: KEL, LUS, WAFR; from the Bay of Biscay southward. R: 1.

Turtoniidae

CLARK, 1855
Micro-mollusks. Oval, smooth shells. Umbones curve over close to the anterior side. Narrow hinge plate with bud-like cardinal (central) teeth with lateral teeth to either side. Circumboreal distribution. One genus: *Turtonia*.

Veneridae

RAFINESQUE, 1815
Venus clams and others

Circular, obliquely oval, or oblong shells, mostly with concentric ribs. Genera also exist with radial ribs or lattice sculpture. They often have nodules, spicules, and scales, especially toward the posterior end. The umbones often point forward (prosogyrate) and are curved. External ligament. The pallial line is always accompanied by a pallial sinus. The animals burrow into sandy or muddy substrates from the littoral to deeper water. It is an extremely large family containing hundreds of species, many of which are edible. It is divided into several subfamilies that sometime differ starkly from one another. Species from the subfamily Chioninae Frizzell, 1936 have oval or rounded shells, often with radial ribs or lattice sculpture. The hinge plate has no lateral teeth. The subfamily Circinae Dall, 1896 contains species that are thick-shelled and oval, often with concentric and radial ribs. No pallial sinus. The lower margin may be crenulated or smooth. The subfamily Clementiinae Frizzell, 1936 contains species with thin shells and wavy concentric ribs. The lower margin is crenulated, while the hinge plate has no lateral teeth. The subfamily Cyclininae Frizzell, 1936 contains species with smooth, round, or oval shells, cream or white in color, with a lower margin that may be crenulated or smooth. The subfamily Dosiniinae Deshayes, 1853 (Artemis shells) contains species with circular shells, either smooth or with low concentric ribs. Shell margin not crenulated. Often with radial bands of chevron markings. Angular pallial sinus. The subfamily Gemminae Dall, 1902 contains small, triangular or more rounded shells that are smooth and very glossy (includes ruby or amethyst "gem clams"). The hinge has no lateral teeth; the lower margin is crenulated. The subfamily Meretricinae J.E. Gray, 1847 contains species with ovate or triangular shells. The surface is usually smooth and glossy (genus *Tivela*) and the lower margin is crenulated. A solid hinge with lateral hinge teeth at right angles. The subfamily Pitarinae Stewart, 1930 contains species with oblong, oval, or triangular shells. The umbones often overhang. The surface is smooth and glossy or else has low concentric ribs. Occasionally, spicules on the posterior end and gaudy coloration (e.g., *Callista*). The subfamily Samarangiinae Keen, 1969 contains one deepwater species from the Indo-Pacific. No pallial sinus. The subfamily Sunettinae Stoliczka, 1870 contains species with an inward curving dorsal margin and oval, smooth, or ribbed shells. Coloration often features chevrons or zigzags. Crenulated lower margin. The subfamily Tapetinae H. & A. Adams, 1857 (carpet shells) contains species with elongated oval shells, often with concentric or lattice ribbing. Lower margin not crenulated. The subfamily Venerinae Rafinesque, 1815 contains thick-shelled species with oval or triangular shells, often with overhanging umbones. Both concentric and radial ribs. Robust hinge teeth. Lower margin usually crenulated. There are hundreds of species in dozens of genera, including: *Amiantis, Anomalocardia, Antigona, Bassina, Callista, Chamelea, Chione, Circe, Circomphalus, Clausinella, Clementia, Cyclina, Cyclinella, Dosinia, Eumarcia, Gafrarium, Gemma, Globivenus, Irus, Lioconcha, Macrocallista, Marcia, Mercenaria, Meretrix, Paphia, Pitar, Placamen, Protothaca, Samarangia, Sunetta, Tapes, Tawera, Timoclea, Tivela, Transenella, Venerupis, Venus.*

Anomalocardia squamosa

(LINNAEUS, 1758)
squamous Venus

D: 25mm. S: a robust, triangular shell. Posterior pinched into a point. Crenulated lower margin. O: defined lattice sculpture. C: amber. Often purple to the posterior and on the interior. H: d1; littoral and sublittoral, sandbars. W: INDP. R: 1.

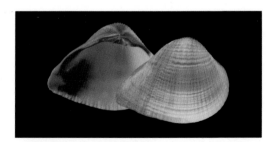

Antigona lamellaris

SCHUMACHER, 1817
lamellate Venus

D: 50mm. S: a robust, elongated, triangular shell. The umbones overhang sharply. O: narrow, raised, wavy concentric ribs. Strong radial sculpture in between. C: cream to amber with

russet marks and bands. Interior rose-red. H: d1; sand and coral reefs to 20m. W: INDP. R: 1.

Bassina disjecta

(PERRY, 1811)
wedding-cake Venus

D: 60mm. S: solid, with a rounded triangular shape. Overhanging umbones. O: broadly interspaced, lamellose concentric ribs. C: cream to white. H: d1–2; sublittoral and deeper to 50m. W: AUS; southern part, Tasmania. R: 2.

Callista chione

(LINNAEUS, 1758)
smooth callista

D: 75mm. S: thick-shelled and oval. O: smooth. C: glossy, amber to russet with dark, radiating bands. H: d1–2; to 100m. W: KEL, LUS; southward from the English Channel. R: 1.

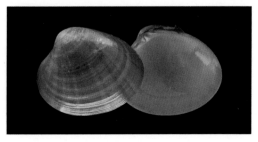

Callista maculata

(LINNAEUS, 1758)
calico clam

D: 50mm. S: thick-shelled and oval. O: extremely low concentric ribs/growth lines. C: amber with russet spots and bands. H: d1; sublittoral, burrows in sand. W: CAR, VIR; United States to Brazil. R: 1. NB: widely eaten.

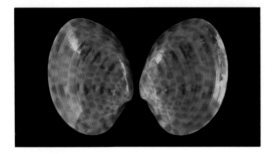

Callista nimbosa

(LIGHTFOOT, 1786)
sunray Venus

D: 120mm. S: thick-shelled and an elongated oval shape. O: very subtle concentric ribs. C: beige with radiating, dark brown stripes. H: d1; sublittoral to 30m. W: CAR, VIR; United States to Texas. R: 1.

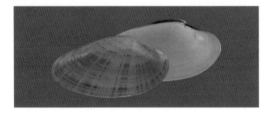

Chamelea striatula

(DA COSTA, 1778)
striated Venus

D: 35mm. S: a solid, triangular shell. Umbones curved to the side. A short, flat area in front of the umbones (lunule). Behind the umbones an oblong area (escutcheon). O: low, but clear, evenly interspaced concentric ribs. C: grayish-white with bands radiating from the umbones made of chevron-shaped dashes. H: d1–2; sublittoral and deeper, burrows in sand. W: KEL, LUS, WAFR. R: 1. NB: the closely related *C. gallina* (Linnaeus, 1758) – chicken Venus – lives in the Mediterranean Sea and has diver-

gent (oblique) ribs running toward the lower margin.

Clausinella fasciata

(DA COSTA, 1778)
wide-ribbed Venus

D: 25mm. S: a solid, triangular shell. Sharply curved umbones. Flat, clear lunule and escutcheon (see above). Lower margin not crenulated. O: irregular, wide, well-interspaced concentric ribs alternate with narrower ribs. C: very variable: creamy white, apricot, pale pink to deep purplish-brown. Dark purple or orange-brown bands often radiate from the umbones. H: d1–2; burrows in sand made of coarse shell fragments. W: KEL, LUS, WAFR, ZAFR. R: 2.

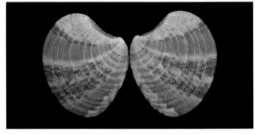

Dosinia exoleta

(LINNAEUS, 1758)
rayed Artemis

D: 50mm. S: a solid, circular shell. Umbones curve over sharply. Lunula flat and clear below the umbones. Lower margin not crenulated. O: even concentric ribs. C: creamy white or yel-

258

lowish-white with radial bands of V-shaped stripes and markings. H: d1–2; burrows deeply in coarse sand from the low-water mark to deeper water. W: KEL, LUS, WAFR. R: 1. NB: *D. lupinus* (Linnaeus, 1758) – smooth Artemis – also occurs in Europe and has a smaller, more delicately striped shell without bands of color.

Lioconcha castrensis

(LINNAEUS, 1758)
camp pitar Venus

D: 35mm. S: a solid, oval shell. Umbones curve over slightly. O: very low concentric growth lines. C: creamy white with chocolate-brown, V-shaped markings. H: d1; sublittoral, shallow water; found in sand. W: INDP. R: 1.

Lioconcha ornata

(DILLWYN, 1817)
ornate pitar Venus

D: 25mm. S: a solid, oval shell. Umbones curve over slightly. O: smooth. Growth lines only. C: creamy white to white with a bright pattern of russet markings and stripes. H: d1; sublittoral. Reefs in sand. W: INDP. R: 1.

Mercenaria mercenaria

(LINNAEUS, 1758)
northern quahog

D: 120mm. S: thick-shelled and obliquely triangular. Umbones curve over. Crenulated lower margin. O: concentric ribs with growth lines in between. C: yellowish-gray to amber. Glossy

white interior, purple at the posterior end. H: d1; burrows into muddy sand. Shallow water. W: KEL, LUS, VIR. R: 1. NB: originally found only in the western Atlantic Ocean. Introduced since to some locations in Europe for commercial fishing. The name "quahog" came from Native Americans, who made beads from these shells to create wampum belts. See Chapter 3.

Meretrix lusoria

(RÖDING, 1798)
poker-chip Venus

D: 70mm. S: a solid, fairly convex, triangular to oval shell. O: smooth. C: creamy white with russet markings or beige with dark brown markings. H: d1; shallow water to 20m. W: INDP; Far East. R: 1.

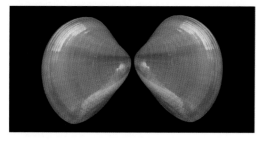

Paphia alapapilionis

RÖDING, 1798
butterfly Venus

D: 75mm. S: thick-shelled and an elongated oval shape. Anterior side shrunken. O: even concentric ribs. C: apricot with radiating bands of dark brown markings. H: d1; sublittoral. W: INDP. R: 1.

Paphia rhomboides

(PENNANT, 1777)
banded carpet shell

D: 60mm. S: a quite solid, oval shell. The underside of the pallial line and the pallial sinus run parallel and create a long, tongue-shaped meander. O: low, regular concentric ribs. C: magenta with deep purple or brown, radiating chevrons and stripes. Interior white or pale pink. H: d1–2; burrows in coarse sand or sand containing gravel and shell fragments. W: KEL, LUS, WAFR. R: 1. NB: the similar, and equally European, golden carpet shell, *P. aurea* (Gmelin, 1791), has a rich golden-yellow interior.

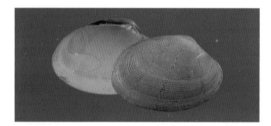

Pitar dione

(LINNAEUS, 1758)
royal comb Venus

D: 40mm. S: a solid, triangular shell. O: wide concentric ribs ending in long, pointed spines. C: creamy white to pale pink with magenta markings and spines. H: d1; sublittoral, along sandy beaches. W: CAR; West Indies. R: 2. NB: *P. lupanaria* (Lesson, 1830)—the prostitute Venus—occurs in the Panamic region and has considerably longer spines.

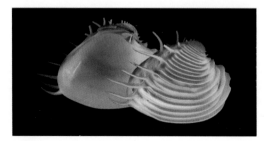

Placamen gravescens

(MENKE, 1843)
heavy Venus

D: 35mm. S: very thick-shelled with a rounded, triangular shell. Sharply overhanging umbones. O: broadly interspaced, very defined concentric ridges. C: creamy white with chocolate-brown radiating bands. H: d1; shallow bays. W: INDP. R: 3.

Sunetta perexcavata

FULTON, 1915
pleated oblong Venus

D: 40mm. S: a solid, rounded oblong shell. Upper margin folded inward, creating a toothlike ridge. O: smooth. C: amber with russet mottling. H: d1; shallow water. W: AUS. R: 1.

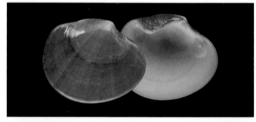

Tapes decussatus

(LINNAEUS, 1758)
grooved carpet shell

D: 75mm. S: a fairly solid, angular shell. Pallial sinus does not extend beyond the center. Base

of pallial line and pallial sinus barely coincide, if at all. Cloven cardinal (central) teeth in both valves. O: strong lattice sculpture. Radial ribs tend to dominate at the anterior and posterior ends. C: amber to brown, often with a checkered pattern, especially toward the posterior. H: d1; burrows in sand or sediment. W: KEL, LUS, WAFR. R: 1.

Tapes literatus

(LINNAEUS, 1758)
lettered Venus

D: 90mm. S: a solid, oblong-oval shell. O: even concentric ribs. C: white to light brown with russet to dark brown mottling, often with V-shaped lines. H: d1; shallow water. W: INDP. R: 1.

Timoclea ovata

(PENNANT, 1777)
oval pygmy Venus

D: 18mm. S: a solid, oval-triangular shell. Umbones approximately central and slightly curved away. Crenulated interior margin. Short pallial sinus. O: defined lattice sculpture. Radial ribs often split toward the lower margin. C: creamy white to light brown. Sometimes dark brown bands radiate from umbones. Light brown periostracum. H: d1–3; burrows in coarse sand. Sublittoral to greater depths. W: KEL, LUS. R: 1.

Tivela ponderosa

(KOCH IN PHILIPPI, 1844)
ponderous tivela

D: 75mm. S: thick-shelled and triangular with a rounded, non-crenulated lower margin. O: smooth. Growth lines only. C: creamy white to deep pink with beige radial bands. H: d1; sublittoral, shallow water. W: INDP; northwestern Indian Ocean. R: 1.

Venerupis senegalensis

(GMELIN, 1791)
pullet carpet shell

D: 50mm. S: a fairly solid, oblong shell. Umbones lie off-center. Pallial sinus extends past the center. Base of pallial line and pallial sinus partly coincide. Cloven cardinal (central) teeth in both valves. O: delicate lattice sculpture. C: yellowish-white or beige, often with bands of russet, V-shaped markings running from the umbones. H: d1; littoral and shallow sublittoral anchored by byssus to shell fragments on and in a sandy substrate. W: ARC, KEL, LUS, WAFR. R: 1. NB: also found on mussel beds and in crevices in intertidal peat, wood, and rock.

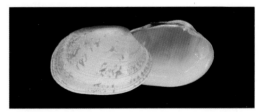

ARCTICOIDEA

NEWTON, 1891
Thick-shelled with umbones pointing forward. External ligament. The animals do not have any long siphons and, as a result, there is no pallial sinus.

Arcticidae

NEWTON, 1891
arctica clams

Robust, round to oval, inflated shells. Smooth or subtle, concentric ribs, and a flaky, brownish-black periostracum. Temperate and cold maritime regions. Sublittoral. An ancient group with numerous fossil species. Only a few modern-day genera: *Akebiconcha, Arctica*.

Artica islandica

(LINNAEUS, 1767)
ocean quahog

D: 125mm. S: a solid, almost circular shell. Umbones clearly curve over to the anterior. Distinct, defined hinge with 3 cardinal and 2 lateral teeth in each valve. Strong, external ligament. No pallial sinus in the pallial line. Lower margin not crenulated. O: smooth. Growth lines only. C: chalky white or pale gray with a thick, flaky, brown to black periostracum. H: d1–2; to over 100m. W: ARC, KEL, LUS, VIR. R: 1.

Trapeziidae

LAMY, 1920
Quite robust, oblong shells. Umbones project well forward. Valves usually slightly gaping. The animals live in the sublittoral and in lagoons and river mouths, often attached within rock crevices and coral. Found in warmer seas in the eastern Atlantic Ocean, Caribbean, Indo-Pacific, and Mediterranean Sea. Only a few genera, including: *Coralliophaga, Fluviolanatus, Trapezium*.

Vesicomyidae

DALL, 1908
Oval to elongated shells, often compressed on either side with concentric growth lines. Prosogyrate umbones (directed forward). Periostracum often thick. Deep-sea species living on sediment sand, and in rock crevices, especially those near to hydrothermal vents as found in the eastern and western Atlantic Ocean. Also found in the Antarctic region. A few genera: *Calyptogena, Vesicomya*.

ASTARTOIDEA

D'ORBIGNY, 1844
Mostly thick-shelled with a distinctively robust hinge. Ornament mostly consists of concentric ribs. Two clear adductor muscle scars.

Astartidae

D'ORBIGNY, 1844
astarte clams

Oval-triangular shells. Umbones generally point forward. The periostracum is dark brown and can have a delicate, microscopically checkered ornament (determining feature). The ligament is external. No siphons and, consequently, no pallial sinus. Found mainly in colder maritime regions, although also found in warmer waters, such as the Mediterranean Sea. The animals live in sand ranging from coarse to fine, lying just under the substrate with the respiratory cavity in the shell posterior just poking above the surface. There are a few dozen modern-day species. These are divided among several genera, including: *Astarte, Digitaria, Goodallia, Tridonta*.

Astarte crenata subequilatera

SOWERBY, 1854
lentil astarte

D: 40mm. S: a thick, oval-triangular shell. O: robust, regular concentric ribs. C: creamy white. Dark brown periostracum. H: d2–3; deeper water. W: ALE, ARC, CAL; colder maritime regions down to northern California. R: 1.

Astarte elliptica

(BROWN, 1827)
elliptical astarte

D: 32mm. S: thick-shelled. Usually slightly longer than its height. Lower margin not crenulated. Pallial line has no sinus. O: wide, low concentric ridges, the number and thickness of which can vary. C: grayish-white with a thick, amber to blackish-brown periostracum. H: d1–3; buried just below the surface of a sandy substrate. Can live at greater depths. W: ARC, KEL. R: 2.

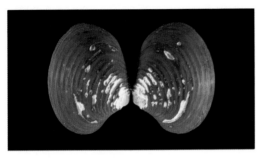

Astarte montagui

(DILLWYN, 1817)
triangular astarte

D: 16mm. S: a robust, roughly triangular shell. The umbones lean over slightly. Lower margin not crenulated. Pallial line without sinus. O: up to 50 narrow concentric ribs. C: amber to pink. Periostracum greenish-yellow to light brown. H: d1–2; party buried in a sandy substrate. W: ARC, KEL. R: 1.

Astarte sulcata

(DA COSTA, 1778)
sulcate astarte

D: 25mm. S: very thick-shelled, almost square. Umbones off-center, curved over. Lower margin usually finely crenulated. Both muscle scars are relatively large. The hinge is solid with 2 lateral teeth in either valve plus 2 cardinal (central) teeth in the right valve and 3 in the left. Ligament largely external. O: 25–40 wide concentric ribs with fine growth lines in between.

C: chalky white. Tawny to deep, dark brown periostracum. H: d1–3; sandy substrate, especially in rather deeper water. W: ARC, KEL. R: 2.

Astarte undata

GOULD, 1841
waved astarte

D: 30mm. S: a rounded triangle shape and thick-shelled. Umbones curved over. O: broadly interspaced, rounded concentric ridges. C: yellowish-white to orange with a tawny periostracum. H: d1–3; 10–200m. W: ARC, KEL; Labrador, United States south to New Jersey. R: 1.

Goodallia triangularis

(MONTAGU, 1803)
little astarte

D: 3mm. S: a solid, triangular shell. Umbones slightly curved over. Very robust hinge. 2 cardinal and 2 lateral teeth in either valve. Crenulated lower margin. O: smooth. Growth lines only. C: yellowish-white to apricot with a pale green to dark brown periostracum. H: d1–3; in

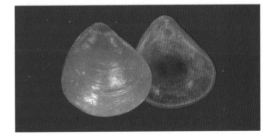

coarse sand from just below the low-water mark to a few hundred meters deep. W: KEL, LUS, WAFR. R: 1.

Cardiniidae

ZITTEL, 1881

Thick, roughly triangular shells. One cardinal and two lateral teeth in the right valve and two kinked cardinal (central) teeth in the left valve. Thick, scaly concentric ridges. Known from fossil records since the Ordovician. Only one modern-day genus containing one species: *Tellidorella cristulata* (Berry, 1963), which is considered to be a "living fossil." Panamic region along the coast between 25 and 100m.

CARDIOIDEA

LAMARCK, 1809

Principally robust, equivalved shells, usually with clear radial ribs. No pallial sinus. Muscle scars virtually the same size.

Cardiidae

LAMARCK, 1809
cockles, giant clams

The radial ribs, variable in their definition, characterize the great majority of species from the family Cardiidae. These may bear scales, nodules, or spines, often diminishing toward the posterior end. The ligament is external. The lower margin of the shell is crenulated; this is usually an extension of the ribs. A heart shape is apparent in most species when both valves are viewed from the side. The large, angular foot is used to burrow quickly into the substrate. Some species are even able to make jumping motions with it. The animals live just below the surface of the ocean floor. Worldwide distribution. Divided into several families. Species from the subfamily Cardiinae Lamarck, 1809 usually have a straight hinge plate and inflated valves that are strongly ribbed. The subfamily Clinocardiinae Kafanov, 1975 contains quite thin-shelled species either with or without ribs (genus *Serripes*). The hinge may be diminished. Shells from the subfamily Fraginae Stewart, 1930 are separated into anterior and posterior sections by an angular, diagonal keel. The hinge is short and angular. Species from the subfamily Laevicardiinae Keen, 1936—egg cockles—have oval to triangular shells and low to virtually invisible ribs. According to recent opinion the subfamily Lymnocardiinae Stoliczka, 1870 with its oval or round shells, usually with rounded ribs, should also include the familiar genus *Cerastoderma* (cockles) as well as genera such as *Hypanis* and *Didacna*. The subfamily Protocardiinae Keen, 1951, contains fossil genera with round to angular shells with radial ribs found exclusively toward the posterior. Species from the subfamily Trachycardiinae Stewart, 1930 have quite large, high shells with thorny and scaly ribs and a short hinge with asymmetrical cardinal (central) teeth. For many years, taxonomists treated Tridacninae Lamarck, 1819—giant clams—separately. Giant clams were even placed in a separate superfamily Tridacnoidea Lamarck, 1819. Nowadays, they are classified as a subfamily within Cardiidae. They are extremely thick-shelled, large, and heavy. They may be elongated or triangular. They have powerfully ridged radial ribs covered in scales. The lower margin is strongly crenulated. Only one cardinal (central) and one posterior lateral tooth are present in the genus *Tridacna*, and the shell valves also have a byssal notch. The genus *Hippopus* has an additional anterior tooth in its hinge but no orifice or notch for the byssus (in mature specimens). Found in the intertidal zone of coral reefs in warm and tropical maritime regions. The animals rest on their hinge in sand or amid corals with the mantle aperture uppermost. The mantle margin may be colored from grayish-white to dark blue depending on the color of the algae present in the fleshy mantle lobes. Some species spend their whole lives attached to the substrate. For others this occurs only in their immature phase.

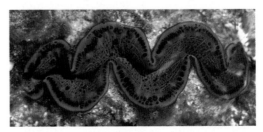

Colored mantle margin of Tridacna maxima in the Red Sea. Photograph: H. Dekker.

The family Cardiidae contains a great many genera, including: *Acanthocardia, Acrosterigma, Cardium, Cerastoderma, Ciliatocardium, Clinocardium, Corculum, Ctenocardia, Fragum, Fulvia, Hippopus, Laevicardium, Nemocardium, Parvicardium, Trachycardium, Tridacna, Vepricardium.*

Acanthocardia aculeata

(LINNAEUS, 1767)
European spiny cockle

D: 100mm. S: fairly thin-shelled and somewhat angular. O: up to 22 wide, low ribs. Sharp, flattened, triangular spicules on the ribs, joined together by a prominent ridge. Fine concentric lines between the ribs. C: amber to purplish-brown with light brown patches. Greenish-brown periostracum. H: d1; burrows in a sandy or muddy substrate. W: KEL, LUS, WAFR. R: 1.

Acanthocardia echinata

(LINNAEUS, 1758)
European prickly cockle

D: 75mm. S: a robust, almost circular shell. O: wide ribs. The grooves between the ribs are almost the same width as the ribs themselves. A groove in the center of each rib contains short, slightly bent spines. C: yellowish-white with light brown mottling. Rust-brown periostracum. H: d1–2; burrows in sandy or muddy substrates. W: KEL, LUS. R: 1.

Acrosterigma angulata

(LAMARCK, 1819)
angular cockle

D: 80mm. S: a fairly solid, oval shell. O: regular, rather angular ribs with small projections at the posterior and anterior ends. C: white to pale

brown with somewhat darker markings. Often yellowish-red or claret-colored at the margin. H: d1; sublittoral, burrows in sand. W: INDP. R: 1.

Cardium costatum

LINNAEUS, 1758
great ribbed cockle

D: 100mm. S: thin-shelled and almost semicircular. Valves gape at the posterior end. O: narrow, hollow, high-keeled radial ribs, very widely interspaced. C: creamy white to pale yellow. H: d1–2; sublittoral and deeper to approx. 50m. W: WAFR; southward to Angola. R: 1.

Cerastoderma edule

(LINNAEUS, 1758)
common European or *edible cockle*

D: 60mm. S: a solid shell, usually slightly longer than its height. Umbones are roughly central. Exterior ligament. O: 22–28 low ribs bearing narrow scales. Interspaces narrower than the ribs. C: white or amber. Young specimens often have dark brown markings around the umbones. H: d1; littoral and sublittoral. Burrow to a depth of 5 cm in sand or mud. W: ARC, KEL, LUS. R: 1. NB: widely eaten.

Corculum cardissa

(LINNAEUS, 1758)
true heart cockle

D: 50mm. S: fairly thin shelled and much compressed on either side. The "back" of the shell is compressed to form a keel. Umbones curve over sharply. Viewed from the side the valves create a perfect heart shape. O: fine radial ribs. The dorsal keel usually bears blunt, spiny projections. C: creamy white or yellow, often with vague orange-brown or violet markings. H: d1; sublittoral on and close to reefs. W: INDP, JAP. R: 2. NB: well-known shell much sought after by collectors. A variety of colors and forms exist.

Ctenocardia victor

(ANGAS, 1872)
Victor's prickly cockle

D: 45mm. S: a solid, angular shell. O: strong ribs covered in recurved spicules and spines. C: white with dark orange blotches. Interior apricot. H: d2; deeper water to over 100m. W: AUS, INDP, JAP. R: 3.

Dinocardium robustum vanhyningi

(CLENCH & SMITH, 1944)
Vanhyning's cockle

D: 100mm. S: very large, thick-shelled, and a rounded, triangular shape. O: strong, fairly low

ribs, partly covered in flattened nodules or scales. C: tawny with dark brown blotches. H: d1; shallow water. W: CAR, VIR. R: 3.

Hippopus hippopus

(LINNAEUS, 1758)
bear paw clam

D: 200mm. S: very thick-shelled and triangular to rhomboid. No byssal notch on upper margin. Large muscle scar in the center. O: up to 14 convex radial ribs varying in width. Also, many much finer radial ribs. C: creamy white with russet mottling. H: d1; shallow water on coral reefs. W: INDP; western part. R: 1. NB: belongs in the subfamily Tridacninae – giant clams.

Fulvia boholensis

VIDAL, 1994
orange cockle

D: 35mm. S: thin-shelled, almost circular. O: dense, regularly interspaced, narrow ribs. C: pale to bright orange. H: d1; sublittoral, burrows in sand and mud. W: INDP. R: 2.

Fragum unedo

(LINNAEUS, 1754)
strawberry cockle

D: 40mm. S: a solid, almost square shell. O: quite low, regularly interspaced ribs covered in narrow, raised scales. C: pale yellow to cream, russet scales. H: d1; sublittoral, burrows in sand. W: AUS, INDP, JAP. R: 1.

Laevicardium attenuatum

(SOWERBY, 1841)
attenuated cockle

D: 65mm. S: quite thin-shelled, elongated, and clearly slanted. O: exceptionally fine radial ribs. Appears almost smooth. C: white or yellow, often with orange-red mottling. Interior light brown to white. H: d1; sublittoral, in sand. W: AUS, INDP, JAP. R: 1.

Laevicardium crassum

(GMELIN, 1791)
Norwegian egg cockle

D: 75mm. S: a quite robust, rather triangular shell. Umbones almost central. O: very low radial ribs. C: pale yellow with orange-red mottling around the umbones. Yellowish-green periostracum. H: d1; burrows in coarse sand and mud, often found in places with a lot of shell fragments. W: KEL, LUS, WAFR. R: 1.

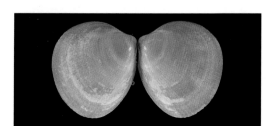

Laevicardium multipunctatum

(SOWERBY, 1841)
many-dotted cockle

D: 50mm. S: a robust, obliquely oval shell. O: low radial ribs, almost smooth. C: grayish-yellow with claret-colored bands and often with a pattern of red dashes and dots. Interior often red. H: d1; burrows in sand in shallow water. W: INDP. R: 3.

Lophocardium annettae

(DALL, 1889)
Annette's cockle

D: 50mm. S: very thin-shelled and convex. O: extremely fine radial as well as concentric ribs. C: orange-brown, often red around umbones and the sides. Interior yellowish-white, red around the margin. H: d1–2; sublittoral and deeper water to 50m. W: CAL, PAN. R: 3.

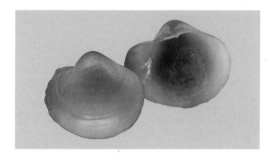

Lunulicardia retusa

(LINNAEUS, 1767)
blunted cockle

D: 40mm. S: a robust, triangular, slanted shell. A strong, diagonal keel runs from the umbones to the lower margin. O: low ribs with narrow interspaces. Subtle spicules and scales on ribs.

267

C: creamy white with russet spots. H: d1–2; sublittoral and deeper water to over 50m. W: AUS, INDP, JAP. R: 2.

Lyrocardium lyratum

(SOWERBY, 1841)
lyrate cockle

D: 50mm. S: thin-shelled but robust and round. O: very narrow, low radial ribs that diminish toward the center. Sharp, quite widely interspaced, oblique grooves on the anterior side fading out before reaching the center. C: creamy white to yellow with red spots. The shell's wine-red periostracum gives it its claret-colored appearance. H: d1–2; shallow to deeper water. W: AUS, INDP, JAP. R: 2.

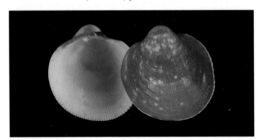

Maoricardium pseudolima

(LAMARCK, 1819)
giant Philippine cockle

D: 150mm. S: thick-shelled and a rounded triangular shape. O: quite low ribs. C: amber with russet bands. Very occasionally white. Interior

paler or white. H: d1; shallow water in the sublittoral, burrows in sand. W: CAR, INDP; East Africa. R: 2. NB: one of the largest cockles.

Nemocardium bechei

(REEVE, 1847)
De la Beche's cockle

D: 60mm. S: a rounded, triangular shell. O: very fine ribs, almost smooth. A confined area to the posterior with a coarse texture caused by fine spicules. C: russet to orange-red. H: d1–2. W: AUS, INDP, JAP. R: 2.

Papyridea aspersa

(SOWERBY, 1833)
Panama paper cockle

D: 40mm. S: thin-shelled and oval. O: fine, dense ribs covered in fine beading. C: cream with russet marbling. H: d1. W: PAN. R: 2.

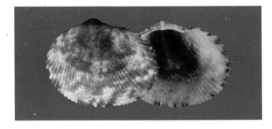

Parvicardium exiguum

(GMELIN, 1791)
exigua cockle

D: 13mm. S: a robust, obliquely triangular shell. A sharp keel runs from the umbones down to the lower posterior margin, giving the shell a crooked, angular appearance. O: up to 22 low ribs that are covered in oval scales or beads. The ribs are wider than the grooves in between. C: yellowish-white to brown. The periostracum is greenish-yellow. H: d1. W: KEL, LUS. R: 1.

NB: fossils are often discolored.

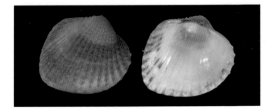

Trachycardium belcheri

(BRODERIP & SOWERBY, 1829)
Belcher's cockle

D: 40mm. S: elongated oval shell. O: angular ribs bearing a great many triangular spicules. C: cream to amber, often with a touch of flaming red around the margins. H: d1. W: PAN. R: 2.

Trachycardium procerum

(SOWERBY, 1833)
slender cockle

D: 70mm. S: very thick-shelled and elongated. O: wide ribs, more angular toward the sides. C: cream with russet mottling; interior paler. H: d1. W: PAN, PER. R: 2.

Tridacna gigas

(LINNAEUS, 1758)
the giant clam

D: 1700mm. S: extremely thick-shelled. An elongated, triangular shell. Umbones virtually in the center. Upper margin gaping (byssal orifice). O: up to 6 very wide radial ribs covered densely with scales. No spatula-like projections. C: grayish-white. H: d1; shallow waters of coral reefs to 20m. W: INDP. R: 1. NB: the largest bivalve in the world. The shells can weigh up to 230 kilograms. The photograph shows a young specimen (see also Chapter 1).

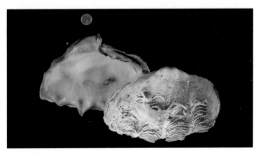

Tridacna squamosa

LAMARCK, 1819
fluted giant clam

D: 300mm. S: thick-shelled, oval to triangular in shape. O: 6 wide radial ribs covered in very pronounced, scaly projections. C: creamy white; young specimens are sometimes pink or pale orange. H: d1; reefs, sublittoral. W: INDP, JAP, ZAFR. R: 1.

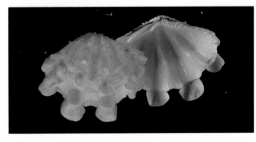

Vepricardium multispinosum

(SOWERBY, 1841)
many-spined cockle

D: 55mm. S: almost circular or oval shell. O: regular, low ribs densely covered in fine

spicules. C: amber, often a touch of magenta around the margins. Interior usually white. H: d1. W: INDP. R: 3.

Hemidonacidae

IREDALE & MCMICHAEL, 1962
Triangular, inequilateral shells, truncated posteriorly. They have no pallial sinus and the lower margin is crenulated. Shallow water, partly buried in sand. Indo-Pacific region. There are only a few species from a single genus: *Hemidonax*.

CARDITOIDEA

J. FLEMING, 1828
Very thick-shelled, usually with thick radial ribs. Umbones often project forward. External ligament. No pallial sinus.

Carditidae

J. FLEMING, 1828
cardita clams

Circular or rectangular (trapezoid) shells, usually having strong, radial ribs covered in scales, lamellae, or nodules. Crenulated lower margin. The animals burrow into the substrate or attach themselves with the byssus to a hard substrate in crevices. Wide distribution, especially throughout warmer maritime regions. Various subfamilies: Carditamerinae Chavan, 1969; Carditellinae Iredale & McMichael, 1962; Carditesinae Chavan in Moore, 1969; Carditinae J. Fleming, 1828; Miodomeridinae Chavan, 1969; Thecaliinae Dall, 1903; Venericardiinae Chavan, 1969. Many genera, including: *Beguina, Cardita, Carditamera, Cardites, Cyclocardia, Strophocardia, Venericardia.*

Cardita affinis

SOWERBY, 1833
similar cardita

D: 50mm. S: a solid, elongated shell. O: 15–20 pronounced, rounded ribs. C: creamy white

with chocolate brown spots. H: d1; sublittoral. W: PAN; Mexico to Peru. R: 1.

Cardita crassicosta

LAMARCK, 1819
Australian or leafy cardita

D: 50mm. S: thick-shelled and rectangular. O: very pronounced ribs, projecting beyond the shell margin to create blunt spines. Ribs also covered in scabrous projections. C: variable: creamy white, bright yellow, pink, or orange-red. H: d1–2; sublittoral and deeper water to 100m. W: AUS. R: 2. NB: species sought-after by collectors.

Cardites bicolor

(LAMARCK, 1819)
two-tone cardita

D: 55mm. S: thick-shelled, oval to triangular in shape. Umbones curve over. O: up to 22 very defined, angular ribs with deep grooves in between. C: cream with russet to dark brown dashes on the ribs. H: d1; in coarse sand with shell fragments, deeper water. W: AUS, INDP. R: 2.

Cardites laticostata

SOWERBY, 1833
wide-ribbed cardita

D: 40mm. S: thick-shelled with a rounded, triangular shape. O: wide ribs with deep grooves in between. C: creamy white with pink, beige, and dark brown markings. H: d1–2; littoral, sublittoral, and deeper to 50m. W: CAL, PAN; California to Peru. R: 1.

Strophocardia megastropha

(GRAY, 1825)
curled cardita

D: 55mm. S: thick shell. Elevated triangular shape with deeply curled umbones. O: fairly low ribs. C: dark pinkish-beige with orange-pink markings. H: d1–2. W: PAN. R: 2.

Condylocardiidae

F. BERNARD, 1897
Micro-mollusks. Either elongated or higher than they are long. Otherwise, triangular, oval, or trapezoid. Radial or concentric ribs. Found in sand in the sublittoral. Wide distribution, including the Caribbean, Indo-Pacific, and Australian regions. Two subfamilies: Condylocardiinae F. Bernard, 1897 and Cuninae Chavan, 1969. Various genera, including: *Americuna, Condylocardia, Condylocuna, Micromeris*.

CHAMOIDEA

LAMARCK, 1809
Thick-shelled and inequivalved. Attached by the umbonal area of one valve to the substrate. Mantle margin has many small tentacles. No byssus. Two adductor muscles and, therefore, scars unlike oysters and thorny oysters (the Ostreidae and Spondylidae families), which they sometimes resemble.

Chamidae

LAMARCK, 1809
jewel boxes

Thick-shelled, often with some calcification and may be covered in scales, lamellae, or spines. Found in all warmer maritime regions from the littoral to a depth of 100meters attached to a hard substrate. They can be difficult to find due to being heavily encrusted. Moreover, they are often very firmly attached to the substrate.

Arcinella cornuta

(CONRAD, 1866)
Florida spiny jewel box

D: 40mm. S: thick-shelled and convex. A slanted, triangular shape. O: distinct, pleated radial ribs covered in scales and other projections. C: creamy white. Interior has rose-red blotches; muscle scars often yellow. H: d1–2; sublittoral and deeper water attached to rocks. W: VIR. R: 2.

Chama lazarus

(LINNAEUS, 1758)
Lazarus jewel box

D: 75mm. S: thick-shelled and oval. Irregularly shaped. O: very coarse, lamellose radial ribs, often bearing flattened, hollow projections, sometimes even branched. C: variable: creamy white, pale yellow, red-orange, pink. H: d1; sublittoral attached to rocks. W: INDP. R: 2–3.

Chama macerophyla

(GMELIN, 1791)
leafy jewel box

D: 60mm. S: thick-shelled and oval. O: a great many strongly sculptured, lamellose ribs. C: yellowish-white to russet. H: d1; shallow water on rocks often cemented together in groups. W: CAR, VIR; southeastern United States to Brazil. R: 3.

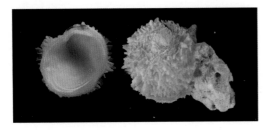

CRASSATELLOIDEA

DE FÉRUSSAC, 1822
Strong shells with a robust hinge and internal ligament. Two muscle scars. Found mostly in deeper water, buried in soft substrates with the respiratory opening in direct contact with the water.

Crassatellidae

DE FÉRUSSAC, 1822
crassatellas

Thick-shelled and either a rounded, triangular shape or else more rectangular. Usually fairly squat. Posterior end often extended and blunt. They mostly have distinct concentric ribs. A wide hinge plate with two oblique cardinal (central) teeth in the right valve and three in the left. Two subfamilies: Crassatellinae De Férussac, 1822 and Scambulinae Chavan, 1952.

Eucrassatella kingicola

(LAMARCK, 1805)
king crassatella

D: 60mm. S: thick-shelled and obliquely triangular. Angular anterior side, rounded posterior side. O: regular concentric ribs, diminishing toward the lower margin. C: beige. Brown periostracum. Interior white; muscle scars brown. H: d1; deep water to 50m. W: AUS. R: 1.

Eucrassatella speciosa

(A. ADAMS, 1852)
Gibbe's crassatella

D: 60mm. S: thick-shelled and oval. Pointed anterior side with an oblique keel running down from the umbones. O: sharp, narrow, densely concentric ribs. C: yellowish-white to light brown with orange-brown markings. Dark beige periostracum. H: d1; sublittoral. W: CAR; West Indies. R: 1.

CYAMIOIDEA

G.O. SARS, 1878
Mainly micro-mollusks with the inhalant and exhalant siphons on the posterior side.

Bernardinidae

KEEN, 1963
Roughly triangular shells, shorter on the anterior side, and longer and rounded on the posterior side. Concentric or radial ribs. No larger than 4.5mm. Found only in the eastern Pacific Ocean. (Formerly classified under Arcticoidea.) Few genera: *Bernardina, Halodakra*.

Cyamiidae

G.O. SARS, 1878
Angular to oval shells with smooth shell margins and smooth, glossy surfaces. Found around Australia, New Zealand, and Antarctica. Two subfamilies: Cyamiinae Philippi, 1845 and Gaimardiinae Hedley, 1916. Several genera, including *Cyamiocardium, Cyamiomactra, Cyamium, Eugaimardia, Gaimardia, Legrandina, Perrierina*.

Galatheavalvidae

KNUDSEN, 1970

A family with only one deepwater species: *Galatheavalva holothuriae* Knudsen, 1970. Found close to East Africa at a depth of 4810 meters, living in close association with sea cucumbers.

Neoleptonidae

THIELE, 1934

Micro-mollusks. Triangular, round, or oval shells. Umbones are central or close to the center. The left valve has a hook-shaped, anterior hinge tooth. Subtle concentric ribs. Found in the littoral and sublittoral of, for example, the Mediterranean Sea and Atlantic Ocean. Several genera: *Arculus, Epilepton, Neolepton, Pachykellia, Puysegeria*.

Sportellidae

DALL, 1899

Elongated, oval shells, sometimes very angular, with a smooth or granulose surface. In *Anisodonta*, the umbones are toward the anterior, while in *Sportella* they are toward the posterior. Found in the littoral and sublittoral of temperate and tropical maritime regions. A few genera: *Anisodonta, Basterotia, Isoconcha, Sportella*.

GALEOMMATOIDEA

J.E. GRAY, 1840

A superfamily with small, thin, often translucent shells. The hinge is often basic and rudimentary. Anterior inhalant orifice, posterior exhalant orifice. Several species live symbiotically with, for example, brittle stars, crabs, or worms. Some species use the foot for crawling. In the past, the many dozens of genera and species were classified within a variety of families and subfamilies (including: Erycinidae Deshayes, 1850; Kellidae Forbes & Hanley, 1848; Leptonidae J.E. Gray, 1847; Montacutidae Clark, 1855; Mysellidae F.R. Bernard, 1983). Two families are employed for this nowadays: Galeommatidae J.E. Gray, 1840 and Lasaeidae J.E. Gray, 1842.

Lasaeidae

J.E. GRAY, 1842

Mainly micro-mollusks but also species measuring up to 25mm. Dozens of genera, including: *Arthritica, Axinoton, Bornia, Borniola, Devonia, Erycina, Galeomma, Hemilepton, Kellia, Lasaea, Lepton, Litigiella, Montacuta,* *Mysella, Pseudopythina, Scacchia, Scintilla, Semierycina, Solecardia, Tellimya, Uncidens, Vasconiella*.

Kellia suborbicularis

(MONTAGU, 1803)
suborbicular Kelly clam

D: 10mm. S: thin-shelled, convex, and oval. Umbones almost central. No pallial sinus. 2 cardinal (central) teeth and 1 lateral tooth in the left valve. 1 cardinal and 2 lateral teeth in the right valve. O: fine concentric ribs and growth lines. C: glossy white, slightly translucent. Amber periostracum, but soon abraded. H: d1–3; attached within rock crevices and other substrates from the littoral to over 200m deep. W: KEL, LUS. R: 2. NB: regularly washed ashore on driftwood and in old oyster shells cemented together.

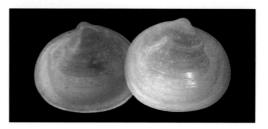

Mysella bidentata

(MONTAGU, 1803)
bidentate mysella

D: 5.5mm. S: thin-shelled, flat, and obliquely oval. Umbones off-center. No cardinal teeth. Right valve has 2 clear lateral teeth; left valve has 2 subtler lateral teeth. Internal ligament. No pallial sinus. O: smooth. Growth lines only. C: white. Amber periostracum. Often covered in rust-colored accretions. H: d1–2; sublittoral and deeper water. Burrows in sand or mud. Often in proximity of other ocean floor dwellers, such as sea urchins, brittle stars, and polychaete worms. W: ARC, KEL, LUS, WAFR. R: 1. NB: can be found in large quantities in light deposits washed ashore.

Tellimya ferruginosa

(MONTAGU, 1808)
oval tellimya

D: 10mm. S: thin-shelled, fairly convex, and elongated. The pallial line displays no sinus. O: fine growth lines, occasionally fine radial ribs as well. C: glossy white with an amber periostracum. Often covered in rust-colored concretions. H: d1–3; sublittoral to greater depths. W: KEL, LUS, WAFR. R: 1. NB: burrows in fine sand and lives in close association with sea urchins, such as *Echinocardium cordatum* and *Spatangus purpureus*.

GLOSSOIDEA

J.E. GRAY, 1847
Round or triangular shells with in-rolled umbones leaning toward the anterior side.

Glossidae

J.E. GRAY, 1847
heart clams

With both valves seen from the side, these shells assume a heart shape. Smooth with coarse growth lines or concentric ribs. Periostracum usually amber, thick, and flaky. External ligament. No pallial sinus. Shells from the genus *Meiocardia* have a sharp, dorsal keel. Found in warm and colder maritime regions, burrowing under a soft substrate. The only modern-day genera are *Glossus* and *Meiocardia*.

Glossus humanus

(LINNAEUS, 1758)
ox-heart clam

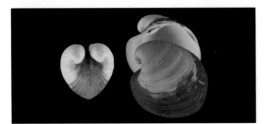

D: 90mm. S: a robust, round shell. The umbonal area is sharply in-rolled to one side. Has a heart shape viewed side-on. O: growth lines only. C: grayish-pink, amber periostracum. H: d1–4; sublittoral and much deeper, between 10 and 1000m. W: KEL, LUS, WAFR. R: 2.

Meiocardia moltkiana

(GMELIN, 1791)
Moltke's heart clam

D: 35mm. S: an oblong shell with a sharp, dorsal keel. O: strong, regularly interspaced ribs. C: cream to white. H: d1; sublittoral, shallow water. W: INDP. R: 3.

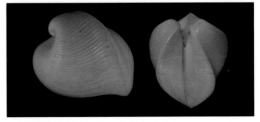

Kelliellidae

P. FISCHER, 1887
Micro-mollusks. Ovoid. Prosogyrate umbones, dorsally angular. Sublittoral to the deep sea. A few genera: *Kelliella, Pauliella, Warrana*.

LUCINOIDEA

J. FLEMING, 1828
Shells that are often round or sometimes more triangular or oblong. Concentric or radial ribs, or smooth. Umbones often point forward (prosogyrate) or curve over. Two muscle scars and no pallial sinus.

Cyrenoididae

H. & A. ADAMS, 1857
Circular valves. Prosogyrate umbones (directed forward) close to the anterior margin. Amber periostracum. External ligament. West Africa, Central America. One genus: *Cyrenoida*.

Fimbriidae

NICOL, 1950
basket lucinas

Thin-shelled, elongated, oval shells. Prominent concentric and radial ribs, reminiscent of basket weaving. Umbones more or less central. A robust hinge with large cardinal (central) and lateral teeth. Indo-Pacific and Australian regions. Only one genus: *Fimbria*.

Fimbria fimbriata

(LINNAEUS, 1758)
common basket lucina

D: 90mm. S: a robust, almost circular shell. Umbonal area fairly squat. Crenulated lower margin. O: lattice sculpture of defined concentric and finer radial ribs. C: creamy white with a yellow sheen. Interior sometimes subtly pink and yellow. H: d1; shallow water. W: INDP. R: 1.

Fimbria sowerbyi

(REEVE, 1841)
Sowerby's basket lucina

D: 75mm. S: a solid, almost circular shell. Lower margin strongly crenulated. O: defined, well-interspaced concentric ribs with rough projections. Finer radial ribs in between. C: cream with orange-red, radiating lines. H: d1; sublittoral to 20m. W: INDP; southwestern part. R: 3.

Lucinidae

J. FLEMING, 1828
lucina clams

Mostly roughly circular shells ranging from fairly robust to thick-shelled. Usually uncolored, cream or white. Either smooth, or with concentric or radial ribs. Some genera (*Divalinga*, *Divaricella*) have divergent, oblique grooves. Anterior muscle scar is narrower and longer than the posterior scar. Found worldwide, both in tropical as well as temperate maritime regions from the littoral to the deep ocean. Several subfamilies, including: Lucininae J. Fleming, 1828; Milthinae Chavan in Moore, 1969; Myrteinae Chavan, 1969. Taken together, dozens of genera, including: *Anodontia, Cardiolucina, Chavania, Codakia, Ctena, Divalinga, Divalucina, Divaricella, Epicodakia, Linga, Loripes, Lucina, Lucinella, Lucinoma, Megaxinus, Miltha, Monitilora, Myrtea, Parvilucina, Phacoides, Rasta*.

Anodontia alba

(LINK, 1807)
buttercup lucina

D: 50mm. S: fairly thin-shelled and round. Umbones virtually in the center. Somewhat flattened to anterior and posterior of the umbones. O: growth lines only. C: exterior white; interior golden yellow (hence buttercup). H: d1; littoral and sublittoral. Burrows in muddy sand in mangroves. W: CAR; West Indies. R: 1.

Codakia paytenorum

(IREDALE, 1937)
interrupted lucina

D: 60mm. S: a solid, circular shell. Umbones virtually in the center; slightly curved over. O: concentric ribs and radiating radial ribs that diminish toward the center. C: yellowish-white; interior lemon yellow and deep orange-red around the margin. H: d1; sublittoral to 10m. W: INDP. R: 1.

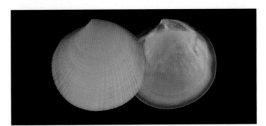

Codakia tigerina

(LINNAEUS, 1758)
Pacific tiger lucina

D: 100mm. S: solid and circular. Umbones virtually in the center, slightly curved over. O: quite delicate lattice sculpture over the whole surface. C: creamy white; interior lemon yellow with an orange-red margin. H: d1; sublittoral to 20m. W: INDP. R: 1.

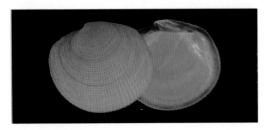

Lucina pectinata

(GMELIN, 1791)
thick American lucina

D: 50mm. S: thick-shelled and round. A slightly flattened, pleated area behind and in front of the umbones. O: very subtle concentric ribs and growth lines. C: yellowish-white. Interior has a wide apricot margin. H: d1; sublittoral, shallow water to 10m. W: CAR, VIR; southeastern United States to Brazil. R: 1.

Lucina pensylvanica

(LINNAEUS, 1758)
Pennsylvanian lucina

D: 50mm. S: a solid, quite convex, round shell. Umbones curved to the side. Lunule clearly visible. A strong keel from the umbones to the posterior lower margin. O: clear, low concentric ribs. C: white. H: d1; sublittoral, shallow water. W: CAR, VIR; southeastern United States, West Indies. R: 1.

Lucinella divaricata

(LINNAEUS, 1758)
dime lucina

D: 11mm. S: a solid, almost round shell. Umbones approximately central. Crenulated lower margin. Internal ligament. O: 60 to 70 irregular, wavy lines run obliquely across the exterior. C: chalky white with a tawny periostracum. H: d1–2; sublittoral and deeper water. W: KEL, LUS. R: 2.

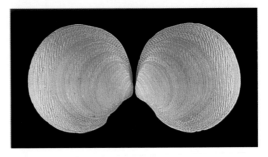

Mactromyidae

COX, 1929
Micro-mollusks with convex, obliquely oval shells, extended toward the posterior. Only one modern-day genus: *Bathycorbis*, found around Australia.

Thyasiridae

DALL, 1901
hatchet shells

Thin-shelled in the shape of rounded triangles with one or more radial, wavy pleats in the posterior dorsal area. Smooth or subtly ornamented, sometimes granulose. A virtually toothless hinge. Found in both warm and cold maritime regions, most species live in deep water, burrowing within soft sediment. Some species live symbiotically with sulfur-oxidizing bacteria. Subfamilies: Axinopsidinae F.R. Bernard, 1983 and Thyasirinae Dall, 1901. A few genera mostly containing smaller shells (just a few millimeters in size), including: *Axinopsida, Axinulus, Leptaxinus, Parathyasira, Thyasira*.

Thyasira flexuosa

(MONTAGU, 1803)
wavy hatchet shell

D: 15mm. S: thin-shelled and almost triangular. Quite pointed umbones. Posterior has 2 clearly undulating ridges. No pallial sinus. Internal ligament. No clear hinge teeth. O: smooth; growth lines only. C: white with a pale amber periostracum. H: d1–3; burrows into fine sand or mud up to depths of 300m. W: KEL, LUS. R: 1.

Ungulinidae

H. & A. ADAMS, 1857
diplodon clams

Ranging from round to triangular and (very) convex. Usually smooth, without ornament, but sometimes with more distinct, irregular growth lines. Mostly in warm maritime regions, but a few species in more temperate areas. A few genera, including: *Diplodonta, Felaniella, Ungulina*.

Diplodonta rotundata

(MONTAGU, 1803)
rotund diplodon

D: 25mm. S: thin-shelled, convex, and almost circular. Slightly angular upper margin. Umbones off-center. O: smooth; growth lines only. C: creamy-white; beige periostracum. H: d1–2; sublittoral to 100m. W: KEL, LUS. R: 2.

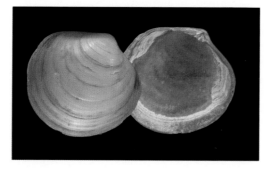

Ungulina cuneata

(SPENGLER, 1782)
rosy diplodon

D: 25mm. S: quite thick-shelled. Irregular shape, usually convex and oval. O: distinct, irregular ribs and growth lines. C: grayish-yellow with a tawny periostracum. Interior rose-red. H: d1; sublittoral. Shallow sandy and muddy substrates to 10m. W: LUS (the Algarve (Portugal) and Gibraltar), WAFR. R: 1.

MACTROIDEA

LAMARCK, 1809
Equivalved and either robust or thin-shelled. Hinge has V-shaped cardinal (central) teeth. Siphons wholly or partially fused. Usually has a pallial sinus.

Anatinellidae

J.E. GRAY, 1853
Rounded, ovoid shells. Angular and slightly gaping on the posterior side. No pallial sinus. Indo-Pacific region. Genus: *Anatinella*.

Cardiliidae

P. FISCHER, 1887
Heart-shaped when viewed side-on. Convex valves. Spirally in-rolled umbones. Partially covered by radial ribs. Developed hinge. No pallial sinus. Indo-Pacific region, Japan. Genus: *Cardilia.*

Mactridae

LAMARCK, 1809
mactra clams or *surf shells*

Large family of oval, oblong, or triangular shells. Umbones lie in the center or point forward. The posterior area is positioned at an angle. Smooth operculum. Well-developed hinge. External ligament with a triangular resilium pad on a depressed chondrophore. In some species the siphons can be withdrawn into the shell. Worldwide distribution. The animals burrow close to the surface of a sandy or muddy substrate. Several subfamilies that can differ from each other markedly. Species from the subfamily Lutrariinae H. & A. Adams, 1856 (otter clams) have elongated, oval shells. The interior is porcelaneous, the exterior is glossy, colored, or a dull white. Prosogyrate umbones. Siphons can only be partly withdrawn, valves gape, lateral hinge teeth are diminished. Wide chondrophore. Species from the subfamily Mactrinae Lamarck, 1809 (mactra clams) usually have oval to triangular shells that gape only slightly. Their umbones are roughly central and they have a well-developed hinge. The siphons can be fully withdrawn. The subfamily Pteropsellinae Keen in Moore, 1969 contains thin-shelled species with rounded, triangular shells and a poorly developed or diminished hinge. Their siphons can be fully withdrawn. The subfamily Zenatiinae Dall, 1895 contains thin-shelled species with elongated, gaping shells. The hinge is well developed and there is a large pit to hold the internal ligament (chondrophore). These subfamilies contain hundreds of species within dozens of genera, including: *Anatina, Darina, Eastonia, Lutraria, Mactra, Mactrellona, Mactrinula, Mulinia, Raeta, Rangia, Spisula, Tresus, Zenatina.*

Eastonia rugosa

(HELBLING, 1779)
rugose mactra

D: 75mm. S: thick-shelled and oval. O: defined lattice sculpture. Radial ribs particularly dominate in the center. C: creamy white to pale yellow. H: d1; sublittoral, shallow water. W: LUS, WAFR. R: 3. NB: distinctive ornament; is unlike most other members of Mactridae.

Lutraria lutraria

(LINNAEUS, 1758)
European otter clam

D: 130mm. S: a robust, flat, elongated, oval shell. Umbones found a third of the way along the upper margin. The pallial line and pallial sinus do not coincide. O: smooth with fine growth lines. C: yellowish-white with a tawny, flaky pe-

riostracum. H: d1; burrows in mud and sand to 50m. W: KEL, LUS, WAFR. R: 1.

Lutraria maxima

JONAS, 1844
snout otter clam

D: 120mm. S: thin-shelled and an elongated oval shape. Pallial line and lower part of the pallial sinus coincide in an almost straight line. O: strong, concentric growth lines. C: creamy white to pale yellow with a dark brown periostracum. H: d1; sublittoral to 10m. W: INDP, JAP. R: 1.

Mactra achatina

HOLTEN, 1802
agate mactra

D: 75mm. S: thin-shelled and oval. Umbones virtually central. Pallial line has a deep sinus. Internal ligament. O: smooth and glossy; fine growth lines only. C: amber with white speckles and stripes. Interior usually white. H: d1–2; sublittoral and deeper to 50m. W: INDP. R: 1.

Mactra chinensis

PHILIPPI, 1846
Chinese mactra

D: 85mm. S: fairly thin-shelled and a triangular oval shape. O: growth lines and low concentric ribs, especially around the lower margin. C: grayish-white to amber, sometimes with subtle, magenta radial bands. Violet interior. H: d1; to 20m. W: INDP, JAP; southern coast of China. R: 1.

Mactra stultorum

(LINNAEUS, 1758)
rayed mactra

D: 65mm. S: thin-shelled and oval. Umbones virtually central. O: smooth and glossy; very fine growth lines only. C: yellowish-white or light brown with purplish-brown bands radiating from the umbones. Violet interior. Tawny periostracum. H: d1; sublittoral, from the shoreline to 25m. W: KEL, LUS. R: 1. NB: the animals have very short siphons and burrow no deeper than 10 cm. Thousands of specimens are often found beached after storms. Often given under the name *M. corallina cinerea* Montagu, 1808.

Mactrellona alata

SPENGLER, 1802
Caribbean winged mactra

D: 90mm. S: quite thin-shelled and a triangular, oval shape. A narrow keel runs from the umbo to the posterior lower margin. O: growth lines and fine concentric ribs. C: milky white; yellowish-gray periostracum. H: d1; sublittoral to 20m. W: CAR. R: 2.

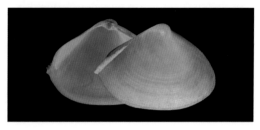

Spisula solida

(LINNAEUS, 1758)
solid mactra

D: 55mm. S: thick-shelled, oval, and rounded on either side. Central umbones. O: smooth exterior; growth lines only. Flattened area on either side of the umbones with fan-like grooves. C: grayish-white. Beige periostracum. H: d1; sublittoral and deeper, burrows in coarse sand. W: KEL, LUS. R: 1.

Spisula subtruncata

(DA COSTA, 1778)
subtruncate mactra

D: 35mm. S: a solid, triangular shell. Anterior slightly more rounded than the rather pointed posterior side (semi-truncated). Umbones virtually central. Flattened area on either side of the umbones with fan-like grooves. Ligament is chiefly internal and held in a triangular pit. O: regular concentric ribs, particularly clear around the lower margin. C: creamy white; yel-

lowish-gray periostracum. H: d1; sublittoral to 20m. W: KEL, LUS. R: 1. NB: can form great banks when washed ashore after storms. A food source for animals such as diving ducks. Commercially fished for human consumption.

Mesodesmatidae

J.E. GRAY, 1839
wedge clams, beach clams, etc.

Solid, oval to elongated, wedge-shaped shells. Anterior longer than posterior. Many species have the shape seen in *Donax* but without a serrated lower margin and with a thick hinge more closely resembling that seen in *Mactra*. Atlantic Ocean, Mediterranean Sea, Indo-Pacific region. Subfamilies: Davilinae Dall, 1895 and Mesodesmatinae J.E. Gray, 1839. Several genera, including: *Anapella, Atactodea, Caecella, Davila, Donacilla, Mesodesma, Monterosatus, Paphies.*

Atactodea striata

(GMELIN, 1791)
striate beach clam

D: 25mm. S: thick-shelled. A rounded triangular shape. O: regular concentric ribs. C: creamy white. Amber periostracum. H: d1; sublittoral, along sandy beaches. W: INDP. R: 1.

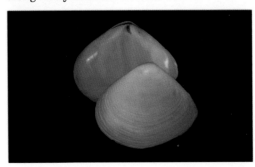

Donacilla cornea

(POLI, 1795)
Mediterranean wedge clam

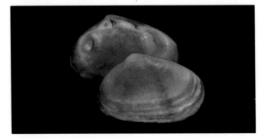

D: 20mm. S: thick-shelled and wedge-shaped. Looks like *Donax* in terms of shape, but lower margin is not crenulated and it has a completely different hinge. O: low growth lines. C: variable: amber to purplish-brown, occasionally in blotches and bands. Interior has roughly the same coloration. H: d1; sublittoral to 20m. W: KEL (south from Brittany, France), LUS, WAFR. R: 1.

Paphies ventricosa

(GRAY, 1843)
toheroa clam

D: 90mm. S: a solid, elongated, wedge-shaped shell. O: growth lines and subtle concentric ribs. C: milky white. Beige periostracum. H: d1; littoral and sublittoral, shallow water alongside sandy beaches. W: AUS; New Zealand. R: 1. NB: widely eaten.

SOLENOIDEA

LAMARCK, 1809
Distinctively narrow, elongated shells with some species measuring over 200mm long. Valves gape at either end. A strong, external ligament. Pallial line has a short pallial sinus.

Pharidae

H. & A. ADAMS, 1858
razor shells and *jackknife clams*

Shells with a clear curvature or else almost straight, and with varying degrees of roundness at either end. A heterodont hinge with one cardinal (central) and one lateral tooth in the right valve and two cardinal and two lateral teeth in the left valve. The ligament is external and very strong. The umbones are not as far forward as in the family Solenidae. Found in all maritime regions from the littoral through to deeper water. They make vertical burrows in fine to coarse sediment. Divided into the subfamilies Pharellinae Tryon, 1884 and Pharinae H. & A. Adams, 1858. Many genera, including: *Cultellus, Ensis, Orbicularia, Pharella, Pharus, Phaxas, Siliqua.*

Cultellus macha

(MOLINA, 1782)
macha jackknife clam

D: 170mm. S: a robust, elongated shell, almost straight-sided. Expanded slightly at the posterior end. Either end is truncated in a straight line. O: growth lines only. C: yellowish-white; thick, amber periostracum. H: d1; sublittoral in sand and mud to 25m. W: MAG, PAT. R: 1.

Ensiculus cultellus

(LINNAEUS, 1758)
cultellus clam

D: 75mm. S: thin-shelled and curved. Rounded at either end. O: irregular growth lines. C: pinkish-beige to olive-green with russet mottling. H: d1; shallow water to 50m. W: INDP, JAP. R: 1.

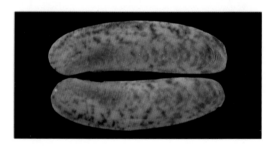

Ensis arcuatus

(JEFFREYS, 1865)
great razor shell

D: 180mm. S: a robust, elongated shell. Length is over eight times its width. Varies from a subtle to a more pronounced curvature. O: growth lines only. C: pink to brownish-purple bands

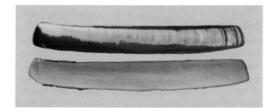

on a paler background. A diagonal line runs from the umbo, dividing the shell's markings into almost precisely vertical and horizontal stripes. Pale green to dark brown, flaky periostracum. Interior white to pale pink. H: d1–2; sublittoral and deeper to 50m in sand. W: KEL, LUS; no further south than Portugal. R: 1.

Ensis directus

(CONRAD, 1843)
Atlantic jackknife clam

D: 160mm. S: quite thin-shelled and clearly curved. Greatly extended: length is over six times its width. Widest in the middle. The anterior (oblong) adductor muscle scar is almost as long as the hinge ligament. O: smooth; growth lines only. C: coloration as for *E. arcuatus*, although the base color tends toward grayish-pink. H: d1; littoral and sublittoral to 20m. W: KEL, LUS, VIR. R: 1. NB: originally an American species. Found along the North Sea coast of Germany at the end of the 1970s. Now common southward from there to France. Sometimes referred to as *E. americanus* (Gould, 1870).

Ensis siliqua

(LINNAEUS, 1758)
giant razor shell

D: 210mm. S: a solid, extremely elongated shell. Completely straight-edged. Length is over six times its width. Rounded anterior end, posterior end angular and slightly wider. O: smooth; growth lines only. C: coloration as in *E. arcuatus*. H: d1–2; sublittoral and somewhat deeper water to 100m. W: ARC, KEL, LUS. R: 2. NB: largest European species of razor shell.

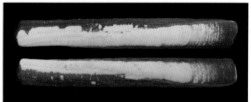

Pharus legumen

(LINNAEUS, 1758)
bean solen

D: 125mm. S: very thin-shelled and straight-sided. Posterior end slightly narrower than the anterior end. O: growth lines only. C: yellowish-white. Periostracum very glossy and greenish-yellow. H: d1; shallow water, mostly alongside sandy beaches. W: KEL, LUS, WAFR. R: 1.

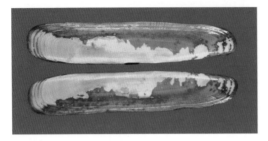

Phaxas pellucidus

(PENNANT, 1777)
little razor shell

D: 30mm. S: very thin-shelled. Elongated, almost to four times its width. Upper margin almost straight, lower margin rounded. Heterodont hinge but with 2 cardinal and no lateral teeth in the right valve. Strong, external hinge ligament. O: smooth; fine growth lines only. C: white or apricot and slightly translucent. Glossy, yellowish-green periostracum. H: d1–2; sublittoral and deeper to 50m. W: KEL, LUS. R: 2.

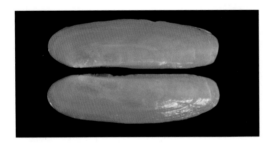

Siliqua costata

SAY, 1822
Atlantic razor clam

D: 50mm. S: thin-shelled and oval. Narrow ends with rounded upper and lower margins. O: smooth. C: grayish-white, sometimes with subtle, pinkish-beige radial bands. Distinct, greenish-yellow to buttercup-yellow perios-

tracum. H: d1; sublittoral along sandy beaches to 20m. W: ARC, KEL, US, VIR. R: 1.

Siliqua radiata

(LINNAEUS, 1758)
sunset siliqua

D: 75mm. S: thin-shelled and oval. Quite wide with narrow front and rear ends and rounded upper and lower margins. O: smooth; growth lines only. C: purplish-brown with bands radiating in cream or white. H: d1; shallow water, muddy substrates. W: INDP. R: 1.

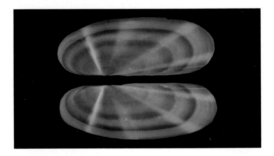

Solenidae

LAMARCK, 1809
razor shells and jackknife clams (continued)

Very narrow, virtually straight-sided shells. Truncated anterior and posterior ends. Only one hinge tooth in both valves. Strong, external ligament. Short, fused siphons. Found in all tropical and temperate maritime regions in the littoral and particularly the sublittoral, as well as in deeper water as well. The animals make vertical burrows in fine to coarse sediment. Genera: *Solen, Solena*.

Solen gordonis

YOKOYAMA, 1920
Japanese jackknife clam

D: 100mm. S: a solid, slender, very straight-sided shell. Anterior edge often cuts in at an angle. O: smooth; growth lines only. C: yellowish-white. Yellowish- to olive-green periostracum. H: d1; littoral and sublittoral, in sand and mud. W: INDP, JAP; China and Japan. R: 1.

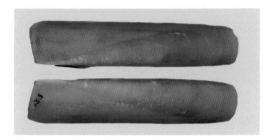

Solen marginatus

PULTENEY, 1799
European razor shell

D: 140mm. S: a robust, completely straight-sided shell. Very elongated. Anterior edge cuts in at an angle. A clear ridge runs parallel along the shell's length. O: growth lines only. C: yellowish-white with an olive-green to brown periostracum. H: d1; littoral and sublittoral to 25m. W: KEL, LUS. R: 1. NB: like many in this and the previous family, this species is edible.

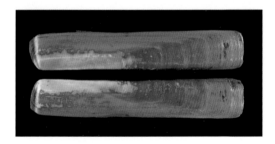

Solen strictus

GOULD, 1861
Gould's jackknife clam

D: 100mm. S: a robust, slender, and completely straight-sided shell. Anterior edge often cuts in at

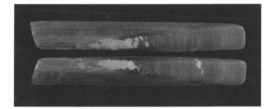

an angle. O: smooth; growth lines only. C: yellowish-white. Yellowish- to olive-green periostracum. H: d1; littoral and sublittoral in sand and mud. W: INDP, JAP; China and Japan. R: 1.

Solen tehuelchus

D'ORBIGNY, 1843
Argentine jackknife clam

D: 100mm. S: a solid, fairly straight-sided shell. Upper and lower margins curve outward slightly. Anterior cuts in at a slight angle. Posterior slightly rounded. O: growth lines only. C: creamy white to pale pink. Yellowish-green periostracum. H: d1; sublittoral to 20m. W: PAT. R: 1.

TELLINOIDEA

DE BLAINVILLE, 1814
An extensive group of bivalves. Their shells range from ovate to almost circular. They are often thin-shelled, although various more robust and thick-shelled species exist. The posterior side is extended and angular in many species. External ligament. Large pallial sinus. Long, separate siphons.

Donacidae

J. FLEMING, 1828
donax clams

Oblong or triangular shells. Often truncated at an oblique angle on the posterior side, while the anterior side is rounded or pointed. The umbones are roughly central. The exterior is smooth or has subtle lattice sculpture. Occasionally, they have stronger ribs or serrated projections around the margins. Crenulated lower margin. External ligament. Clear pallial sinus. Found in both warm as well as temperate maritime regions. They burrow in sand or mud just below the substrate surface. Many genera, including *Capsella, Chion, Cuneus, Donax, Galatea, Hecuba, Latona*.

Donax bipartitus

SOWERBY, 1892
South African donax

D: 23mm. S: a solid, elongated, quite narrow shell. Posterior sharply truncated. O: anterior side is smooth, central section has subtle concentric ornament, and posterior side has stronger concentric grooves and finer radial ribs. C: creamy white to grayish-white. Interior white; posterior side violet. H: d1; sublittoral in coarse sand. From the splash zone to 25m. W: ZAFR. R: 1.

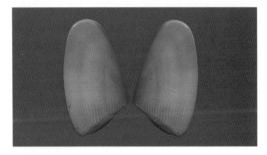

Donax denticulatus

LINNAEUS, 1758
toothed donax

D: 25mm. S: a solid, triangular shell. O: clear radial ribs ending in small, sharp projections at the margin. Very faint sculpture between the ribs. C: variable: often grayish-white with purple stripes. H: d1; littoral and sublittoral, along sandy beaches. W: CAR, VIR; United States to Brazil. R: 1.

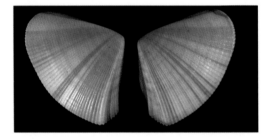

Donax rugosus

LINNAEUS, 1758
rugose donax

D: 50mm. S: a solid, elongated oval shell. Posterior side sharply truncated. O: low, radial grooves and concentric ribs. A granulose structure toward the posterior. C: very variable: creamy white, apricot, and purple, with or without concentric or radial bands. H: d1;

splash zone and sublittoral along sandy beaches. W: WAFR. R: 1.

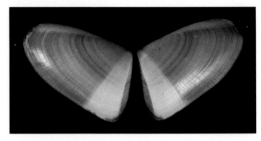

Donax serra

DILLWYN, 1817
saw donax

D: 50mm. S: a solid, oval shell. Lower margin at the truncated posterior end is more strongly and sharply crenulated than elsewhere. O: fine concentric and radial ribs. Posterior end has defined, rough sculpture. C: beige. Russet periostracum. Interior purple. H: d1; shallow water, splash zone and sublittoral of sandy beaches. W: ZAFR. R: 1.

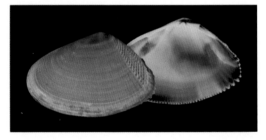

Donax striatus

LINNAEUS, 1767
striate donax

D: 25mm. S: a solid triangular to elongated shell. Lower anterior margin curves outward. Posterior is pointed. O: clear radial ribs across the whole shell. C: variable: grayish-white to mauve, uniformly or in bands. Interior white or purple. H: d1; littoral and sublittoral. W: CAR. R: 1.

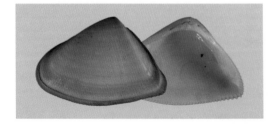

Donax trunculus

LINNAEUS, 1758
truncate donax

D: 30mm. S: a solid, elongated oval shell. Posterior side more sharply truncated than in *D. vittatus*. O: fine radial ribs. C: variable, creamy white, apricot, or mauve. Interior ochre to deep purple. H: d1; littoral and sublittoral along sandy beaches. W: KEL (from Brittany southward), LUS, WAFR. R: 1. NB: much used in soups and in the Spanish dish paella.

Donax vittatus

(DA COSTA, 1778)
banded donax

D: 40mm. S: a robust, elongated, triangular shell. Posterior truncated, tapering to a slight point. O: fine radial ribs fan out from the umbo crossed by growth lines. C: apricot to mauve with an olive-green periostracum. Interior often purple, sometimes orange. H: d1; sublittoral— splash zone to 25m, along sandy beaches. W: KEL, LUS. R: 2.

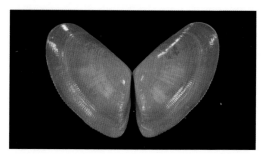

Hecuba scortum

(LINNAEUS, 1758)
leather donax

D: 90mm. S: thick-shelled and triangular. Sharply pointed posterior. O: defined lattice sculpture. Concentric ribs stronger and more widely interspaced toward the anterior. C: grayish-white; extremities and interior purple. Dark

brown periostracum. H: d1; sublittoral in muddy bays. W: INDP. R: 1. NB: concentric ribs may bear spiny projections, especially toward the posterior.

Latona cuneata

(LINNAEUS, 1758)
cuneate donax

D: 40mm. S: a solid, elongated oval shell. Umbones almost central. O: smooth; ribbed toward the posterior. C: variable, often yellowish-green or cream with brown, radiating bands. Interior deep purple. H: d1; sublittoral in sand. W: INDP. R: 1.

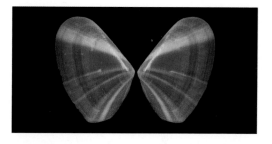

Latona faba

(GMELIN, 1791)
Pacific bean donax

D: 18mm. S: quite thick-shelled and an elongated oval shape. Truncated on either side. O: concentric ribs. C: yellowish-white, marbled with russet spots or radial bands. H: d1; sublittoral. Shallow water and the splash zone along sandy beaches. W: INDP. R: 1.

285

Psammobiidae

J. FLEMING, 1828

sanguin and gari clams (sunset clams)

Thin-shelled to relatively robust. Valves gape to varying degrees at either end. Elongated oval shells. The surface may be smooth or sculpted. They are often brightly colored with bands of color radiating from the umbones, reminiscent of the setting sun. The ligament is located externally on a wide ridge (ligament shelf). A clear, deep pallial sinus. Found in both warm as well as temperate maritime regions, the animals burrow into sand, sediment, or gravel, especially in the littoral and sublittoral, and in estuaries and mangrove swamps. Some species also live in deeper water. Two subfamilies: Psammobiinae J. Fleming, 1828 and Sanguinolariinae Grant & Gale, 1931. Many genera, including: *Asaphis, Gari, Heterodonax, Nuttallia, Psammobia, Psammotellina, Sanguinolaria, Soletellina*.

Asaphis deflorata

(LINNAEUS, 1758)
gaudy asaphis

D: 60mm. S: a robust, oblong shell. O: lattice sculpture. Toward the anterior and posterior ends rather more defined radial ribs that may bear scales. C: variable: yellow, orange, pink, or violet, often in radial bands. H: d1; littoral and sublittoral, mangroves. W: CAR; Florida to Brazil. R: 1.

Asaphis violascens

(FORSKÄL IN NIEBUHR, 1775)
Pacific asaphis

Gari depressa

(PENNANT, 1777)
depressed gari

D: 67mm. S: a solid, oblong shell. O: pronounced lattice sculpture; radial ribs wider apart at the anterior and posterior ends. C: yellow, pink, or purple, often in radial bands. H: d1; sublittoral. Burrows in coarse sand. W: AUS, INDP, JAP. R: 1.

Gari amethysta

(WOOD, 1815)
amethyst gari

D: 60mm. S: a robust, elongated shell. Posterior end tapers to an angle with 1–2 rounded keels running to the posterior end from the umbones. O: fine, dense concentric ribs in the central section; stronger ribs toward the anterior side. C: pale pink with magenta mottling and, occasionally, radial stripes. H: d1; shallow water. W: INDP. R: 1.

Gari costulata

(TURTON, 1822)
quarter-striped gari

D: 25mm. S: fairly thin-shelled. A flattened, elongated oval shell. Slightly truncated posterior end. O: regular growth lines and fine concentric ribs – up to 20 radial ribs in the posterior section. C: pink to purple with subtle radial stripes. H: d1–2; sublittoral and deeper to 50m. W: KEL, LUS, WAFR, ZAFR. R: 3.

D: 70mm. S: a solid, fairly flat, oval shell. Truncated, rounded posterior. O: low, concentric ribs. C: cream, pale yellow, magenta. Usually with violet radial stripes. H: d1–2; sublittoral and deeper to 50m. W: KEL, LUS, WAFR. R: 1.

Gari fervensis

(GMELIN, 1791)
Faeroe gari

D: 50mm. S: a solid, elongated shell. Posterior tapers to an angle with a sharp keel to the rear running from the umbo. O: quite pronounced concentric ribs, especially on the right valve and in the area around the keel. C: creamy white to pale pink with orange-red stripes radiating from the umbones. Glossy purple interior. Amber periostracum. H: d1–2; sublittoral and deeper to 100m. W: KEL, LUS, WAFR. R: 2.

Heterodonax bimaculatus

(LINNAEUS, 1758)
small false donax

D: 18mm. S: a solid, compact, oval shell. Truncated posterior end. O: low concentric ribs. C: variable: creamy white, apricot to purple, often with russet bands of color composed of chevron-like markings. H: d1; littoral and sublittoral, the splash zone on beaches. W: CAR; Florida, West Indies. R: 1.

Sanguinolaria sanguinolenta

(GMELIN, 1791)
Atlantic sanguin

D: 50mm. S: thin-shelled and oval. Pointed posterior end, rounded anterior end. O: growth lines only. C: pale pink, umbones and interior darker. H: d1; sublittoral, shallow water. W: CAR; Texas to Brazil. R: 3.

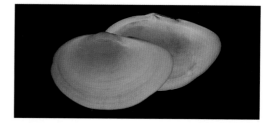

Semelidae

STOLICZKA, 1870
semele clams

These clams range from being exceptionally thin-shelled to fairly robust. They may be rounded, oval, or egg-shaped. Some species' valves gape slightly. Lateral teeth may sometimes be present in the hinge. The ligament is partly internal with an embedded resilium pad. Deep pallial sinus. Wide distribution. Although chiefly found in sediment and mud in shallow water, some species live much deeper. Subfamilies: Scrobiculariinae H. & A. Adams, 1856 and Semelinae Stoliczka, 1870. The posterior part of the valves in the latter subfamily are often slightly bent to the side and their hinges contain lateral teeth. Members of Scrobiculariinae mainly occur in Europe and have quite large, flattened, oval shells but no lateral teeth in the hinge. Only a few genera: *Abra, Cumingia, Ervilia, Iacra, Leptomya, Scrobicularia, Theora, Semele, Syndosmya*.

Abra alba

(W. WOOD, 1802)
white semele

D: 22mm. S: very thin-shelled and ovate. Umbones not central. Posterior end slightly angled.

A slanted, triangular ligamental pit just behind the umbones on the inside. O: smooth; very fine growth lines only. C: glossy white; the living animal often lends a bluish hue to the shell. Tawny periostracum. H: d1–2; sublittoral and slightly deeper water. W: KEL, LUS, WAFR. R: 1.

Abra nitida

(O.F. MÜLLER, 1776)
glossy semele

D: 15mm. S: very thin-shelled and elliptical. Looks like *A. alba* in terms of shape but umbones are almost central. O: smooth, very glossy, sometimes slightly translucent. C: very glossy white. H: d1–2; deep water. W: ARC, KEL, LUS. R: 3.

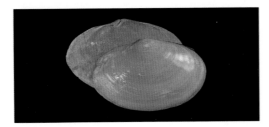

Abra prismatica

(MONTAGU, 1808)
prismatic semele

D: 24mm. S: very thin-shelled and elongated. Umbones not centered. Posterior end clearly pointed. O: smooth; very fine growth lines only. C: very glossy white. H: d1–2; deep water. W: KEL, LUS. R: 3.

Scrobicularia plana

(DA COSTA, 1778)
flat furrow clam

D: 60mm. S: quite a thin, very flat, oval to round shell. Equilateral. Anterior side rounded; posterior side very slightly truncated. Hinge missing lateral teeth, unlike *Abra* species. A large, triangular resilium pit below the umbones of both valves. O: dense concentric ribs and growth lines. C: grayish- or yellowish-white. Amber periostracum. H: d1; littoral and sublittoral, especially muddy substrates and exposed sandbars. W: KEL, LUS, WAFR. R: 1.

Solecurtidae

D'ORBIGNY, 1846
solecurtus clams

Rectangular to oval shells with rounded extremities. Roughly equilateral and gaping at either end. Ornament is often with oblique (converging) radial grooves. These animals dig burrows a few tens of centimeters deep into sand or mud and are chiefly found in warmer maritime regions. Subfamilies: Novaculininae Ghosh, 1920 and Solecurtinae D'Orbigny, 1846. Only a few genera, including *Azorinus, Novaculina, Protagelus, Sinonovacula, Solecurtus, Tagelus*.

Azorinus chamasolen

(DA COSTA, 1778)
antique razor clam

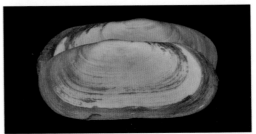

D: 55mm. S: oval, flattened shell. Rounded anterior and posterior margins. Umbones asymmetrical. Lower margin often slightly curved inward. O: regular, concentric growth lines only. C: white with an amber periostracum. H: d1–2; sublittoral and deeper water. W: KEL, LUS. R: 2.

Sinonovacula constricta

(LAMARCK, 1818)
constricted razor clam

D: 50mm. S: a fairly robust, straight-sided, elongated oval shell. O: distinct growth lines. C: yellowish-white; tawny periostracum. H: d1; shallow water at river mouths and bays in mud. W: INDP. R: 1.

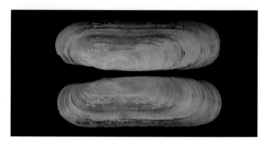

Solecurtus scopula

(TURTON, 1822)
white solecurtus

D: 80mm. S: oval, convex shell. Anterior and posterior ends truncated. O: concentric growth lines and narrow, oblique radial ribs, diminishing or disappearing at the furthest extremities. C: white; grayish-yellow periostracum. H: d1–2; sublittoral and deeper water. W: LUS, WAFR. R: 2.

Solecurtus strigilatus

(LINNAEUS, 1758)
scrapper solecurtus

D: 75mm. S: a wide, convex, oval shell. Asymmetrical umbones. Anterior and posterior ends quite sharply truncated. O: concentric growth lines and oblique, wavy radial ribs. C: pink and cream, usually with paler rays fanning out from

the umbones. H: d1; sublittoral, burrows in sand. W: LUS, WAFR, ZAFR. R: 1.

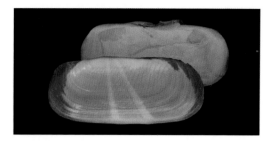

Tagelus divisus

(SPENGLER, 1794)
purplish American tagelus

D: 35mm. S: narrow, flat, slightly curved. Umbones virtually central. O: smooth, only very vague growth lines. C: white with purple radiating bands and blotches. Amber periostracum. H: d1; shallow water, burrows in sand and mud. W: CAR, VIR; United States to Brazil. R: 1.

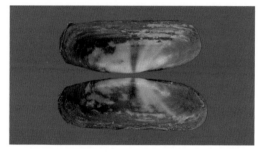

Tagelus dombei

(LAMARCK, 1818)
Dombey's tagelus

D: 90mm. S: narrow, flat shell. Posterior wider than anterior. Umbones just off-center. O: low concentric growth lines. C: grayish-yellow with slight grayish-violet blotches and bands. Sometimes paler rays. Brown periostracum. H: d1; sublittoral. W: PAN, PER; Mexico, Peru. R: 1.

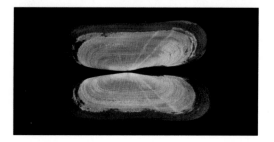

Tellinidae

DE BLAINVILLE, 1814
tellins

Mostly inequilateral shells, often shorter on the posterior side and slightly curved to the right. In many species, the right valve is a little larger and rather more convex. The surface has concentric ribs or else is smooth, sometimes with radial grooves or some other radial ornament. They are often brightly colored and patterned. Worldwide distribution. They burrow in soft sand and mud, many species resting on their left side just under the surface of the substrate, searching the surface for food particles with their long or short siphons that can be either fused or separate. Subfamilies: Macominae Olsson, 1961; Tellininae De Blainville, 1814. Members of the first subfamily have no lateral hinge teeth, while those from the other subfamily do. There are simply dozens of genus names currently in use. However, for the sake of convenience, many official publications still place the majority of species within the genus *Tellina*, with the various genus names used as a subgenus name. That principle has been employed in this encyclopedia too. Genera: *Angulus, Arcopagia, Fabulina, Moerella, Oudardia, Serratina*. Other genera to come under Tellinidae include: *Cymatoica, Exotica, Gastrana, Leporimetis, Macalia, Macoma, Psammotreta, Strigilla, Tellidora*.

Macoma balthica

(LINNAEUS, 1758)
Baltic macoma

D: 30mm. S: a robust, round to triangular shell. Fairly convex. Posterior end slightly angled, umbones in the center. External ligament. Clear pallial sinus. O: growth lines only. C: cream, yellow, orange, or pink, especially the interior and around the umbonal area. H: d1; littoral and sublittoral, burrows deeply in relatively fine sand or sediment. W: ARC, KEL; both sides of the Atlantic Ocean. R: 1.

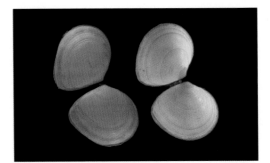

Macoma calcarea

(GMELIN, 1791)
chalky macoma

D: 50mm. S: quite thin-shelled and an elongated oval shape. Umbones off-center and fairly flattened. O: growth lines only. C: chalky white; beige periostracum. H: d1; in rather deeper water. W: ALE, ARC, KEL (both sides of the Atlantic Ocean), JAP. R: 1.

Tellina crassa

PENNANT, 1777
thick tellin

D: 50mm. S: thick-shelled, flattened, and an oblique oval shape. Umbones off-center. Deep, wide pallial sinus. External ligament. O: regular concentric ribs with fine radial ribs in between. C: creamy white or pale yellow with orange-red bands fanning out from the umbones. H: d1; burrows in coarse sand with shell fragments. W: KEL, LUS, WAFR. R: 2.

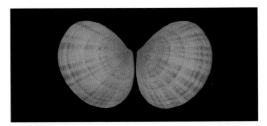

Tellina donacina

LINNAEUS, 1758
donax tellin

D: 25mm. S: quite thin-shelled and elongated. Angled posterior end. Umbones off-center. O: fine concentric sculpture. C: pale yellow or orange with interrupted bands of orange, red, or mauve radiating from the umbones. H: d1–2; sublittoral and deeper to over 80m. W: KEL, LUS, WAFR. R: 2.

Tellina foliacea

(LINNAEUS, 1758)
foliated tellin

D: 75mm. S: a large, quite solid, flat shell. Umbones roughly central. O: a sharp ridge runs to the posterior (this side is often covered in beading and spicules). C: orange-red, interior magenta. H: d1. W: INDP. R: 1.

Tellina linguafelis

(LINNAEUS, 1758)
cat's-tongue tellin

D: 60mm. S: a solid, rounded, triangular shell. Posterior end slightly angular and ridged. O: surface covered in small rough scales. C: creamy white with red-orange rays. H: d1; sublittoral. W: INDP. R: 1.

Tellina listeri

RÖDING, 1798
speckled tellin

D: 60mm. S: a robust, elongated shell. Prominent ridge at pointed posterior end. O: clear,

defined concentric ribs. C: pink with purplish-brown dashes and stripes. H: d1–2; sublittoral and deeper water. W: CAR, VIR; United States to Brazil. R: 1.

Tellina planata

LINNAEUS, 1758
flat tellin

D: 65mm. S: a solid, flat, broadly oval shell. Pointed posterior end. O: smooth with a ridge toward the posterior side. C: orange-gray; interior apricot. H: d1; sublittoral. W: LUS, WAFR. R: 1.

Tellina pulcherrima

SOWERBY, 1825
beautiful tellin

D: 40mm. S: a robust, elongated, oval shell. Posterior side acutely angled. O: Posterior ridge. Concentric ribs and sharp, scaly projections on the anterior and posterior sides. C: creamy white or white with orange-red rays. H:

d1; sublittoral. W: INDP, JAP. R: 3.

Tellina radiata

LINNAEUS, 1758
sunrise tellin

D: 100mm. S: a large, solid, elongated shell. Slightly pointed posterior end. O: smooth. C: glossy creamy white to pure white with wide rays in rose red. H: d1. W: CAR. R: 1.

Tellina rostrata

LINNAEUS, 1758
rostrate tellin

D: 75mm. S: thin-shelled and elongated. Posterior end narrows very sharply. O: smooth; growth lines only. Slight ridge toward posterior. C: glossy orange-red. H: d1; sublittoral to 20m. W: INDP. R: 3.

Tellina scobinata

LINNAEUS, 1758
rasp tellin

D: 60mm. S: solid, almost circular shell. O: slight posterior ridge. Defined, scabrous projections over whole shell. C: creamy white, sometimes

with vague, brown blotches. Interior white with yellow. H: d1; shallow water. W: INDP. R: 1.

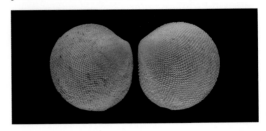

Tellina tenuis

DA COSTA, 1778
thin tellin

D: 30mm. S: thin-shelled and quite flat. Posterior slightly angled. O: growth lines only. C: uniform orange or pink, or pale pink with dark pink bands. H: d1; sublittoral to 20m. W: KEL, LUS, WAFR. R: 1. NB: seen to the right in the photograph is the species *T. fibula* (Gmelin, 1791) – the story tellin. It has the same occurrence and measures up to 25mm. Its right valve has fine grooves running obliquely across the shell.

Tellina virgata

(LINNAEUS, 1758)
striped tellin

D: 75mm. S: a solid, elongated oval shell. O: defined concentric ribs. Posterior end has ridges. C: yellowish-white with wide, pink to purplish-brown rays. H: d1; sublittoral to 30m. W: INDP, JAP. R: 1.

ORDER MYOIDA

GOLDFUSS, 1820

SUBORDER MYINA

GOLDFUSS, 1820

MYOIDEA

LAMARCK, 1809

Animals with very well-developed siphons. Hinge has one or two reduced teeth or else is toothless. Widely gaping valves, oval or ovoid, often slightly inequivalved. Ligament usually internal. They burrow in sand or bore into a hard substrate.

Corbulidae

LAMARCK, 1818
corbula clams

Distinctively inequivalved shells: in some species, the right valve is considerably larger than the left, and partly encloses it. Anterior rounded. Posterior often narrower, angular, or beaked. Wide distribution: found both in warm and cold maritime regions, and also in estuarine water. Two subfamilies: Corbulinae Lamarck, 1818 and Lentidiinae H.E. Vokes, 1945. Genera: *Anisocorbula, Lentidium, Notocorbula, Potamocorbula, Solidicorbula, Varicorbula*.

Notocorbula tunicata

HINDS, 1843
angular corbula

D: 50mm. S: thick-shelled and angular. Right valve larger and more convex. Umbones are central and sharply in-rolled. O: quite widely inter-spaced concentric ribs. Several angular ridges run from the umbones to the posterior end. C: creamy white, often beige between the ribs. H: d1; sublittoral and deeper water. W: INDP. R: 2.

Solidicorbula erythrodon

(LAMARCK, 1818)
red-toothed corbula

D: 12mm. S: thick-shelled. An elongated, triangular shell. Posterior side thickened internally. O: defined, slanting concentric ribs. C: chalky white; interior white with a touch of purple. Shell margins red-orange. H: d1; sublittoral to 20m. W: JAP. R: 1.

Varicorbula gibba

(OLIVI, 1792)
common Atlantic corbula

D: 13mm. S: quite thick-shelled and triangular. Right valve significantly larger and more convex than the left. Umbones central, sharply in-rolled. O: dense concentric ribs. 2 slight ridges running from the umbo to the posterior. Left valve flatter and less strongly ribbed; usually has stronger radial sculpture. C: tawny or pink; beige, fibrous periostracum. H: d1–3; sublittoral to greater depths. W: ARC, KEL, LUS, WAFR. R: 1.

Erodonidae

WINCKWORTH, 1932
Same shape as for Corbulidae but with a chondrophore (depression holding internal ligament) in the hinge. Mud flats and estuarine water. From Brazil to Argentina. One genus: *Erodona*.

Myidae

LAMARCK, 1809
soft-shell clams

Elongated, gaping shells that are angled or sharply truncated at the posterior end. Large chondrophore in the left valve. Toothless hinge (desomdont). Deep pallial sinus. Long, fused siphons surrounded by a corneous periostracum. Animals byssate only when immature. Some species reach up to 100mm or more in size. The animals burrow down to half a meter deep in muddy sand. Only a few genera, including *Mya, Paramya, Sphenia, Tugonia*.

Mya arenaria

LINNAEUS, 1758
soft-shell clam

D: 130mm. S: a solid, ovate shell. Umbones almost central. Anterior rounded; posterior pointed. Gapes wide. Very long, fused siphons in a parchment-like, periostracum-encased tube. O: regular growth lines only. C: chalky white to yellowish-white with rust-brown blotches. H: d1; littoral and sublittoral, burrowing 40 cm deep in fine sand or sediment. W: ALE, CAL, JAP, KEL. R: 1. NB: edible.

Mya truncata

LINNAEUS, 1758
truncate soft-shell clam

D: 75mm. S: a robust shell, distinctly truncated on one side. Umbones roughly central. Chondrophore projects in left valve. O: growth lines only. C: white or yellowish-white. Dark brown, flaky periostracum. H: d1–2; burrows up to 30 cm deep in muddy sand. Sublittoral and deeper to 70m. W: ALE, ARC, CAL, JAP, KEL. R: 2. NB: the siphonal tube seen in the photograph is considerably longer in living animals (this also applies to *M. arenaria*).

Spheniopsidae

GARDNER, 1928
Micro-mollusks. Triangular shells with concentric ribs. Right valve has two cardinal (central) teeth. Left valve is toothless. Clear pallial sinus. One genus: *Grippina*, found in the Californian region.

GASTROCHAENOIDEA

J.E. GRAY, 1840
Widely gaping shells. The living animal bores a tunnel into wood, coral, or rock. The tunnel-burrow is bottle-shaped and has a calcareous lining. Only one family: Gastrochaenidae.

Gastrochaenidae

J.E. GRAY, 1840
rock-borer clams

Elongated and thin-shelled. Gaping widely at the anterior end. External ligament. Deep pallial sinus. Only a few genera, including *Cucurbitula, Gastrochaena, Spengleria*.

Gastrochaena dubia

(PENNANT, 1777)
European rock borer

D: 25mm. S: thin-shelled and an elongated, oval shape. Anterior end gapes very widely. O: dense growth lines. C: chalky white; beige periostracum. H: d1; sublittoral, lives in self-bored holes in limestone and large shells, such as oysters. W: KEL, LUS. R: 3.

HIATELLOIDEA

J.E. GRAY, 1824

The animals live in crevices and holes or burrow into hard or softer sediment. Often found in bore tunnels made by other organisms.

Hiatellidae

J.E. GRAY, 1824

geoduck, panope, hiatella, and saxicave clams

Thick-shelled and gaping. An oval to trapezoid shape. External ligament. Byssate on rocks and other substrates or found in rock crevices. Some also burrow deeply into mud. Circumpolar, but also found in more temperate regions such as the Mediterranean Sea. Many genera, including: *Cyrtodaria, Hiatella, Panomya, Panopea, Saxicavella.*

Hiatella artica

(LINNAEUS, 1767)
Arctic hiatella

D: 25mm. S: thick-shelled and an elongated, rectangular shape. Often very distorted. O: irregular growth lines. 2 clear keels, usually with spicules, run from the umbo to the posterior side. C: chalky white; beige periostracum. H: d1–3; littoral, sublittoral, and deeper water. Attached by byssus to rocks, root clumps, wood, and many other substrates and objects, both floating and fixed. W: ALE, ARC, CAR, INDP, KEL, LUS, PAN, WAFR, ZAFR. R: 1.

Hiatella rugosa

(LINNAEUS, 1767)
rugose hiatella

D: 35mm. S: elliptical, oval shell. O: distinct growth lines, no spiny keels. C: chalky white; beige periostracum. H: d1–2; littoral and sublittoral, also in deeper water. Chiefly found in rock crevices, usually in bore tunnels made by

rock-boring mollusks. W: ALE, ARC, CAR, INDP, KEL, LUS, PAN, WAFR, ZAFR. R: 1. NB: some consider this to be a subspecies or a particular ecological form of *H. arctica.*

SUBORDER PHOLADINA

H. & A. ADAMS, 1858

PHOLADOIDEA

LAMARCK, 1809

Bivalves that have adapted to a distinctive lifestyle. The animals bore holes in intertidal peat, wood, rock, coral, etc. The bore tunnel then becomes their permanent home.

Pholadidae

LAMARCK, 1809

piddocks, pholads

Ranging from thin-shelled to quite robust, these shells are extremely elongated and gape at either end. Ornament of radial and concentric ribs, often with rough projections, particularly at intersections. Ligament missing. The upper margin is turned outward, this is where the anterior adductor muscle is attached, usually covered by a third accessory shell plate (sometimes more than one) made of calcite. A spoon-like projection is also visible within each valve (apophysis). Divided into several subfamilies: Jouannetiinae Tryon, 1862; Martesiinae Grant & Gale, 1931; Pholadinae Lamarck, 1809. Many genera, including: *Barnea, Cyrtopleura, Jouannetia, Lignopholas, Martesia, Parapholas, Pholadidea, Pholas, Zirfaea.*

Barnea candida

(LINNAEUS, 1758)
white piddock

D: 50mm. S: very thin-shelled and an elongated, oval shape. Umbones and upper margin partially reflected. A thin, curved apophysis projects within the valves. Where there are 2 valves, a third (accessory) shell plate should be found between them at the hinge. O: concentric and radial ribs (lattice sculpture). Scaly spines at intersections. C: white; yellowish-gray periostracum. H: d1; found in self-bored passages in wood, intertidal peat, and softer rock types. W: KEL, LUS, WAFR. R: 1.

Barnea dilatata

(SOULEYET, 1843)
wide piddock

D: 80mm. S: very thin-shelled and a wide, oval shape. Very gaping habit. O: widely interspaced lattice sculpture. C: white. H: d1; sublittoral, makes deep tunnels in firm clay. W: INDP, JAP; China and Asia. R: 2. NB: the animal and its siphons are edible.

Barnea parva

(PENNANT, 1777)
little piddock

D: 40mm. S: a solid, elongated shell. Gaping anterior and posterior ends. Lower margin

curves inward just below the umbonal area. Reflected upper margin. Interior has a thin curved tooth (apophysis). Has a third (accessory) shell plate. O: delicate lattice sculpture with scales at intersections. C: chalky white; grayish-yellow periostracum. H: d1; sublittoral to approx. depth of 20m. Bores into chalk, wood, and peat. W: KEL, LUS. R: 3.

Cyrtopleura costata

(LINNAEUS, 1758)
angel wing

D: 150mm. S: thin-shelled and an elongated oval shape. Reflected umbones and upper margin. Apophysis within. Has an accessory shell plate. O: lattice sculpture; area below umbones has more broadly interspaced and pronounced radial ribs. Fluted scales at intersections. C: creamy white and, rarely, a hint of magenta. H: d1; tunnels into clay and mud. W: CAR. R: 2.

Pholas dactylus

LINNAEUS, 1758
European piddock

D: 120mm. S: a robust, extremely elongated shell. Distinctly gaping. Reflected upper margin and umbones containing radiating cavities. The lower margin curves inward below the umbonal area. Apophysis within. A complex arrangement of 3 accessory shell plates at the hinge when both valves are intact. O: concentric grooves crossed by radial ribs. Rough projections at intersections. C: white or cream. H: d1; bores into clay and sandstone. W: KEL, LUS. R: 1. NB: living animals emit a bluish, phosphorescent light in the dark.

Pholas orientalis

(GMELIN, 1791)
oriental piddock

D: 125mm. S: thin-shelled and elongated. Reflected upper margin. O: concentric growth lines and also radial ribs across half of the shell with scales. An accessory shell plate. C: white. H: d1; sublittoral, bores into clay and soft limestone. W: AUS, INDP. R: 2.

Zirfaea crispata

(LINNAEUS, 1767)
oval piddock

D: 85mm. S: a solid, wide, oval shell. Very gaping anterior and posterior margins. Reflected upper margin. A thin, curved apophysis within. A small accessory shell plate. O: a shallow groove down the center of the shell exterior dividing its ornament into two. Strong, wavy concentric ribs below the umbones. C: chalky white; beige periostracum. H: d1; bores into rock, clay, wood, and peat. Found to a depth of approx. 25m. W: ALE, ARC, KEL, LUS. R: 2.

Teredinidae

RAFINESQUE, 1815
shipworms

Long, worm-like animals that bore tunnels into wood. They line these burrows with a calcareous secretion. The very small shells cover only a small part of the animal at the front. The short siphons are protected by two paddle-shaped, calcareous shutters or "pallets." These pallets are important to the identification of different species. In the past, these animals caused great damage to the wooden hulls of ships, harbor pilings, etc. Subfamilies: Bankiinae Turner, 1966; Kuphinae Tryon, 1862; Teredininae Rafinesque, 1815. Many genera, including: *Bankia, Kuphus, Lyrodus, Nototeredo, Psiloteredo, Teredo, Teredora*.

Psiloteredo megotara

(HANLEY IN FORBES & HANLEY, 1848)
floating timber shipworm

D: 12mm. S: shells differ from those of *T. navalis* due to the shape of the "ear," which is larger and projects above the shell. Pallets have a straight spine; not notched at the top. O: as for *T. navalis*. C: white. H: d1; as for *T. navalis*. W: wide distribution. R: 2.

Teredo navalis

LINNAEUS, 1758
common shipworm

D: shells 12mm; pallets 7mm. S: thin-shelled and obliquely triangular, roughly divided into an anterior, central, and posterior section (the "ear"). The latter does not project above the shell in *T. navalis*. The pallets have a curved spine and are slightly notched at the top. O: central section has horizontal and vertical ribs. Anterior section has horizontal ribs; the ear is virtually smooth. C: chalky white. H: d1–3; bores into wood. W: nearly worldwide distribution. R: 1.

Xylophagaidae

PURCHON, 1941
wood borers

These animals bore into wood and have shells like those of *Teredo*, but they lack pallets, and the shells are larger (up to 15mm), covering the whole body. The burrows are not lined with any calcareous secretions. Found in timber on the ocean floor down to great depths. A few genera, including: *Xylophaga, Xyloredo, Xylopholas.*

Xylophaga dorsalis

(TURTON, 1819)
common wood borer

D: 13mm. S: quite thin-shelled and convex. Can be divided into several parts. 2 accessory shell plates between, and partially covering, the umbones. Both valves seen together are circular in outline. Only the posterior sections fit snugly. No pallets. Body much shorter than that of shipworms. O: central section has wavy keels and oblique concentric lines. Anterior section has horizontal ribs. Posterior section virtually smooth. C: chalky white. H: d1–3; bores into sunken timber in deep water. W: ALE, ARC, KEL, LUS. R: 3.

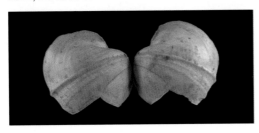

SUBCLASS ANOMALODESMATA

DALL, 1889
A subclass of highly developed bivalves in which some groups possess very specialized, W-shaped gills. Hinge has poorly developed teeth or is toothless. External ligament or a spoon-shaped, calcareous projection in the valves (lithodesma).

ORDER PHOLADOMYOIDA

NEWELL, 1965

PHOLADOMYOIDEA

J.E. GRAY, 1847

Parilimyidae

MORTON, 1982
Rounded to triangular in shape and thin-shelled. Equivalved. Anterior and posterior ends truncated and gaping. Umbones roughly central, projecting inward. Granulose surface or fine radial ribs. Atlantic and Indo-Pacific regions in shallow and deep water. A few genera: *Nipponopanacca, Panacca, Parilimya.*

Pholadomyidae

J.E. GRAY, 1847
Elongated, oval shells with the umbo projecting toward the anterior. Equivalved, gaping at the rear. Nodulose radial ribs. Resilium in a chondrophore (depression). No lithodesma. Worldwide occurrence. Only one genus, *Pholadomya*, found in deep water.

CLAVAGELLOIDEA

D'ORBIGNY, 1844
A very small superfamily. Only one family containing some distinctly aberrant bivalves in terms of their shape.

Clavagellidae

D'ORBIGNY, 1844
watering pot shells

The shells themselves are extremely small and nacreous. A calcareous tube secreted by the mantle grows out from one or both of the embryonic valves. This tube is open at the rear, while at the front it is sealed with a perforated disk fringed with small tubes, reminiscent of a watering pot spout. Water and food particles are drawn in through the perforated disk. The animals may attach themselves to a hard substrate, bore into a soft substrate, or stick vertically out of sandy sediment, spending their whole lives in that position. They occur in warmer maritime regions (the Red Sea, Mediterranean Sea, and Indo-Pacific). Only a few species contained within several genera: *Brechites, Clavagella, Humphreysia.*

Brechites penis

(LINNAEUS, 1758)
common watering pot

D: 120mm. S: a tube-shaped shell with a porous, rounded anterior encircled by a crinkled "fringe." O: smooth or crinkled tube. C: white. H: d1; in sand to 50m. W: INDP; Taiwan. R: 2. NB: the very small shell valves that have merged into the tube can be made out in the photograph as vague nodules just under the tube's fringe.

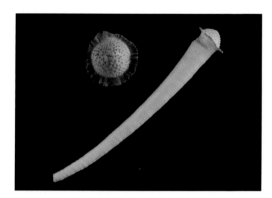

PANDOROIDEA

RAFINESQUE, 1815.
Elongated, inequivalved shells. Interior sometimes nacreous. Internal ligament. Unattached or byssate.

Cleidothaeridae

HEDLEY, 1918
Very inequivalved shells. The right valve is convex and calcified – cemented to a hard substrate. The left valve is flat. Interior is nacreous. Umbones curved over. Resilium in a large lithodesma (narrow calcareous plate strengthening the ligament). Only found around Australia. Genus: *Cleidothaerus*.

Lyonsiidae

P. FISCHER, 1887
Elongated, oval shells becoming beak-like and gaping toward the posterior end. Generally inequivalved. Interior is nacreous. Yellowish periostracum. Wide distribution. Byssate on hard substrates. Only a few genera, including: *Entodesma, Lyonsia, Ostomya*.

Myochamidae

BRONN, 1862
Inequivalved shells. The convex valve encloses the flat one. Unattached or cemented to a substrate by the right valve. Western part of the Indo-Pacific region and around Australia. Genera: *Myadora, Myochama*.

Pandoridae

RAFINESQUE, 1815
Pandora clams

Thin-shelled and extremely inequivalved. The left valve is convex, while the right valve is completely flat. Posterior side grows into a beaked shape in many species. Valve interiors coated with silvery white nacre. Resilium with lithodesma. Occur on silty substrates with the left valve uppermost. Only genus known: *Pandora*.

Pandora gouldiana

DALL, 1886
Gould's Pandora

D: 40mm. S: a robust, oval shell. Rounded anterior, pointed posterior. Inequivalved. Left valve more convex than the right. O: low growth lines, upper margin almost straight with a ridge running from the umbo. C: glossy white. White, nacreous interior. H: d1–3; sublittoral and deep water to 200m. W: KEL (North American part), VIR. R: 1.

Pandora inaequivalvis

(LINNAEUS, 1758)
unequal Pandora

D: 40mm. S: solid, elongated, very inequivalved shell. Left valve very convex, right valve completely flat. O: low growth lines. Some slight ridges run along the posterior, from umbo to curved upper margin. C: glossy white to pale yellow. Silvery white, nacreous interior. H: d1; littoral and sublittoral, shallow water. Burrows in mud and fine sand. W: KEL, LUS. R: 1.

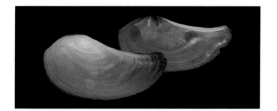

THRACIOIDEA

STOLICZKA, 1870

A superfamily comprised of several families chiefly inequivalved and possessing very thin shells without true hinge teeth. The shells are porcelaneous or slightly nacreous but not thickly so. The umbones curve toward each other. The ligament is sunken in a V-shaped lithodesma.

Laternulidae

HEDLEY, 1918
lantern clams

Very thin-shelled and partly translucent. The anterior is rounded. The posterior is gaping and may extend into a beak or be truncated to some extent. Equivalved and convex. The surface is granulose, sometimes bearing blunt, radial spicules. They burrow in mud and sediment in the intertidal zone and amid sea grass in regions such as the Mediterranean Sea and the Indo-Pacific. Most familiar genus: *Laternula*.

Laternula anatina

(LINNAEUS, 1758)
duck lantern clam

D: 60mm. S: thin-shelled and an elongated oval shape. Anterior rounded; posterior bluntly angled and curved slightly upward. O: growth lines and finely granulose. C: yellowish-white; grayish-white periostracum. H: d1; shallow water, in mud and sediment. W: INDP. R: 2.

Laternula laterna

(LAMARCK, 1818)
common lantern clam

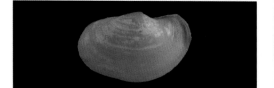

D: 80mm. S: thin-shelled and oval. Posterior is narrow and rounded. O: growth lines, granulose. C: grayish-white. H: d1; sublittoral in sand and mud. W: AUS. R: 1.

Periplomatidae

DALL, 1895
spoon clams

Thin-shelled and oval. Gaping and truncated to the rear. The right valve is more convex than the left. Umbones often slightly split. Sometimes a slightly nacreous interior. Toothless hinge. Resilium in a spoon-shaped chondrophore (depression) with or without a lithodesma. The animals rest horizontally in sediment from the littoral to the sublittoral and are found in the Atlantic Ocean, Mediterranean Sea, and the eastern and western Pacific Ocean. A few genera: *Cochlodesma, Halistrepta, Periploma*.

Cochlodesma praetenue

(PULTENEY, 1799)
European spoon clam

D: 40mm. S: very thin-shelled and oval. Anterior rounded; posterior slightly truncated. Hinge has a spoon-shaped resilium groove (lithodesma). A fairly defined ridge runs on the inside from the umbo to the anterior muscle scar. O: smooth. C: white. H: d1–2; sublittoral. Burrows in fine sand to depths of over 100m. W: KEL, LUS. R: 2.

Periploma angasi

CROSSE & FISCHER, 1864
Angas' spoon clam

D: 75mm. S: thin-shelled and oval. Very inequivalved. O: low growth lines. Sometimes slight concentric ribs. C: white; grayish-yellow periostracum. H: d1; shallow water. W: AUS; southern part. R: 2–3.

Periploma margaritaceum

(LAMARCK, 1801)
unequal spoon clam

D: 20mm. S: a round to angular, truncated shell. Very inequivalved. O: smooth; growth lines only. C: white. H: d1; littoral and sublittoral. Burrows in sand. W: VIR. R: 1.

Thraciidae

STOLICZKA, 1870
thracia clams

Extremely thin-shelled. The anterior is rounded, while the posterior is truncated to some degree. The right valve is larger than the left and overlaps it. The surface is finely granulose or has concentric grooves and ribs. Hinge teeth are absent but there is an angular chondrophore. The anterior muscle scar is more defined than the posterior one and the pallial sinus is deep. Chiefly found in temperate to cold maritime regions: Atlantic Ocean, Pacific Ocean. Sublittoral and deeper. They burrow in fine or semi-coarse sand. Only a few genera, including: *Cyathodonta, Thracia, Thracidora*.

Thracia adenensis

MELVILL, 1898
Arabian thracia

D: 30mm. S: thin-shelled and elongated. Rounded anterior; angular, truncated posterior. Umbones off-center. Left valve slightly more convex than the right. A slight or prominent ridge runs obliquely from the umbo toward the posterior. O: granulose surface, most obvious toward the posterior. C: white; yellowish-gray periostracum. H: d1; sublittoral and deeper water. W: INDP. R: 2.

Thracia convexa

(W. WOOD, 1815)
convex thracia

D: 65mm. S: thin-shelled and a rounded, triangular shape. The truncated posterior is lower than the anterior side. Umbones central. Left valve more convex than the right. O: growth lines and quite coarsely granulose, particularly toward the posterior. C: chalky white; yellowish-gray periostracum. H: d1–2; deeper water, 15m and below. W: KEL, LUS. R: 3.

Thracia papyracea

(POLI, 1791)
paper thracia

D: 30mm. S: thin-shelled and an elongated, oblong shape. Rounded anterior; angular, truncated posterior. Left valve slightly more convex. A ridge runs obliquely toward the posterior from the umbo. O: concentric growth lines. Very faintly granulose. C: white. H: d1–2; burrows in fine sand. W: KEL, LUS, WAFR. R: 2.

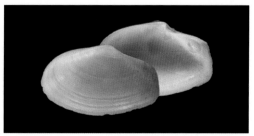

ORDER SEPTIBRANCHIA

PELSENEER, 1888

A group of bivalves that filter food particles from water by passing it through gills modified into septa that run transversely across the mantle cavity.

POROMYOIDA

DALL, 1886

Poromyidae

DALL, 1886
poromyid clams

Thin-shelled, these convex deep-sea clams may be oval, rhomboid, or triangular in shape. The surface is smooth or granulose. The interior has a thin, glossy layer of nacre. Two subfamilies: Cetomyinae Krylova, 1997 and Poromyinae Dall, 1886. Genera: *Cetoconcha, Cetomya, Lissomya, Poromya*.

CUSPIDARIOIDEA

DALL, 1886

Cuspidariidae

DALL, 1886
cuspidaria clams

Thin-shelled and slightly inequivalved: the left valve is rather more convex than the right. The anterior side is rounded, while a beak-like growth extends from the posterior side varying in length (rostrum). The interior is dull and not nacreous. They have a wide distribution and, while also occurring elsewhere, are chiefly found in deeper and colder waters: the Arctic, Atlantic Ocean, Mediterranean Sea, western Pacific Ocean, Australia. Various genera, including: *Cardiomya, Cuspidaria* and *Myonera*.

Cardiomya alcocki

(E.A. SMITH, 1884)
Alcock's cuspidaria

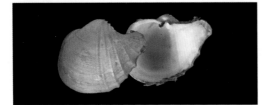

D: 8mm. S: thin-shelled. Wide, rounded anterior. Pointed posterior. O: fine concentric riblets and growth lines. Clear, wavy radial ribs at the rear end. C: creamy white; brownish-gray periostracum. H: d2–3; deep water. W: INDP, JAP. R: 3.

Cuspidaria cuspidata

(OLIVI, 1792)
West European cuspidaria

D: 20mm. S: thin-shelled. Rounded anterior. Posterior has a short, fairly wide beak. Left valve slightly more convex than the right. O: strong growth lines. C: chalky white; brown periostracum, often incorporating grains of sand. H: d1–3; deep water, from 15m to great depths. W: ARC, KEL, LUS, WAFR. R: 3.

Cuspidaria japonica

KURODA, 1948
Japanese cuspidaria

D: 30mm. S: thin-shelled and oval with a fairly long, thin beak. O: growth lines only. C: grayish-white; amber periostracum. H: d2; 100–200m. W: JAP. R: 3.

Cuspidaria kawamurai

KURODA, 1948
Kawamura's cuspidaria

D: 60mm. S: quite robust, oval shell with very narrow, long, slightly curved rostrum. O: strong growth lines. C: chalky white; beige periostracum. H: d2–4; to 640m. W: INDP, JAP. R: 3.

VERTICORDIOIDEA

STOLICZKA, 1871

Verticordiidae

STOLICZKA, 1871
verticord clams

Mostly quite small, round or slightly angular shells. Smooth or granulose, or with radial ribs or nodules and spines. Umbones often prominent, inflated, and rolled forward. Periostracum is thin, often with grains of sand attached. Sil-very white, nacreous interior. Chiefly found in deep water in the Arctic, Atlantic Ocean, Mediterranean Sea, and western Pacific Ocean. A number of genera, including: *Euciroa, Halicardia, Laevicordia, Lyonsiella, Policordia, Verticordia*.

Lyonsiella compressa

(LOCARD, 1898)
pentagonal verticord clam

D: 14mm. S: thin-shelled, almost pentagonal, and fairly flat. O: without radial ribs, unlike many species from this family. C: grayish-white; white interior with spots of glossy nacre. H: d1–4; 10–3700m. W: LUS, WAFR; Canary Islands, North African coast (Tunisia, Egypt). R: 4.

12. Class Scaphopoda

KEFERSTEIN IN BRONN, 1862

tusk shells

This is a small class containing only a few hundred species in total.

The shells are tube-shaped and look like elephants' tusks. The tube is usually slightly curved and is open at either end. The anterior end is wider than the posterior (apical) end. During the growth process, the narrow end occasionally becomes constricted or partly sealed. The shell may also have longitudinal grooves or ring-shaped growth lines. There are also a small number of groups with a slightly aberrant shape (e.g., *Cadulus*). Caecidae shells from the class Gastropoda superficially resemble tusk shells but are very small, open only on one side, have an operculum, and are spirally wound at the juvenile stage. Tusk shells are maritime animals. While some species live in the littoral, by far the majority live in deep to extremely deep water. The animals burrow into the ocean floor at an angle with just the narrow end poking above the sediment. They have no gills and extract oxygen via the mantle. However, they do have a radula. Their food consists of foraminifers and other micro-organisms which are caught using very small tentacles.

There are only a few families, which are divided into two orders. There are no subfamilies. Only Dentaliidae feature as collectors' items. The others are quite insignificant in size and usually rare.

ORDER DENTALIIDA

DA COSTA, 1776

Dentaliidae

CHILDREN, 1834
tusk shells

Tube-shaped shells, most closely resembling elephants' tusks. They range from almost straight to strongly curved. There is an opening at either end, although they may sometimes appear to be almost sealed at the narrowest end. This narrow end occasionally has a notch or slit. They may have spiral and longitudinal grooves. A number of genera, including: *Antalis, Coccodentalium, Dentalium, Fissidentalium, Pictodentalium, Striodentalium*.

Two European species are shown in the top photograph. Above: *Dentalium vulgare* Da Costa, 1778—common tusk. Below: *D. entalis* Linnaeus, 1758—smooth tusk. The first lives in both shallow and deep water. The second lives only in deep water (the North Sea).

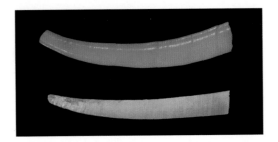

The second photograph shows the following non-European species: (from the top) *Fissidentalium floridense* Henderson, 1920—Florida tusk; *F. vernedei* Sowerby, 1860—Vernede's tusk; *Dentalium aprinum* Linnaeus, 1767—boar's tusk; *D. elephantinum* Linnaeus, 1758—elephant tusk; *Pictodentalium formosum* A. Adams & Reeve, 1850—beautiful tusk. These species are not shown to scale. They measure, respectively, 60, 140, 75, 100, and 100mm. The majority live in the Indo-Pacific region.

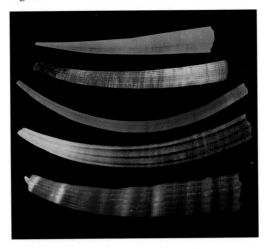

In addition to the family Dentaliidae, the order Dentaliida also contains various other families, including: Anulidentaliidae Christikov, 1975; Calliodentaliidae Christikov, 1975; Fustiaridae Steiner, 1991; Gadilinidae Christikov, 1975; Laevidentaliidae Palmer, 1974; Omniglyptidae Christikov, 1975; Rhabdidae Christikov, 1975.

The order Gadilida Starobogatov, 1974, contains various, mostly small, species belonging to, for example, the families Entalinidae Christikov, 1979; Gadilidae Stoliczka, 1868; Pulsellidae Boss, 1982; Wemersoniellidae Scarabino, 1986. The photograph shows two examples from this group that so often possess extremely small shells. (Images made using a Scanning Electron Microscope.)

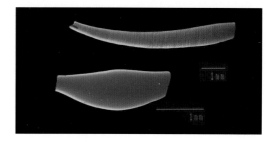

13. Class Cephalopoda

CUVIER, 1797

squids, octopuses, cuttlefishes, and nautiluses

These animals may be elongated (arrow-shaped) or more rotund, possessing eight tentacles (octopuses), ten tentacles (squids, cuttlefishes), or numerous small tentacles (nautiluses). The head and foot are fused, forming what is referred to as a cephalopodium. Breathing is performed by gills and there is a radula. Of all the mollusks, the cephalopods are by far the most evolved, having highly developed senses and organs, such as eyes, beak-shaped jaws, and a nervous system. They are active swimmers and carnivorous predators that populate maritime environments all over the world. The largest living mollusk, *Architeuthis*, measures at least 22 meters, including its extended tentacles. It is believed that even larger animals live in the deep sea judging by the stomach contents of sperm whales and sucker marks found on baleen whales. Nowadays, the world has fewer than 1000 species of cephalopod; however, from studies of fossil records it is known that in the distant past at least ten times that number populated the world's seas. Ammonites are a very well known example of these—shell-bearing ancestors of species still living today. Although many modern species are shell-less, shell-bearing species do still occur. The shells can be both internal and external. In the case of external shells, they take the form of a large, horn-like snail shell, lined with nacre within. When internal, the shell is present in the dorsal region or spiral in shape (one species). The genus *Argonauta* creates papery pseudo-shells, made to hold eggs. This encyclopedia includes only a few shell-bearing species of cephalopod. None of the other orders, subfamilies, and families will be discussed further.

SUBCLASS NAUTILOIDA

AGASSIZ, 1847

ORDER NAUTILIDA

AGASSIZ, 1847

Nautilidae

DE BLAINVILLE, 1825

nautiluses

Spirally wound shells, partitioned into chambers that are joined to one another by a hollow tube. Nacreous interior. Genera: *Nautilus* and *Allonautilus*, containing six modern-day species. Chiefly found in tropical waters (Indo-Pacific).

Nautilus pompilius

LINNAEUS, 1758

chambered nautilus

D: 150mm. S: quite thin-shelled but robust with a large final whorl and a wide aperture. No umbilicus. Nacreous partitions divide interior into chambers joined together by a hollow tube (see Chapter 2). O: smooth; growth lines only. C: white with russet, zebra stripes, which disappear on the last part of the shell. Rich, greenish-blue to silvery white, nacreous interior. H: d1–4; all depths. W: INDP; empty shells also wash ashore elsewhere. R: 2. NB: the shells of *N. macromphalus* Sowerby, 1849—the New Caledonia nautilus—and *N. scrobiculatus* Lightfoot, 1786—the umbilicate nautilus—show close similarities but are just a little bigger (180mm), have a clear umbilicus, and are rarer.

SUBCLASS COLEOIDEA

BATHER, 1888

A number of orders, suborders, and families. Only a few examples are discussed here.

Argonautidae

TYRON, 1879
argonauts (paper nautiluses)

Paper-thin, fragile shells. Spirally wound like a snail shell. They are not partitioned into separate chambers, unlike both *Nautilus* and *Spirula*. The shell is not permanently attached to the animal and is not, in fact, a true shell at all but a pseudo-shell or "cradle" in which the female deposits her eggs. The males are very small and have no shell. At least five cosmopolitan, free-swimming species are to be found in tropical seas. In the photograph, from left to right, the pseudo-shells of: *Argonauta argo* Linnaeus, 1758—common paper nautilus; *A. hians* Lightfoot, 1786—brown paper nautilus; *A. nodosa* Solander, 1786—nodose paper nautilus. Their measurements are respectively: up to 200mm; up to 70mm; and up to 180mm.

Sepiidae

LEACH, 1817
cuttlefishes

An extremely large cephalopod family containing over 100 species. Cuttlefishes have relatively rotund bodies with eight short and two long tentacles covered in suckers. The longer arms are expanded at the ends and serve as grips. One of the shorter arms is used in mating. There are well-developed eyes on either side of the head. The mouth contains chitinous, beak-like jaws. If it senses danger, the animal ejects black, or dark purple, ink into the water. This ink was used in the distant past for writing (sepia ink). The dorsal area of the animal contains a dorsal shield or shell and takes the form of an oval, calcareous plate that is quite brittle on one side, composed of numerous, thin, soft layers. When the animal dies (many species live only a year), the shells continue to float in the water and sometimes wash ashore on beaches in huge numbers. Most species can be identified by their shells. The photograph shows a number of *Sepia* shells. From left to right: both sides of a shell from *Sepia officinalis* Linnaeus, 1758—common cuttlefish; *S.*

orbignyana De Férussac, 1826—Orbigny's cuttlefish; *S. elegans* D'Orbigny, 1826—elegant cuttlefish; *S. gibbosa* Ehrenberg, 1831—bulging cuttlefish (side view to illustrate the humpbacked bulge found on the soft side of some cuttlefishes). Occurrence: European waters; *S. gibbosa* is found in the Red Sea.

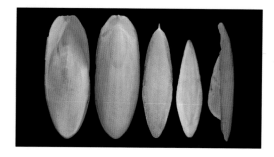

Spirulidae

OWEN, 1836
spirulas

Only one genus containing one species. The shell is contained within the body of the mollusk and is curled like an antique post horn. The animals swim with their heads below and the shell uppermost. The shell operates as a hydrostatic organ in the same way as for *Nautilus* species.

Spirula spirula

(LINNAEUS, 1758)
common spirula

D: 35mm. S: a planospiral shell with the whorls closely coiled but separate from each other. Just as in Nautilus, partitions divide the whorls into chambers linked to one another by a hollow tube. O: smooth, glossy, and polished. C: yellowish-white or cream. Very glossy yellowish-white to grayish-white, nacreous interior. H: pelagic animals, the shell is used for ascent and descent. W: found in all tropical seas. R: 3. NB: shells sometimes wash ashore after storms.

Credits

Various people and institutions in the Netherlands have helped to bring about the publication of this encyclopedia. First and foremost, our thanks go to P.L. van Pel (Egmond aan Zee), H. Dekker (Winkel), and all those from the Malacological Department of the Zoological Museum in Amsterdam who facilitated, and assisted directly with, the photographs and naming of hundreds of shell species. Our further thanks extend to H.H. Dijkstra, J.J. ter Poorten, B. Gras, R. Vink and H.H. Kool for the verification of names and to I. van Lente, M.R. de Bruyne and K. Jonges for corrections. J. Goud (Naturalis, Leiden) and R.G. Moolenbeek (Zoological Museum, Amsterdam) supplied SEM photographic material. Other photographic material was used from the archives of P.L. van Pel, H. Dekker, R.H. de Bruyne, and PICTAN (the photographic archive of the ANEMOON Foundation). D.A.B. Iliohan produced the anatomical and structural diagrams. H. Dekker verified scientific names and compiled the taxonomic overview. The majority of shells photographed can be found in the collections of P.L. van Pel, I.E.M. Peeters, and the Zoological Museum, Amsterdam, with some other shells having come from the collections of R.H. de Bruyne and H. Bielderman as well. R.H. de Bruyne and A. Gmelig Meyling Sr. produced the photographs.

Useful addresses

The American Malacological Society
Publications: *The American Malacological Bulletin* and the *AMS newsletter*.
Address: 4201 Wilson Blvd., STE 110-455, Arlington, VA 22203-1859.
http://erato.acnatsci.org/ams/

Conchologists of America
Publication: *American Conchologist*. 698 Sheridan Woods Drive, West Melbourne, FL 32904-3302
http://coa.acnatsci.org/conchnet/

Bailey-Matthews Shell Museum
P.O. Box 1580, 3075 Sanibel-Captiva Road, Sanibel, FL 33957
http://www.shellmuseum.org/

Jacksonville Shell Club
1010 N. 24th Street, Jacksonville Beach, FL 32250-2883
http://www.jaxshells.org/

North Texas Conchological Society
804 Westbrook Drive, Plano, TX 75075
http://outdoorplace.org/shells

Northern California Malacological Club
121 Wild Horse Valley Road, Novato, CA

Of Sea and Shore
Publications: *Of Sea and Shore Magazine*; various publications and directories. P.O. Box 219, Port Gamble, WA 98364
http://www.ofseaandshore.com

Oregon Society of Conchologists
4746 N.E. Everett Street, Portland, OR 97213

Palmetto Shell Club
1191 Sawyer Avenue, Orangeburg, SC 29115
http://www.molluscs.net/Palmetto_Shell_Club.htm

Philadelphia Shell Club (oldest malacological center in USA)
Academy of Natural Sciences, Benjamin Franklin Parkway & 19th Street, Philadelphia, PA 19103
http://erato.acnatsci.org/psc/

San Diego Shell Club
Publication: *The Festivus*. 3883mt. Blackburn Avenue, San Diego, CA 92111
http://www.molluscs.net/SanDiegoShell-Club/index.html

St Petersburg Shell Club
P.O. Box 66873, St Pete Beach, FL 33736
http://web.tampabay.rr.com/shellclub/

Treasure Coast Shell Club
P.O. Box 279, Palm City, FL 34990
http://members.aol.com/TCoastShellClub/

University of Michigan Museum of Zoology – Mollusk Division
Publications: four malacological journals
1109 Geddes Avenue, Ann Arbor, MI 48109-1079
http://www.ummz.lsa.umich.edu/mollusks/

Taxonomic overview

Given that the order of entries employed in this encyclopedia differs from the taxonomic order, a taxonomic overview is provided below to enable comparison.

Phylum: Mollusca Cuvier, 1795
Subphylum: Aculifera Hatschek, 1891
Class: Aplacophora Von Ihering, 1876
Subclass: Chaetodermomorpha Pelseneer in Lankester, 1906
   Family: Chaetodermatidae Von Ihering, 1786
   Family: Limifossoridae Salvini-Plawen, 1968
   Family: Prochaetodermatidae Salvini-Plawen, 1968
Subclass: Neomeniomorpha Pelseneer in Lankester, 1906
   approximately 20 families
Class: Polyplacophora Blainville, 1816
Order: Neoloricata Bergenhayn, 1955
Suborder: Lepidopleurina Thiele, 1910
   Family: Ferreiraellidae Dell' Angelo & Palazzi, 1991
   Family: Hanleyidae Bergenhayn, 1955
   Family: Leptochitonidae Dall, 1889
   Family: Nierstraziellidae Sirenko, 1992
Suborder: Choriplacina Starobogatov & Sirenko, 1975
   Family: Choriplacidae Ashby, 1928
Suborder: Ischnochitonina Bergenhayn, 1930
   Family: Ischnochitonidae Dall, 1889
    subfamily: Callistoplacinae Pilsbry, 1893
    subfamily: Callochitoninae Plate, 1901
    subfamily: Chaetopleurinae Plate, 1899
    subfamily: Ischnochitoninae Dall, 1889
    subfamily: Lepidochitoninae Iredale, 1914
    subfamily: Schizoplacinae Bergenhayn, 1955
   Family: Chitonidae Rafinesque, 1815
    subfamily: Acanthopleurinae Dall, 1889
    subfamily: Chitoninae Rafinesque, 1815
    subfamily: Toniciinae Pilsbry, 1893
   Family: Mopaliidae Dall, 1889
    subfamily: Mopaliinae Dall, 1889
    subfamily: Katharininae Jakovleva, 1952
   Family: Schizochitonidae Dall, 1889
Suborder: Acanthochitonina Bergenhayn, 1930
   Family: Acanthochitonidae Pilsbry, 1893
    subfamily: Acanthochitoninae Pilsbry, 1893
    subfamily: Cryptochitoninae, Pilsbry, 1893
   Family: Cryptoplacidae H. & A. Adams, 1858
Subphylum: Conchifera Gegenbauer, 1878
Class: Monoplacophora Odhner, 1940
Order: Monoplacophorida Wenz Knight, 1952
Superfamily: Tryblidioidea Pilsbry in Zittel-Eastman, 1899
   Family Laevipilinidae Moskalev, Starobogatov & Filatova, 1983
   Family Monoplacophoridae Moscalev, Starobogatov & Filatova, 1983
   Family Neopilinidae Knight & Yochelson, 1958

   Family Vemidae Moskalev, Starobogatov & Filatova, 1983
Class: Gastropoda Cuvier, 1795
Subclass: Eogastropoda Ponder & Lindberg, 1996
Order: Patellogastropoda Lindberg, 1986
Suborder: Patellina Von Ihering, 1876
Superfamily: Patelloidea Rafinesque, 1815
   Family: Patellidae Rafinesque, 1815
Suborder: Nacellina Lindberg, 1988
Superfamily: Nacelloidea Thiele, 1891
   Family: Nacellidae Thiele, 1891
Superfamily: Acmaeoidea Carpenter, 1857
   Family: Acmaeidae Carpenter, 1857
    subfamily: Acmaeinae Carpenter, 1857
    subfamily: Pectinodontinae Pilsbry, 1891
   Family: Lepetidae J.E. Gray, 1850
    subfamily: Lepetinae J.E. Gray, 1850
    subfamily: Propilidiinae Thiele, 1892
   Family: Lottiidae J.E. Gray 1840
    subfamily: Lottiinae J.E. Gray, 1840
    subfamily: Patelloidinae Chapman & Gabriel, 1923
    subfamily: Rhodopetalinae Lindberg, 1981
Suborder: Lepetopsina McLean, 1990
Superfamily: Lepetopsoidea McLean, 1990
   Family Lepetopsidae McLean, 1990
   Family Neolepetopsidae McLean, 1990
Subclass: Orthogastropoda Ponder & Lindberg, 1996
Superorder: Cocculiniformia Haszprunar, 1987
Superfamily: Cocculinoidea Dall, 1882
   Family: Bathysciadiidae Dautzenberg & H. Fischer, 1900
   Family: Cocculinidae Dall, 1882
Superfamily: Lepetelloidea Dall, 1882
   Family: Addisoniidae Dall, 1882
    subfamily: Addisoniinae Dall, 1882
    subfamily: Helicopeltinae Marshall, 1996
   Family: Bathyphytophilidae Moskalev, 1978
   Family: Choristellidae Bouchet & Warén, 1979
   Family: Cocculinellidae Moskalev, 1971
   Family: Lepetellidae Dall, 1882
   Family: Osteopeltidae Marshall, 1987
   Family: Pseudococculinidae Hickman, 1983
    subfamily: Caymanabyssiinae Marshall, 1986
    subfamily: Pseudococculininae Hickman, 1983
   Family: Pyropeltidae Mclean & Haszprunar, 1987
Superorder: 'Hot Vent Taxa' Ponder & Lindberg, 1997
Order: Neomphaolida Sitnikova & Starobogatov, 1983
Superfamily: Neomphaloidea McLean, 1981
   Family: Neomphalidae McLean, 1981
Superfamily: Peltospiroidea McLean, 1989
   Family: Peltospiridae McLean, 1989
Superorder: Vetigastropoda Salvini-Plawen 1980
Superfamily: Pleurotomarioidea Swainson, 1840
   Family: Pleurotomariidae Swainson, 1840
   Family: Scissurellidae J.E. Gray, 1847
    subfamily: Schizotrochinae Iredale & McMichael, 1962

309

subfamily: Scissurellinae J.E. Gray, 1847
subfamily: Temnocinclinae McLean, 1989
Superfamily: Haliotoidea Rafinisque, 1815
  Family: Haliotidae Rafinesque, 1815
Superfamily: Lepetodriloidea McLean, 1988
  Family: Gorgoleptidae McLean, 1988
  Family: Lepetodrilidae McLean, 1988
  Family: Sutilizonidae McLean, 1989
Superfamily: Fissurelloidea Flemming, 1822
  Family: Fissurellidae Flemming, 1822
    subfamily: Diodorinae Wenz, 1938
    subfamily: Emarginulinae J.E. Gray, 1834
    subfamily: Fissurellidinae Pilsbry, 1890
    subfamily: Fissurellinae Flemming, 1822
    subfamily: Hemitominae Kuroda, Habe & Oyama, 1971
    subfamily: Scutinae Christiaens, 1973
  Family Clypeosectidae McLean, 1989
Superfamily: Trochoidea Rafinesque, 1815
  Family Pendromidae Warén, 1991
  Family Skeneidae Clark, 1851
  Family Trochaclididae Thiele, 1928
  Family Trochidae Rafinesque, 1815
    subfamily: Calliostomatinae Thiele, 1924
    subfamily: Eucyclinae Koken, 1897
    subfamily: Halistylinae Keen, 1958
    subfamily: Lirulariinae Hickman & McLean, 1990
    subfamily: Margaritinae Stoliczka, 1868
    subfamily: Solariellinae Powell, 1951
    subfamily: Stomatellinae J.E. Gray, 1840
    subfamily: Tegulinae Kuroda, Habe & Oyama, 1971
    subfamily: Thysanodontinae Marshall, 1988
    subfamily: Trochinae Rafinesque, 1815
    subfamily: Umboniinae H. & A. Adams, 1854
  Family Turbinidae Rafinesque, 1815
    subfamily: Angariinae Thiele, 1921
    subfamily: Colloniinae Cossmann, 1916
    subfamily: Gabrieloninae Hickman & McLean, 1990
    subfamily: Liotiinae H. & A. Adams, 1854
    subfamily: Moelleriinae Hickman & McLean, 1990
    subfamily: Phasianellinae Swainson, 1840
    subfamily: Prisogasterinae Hickman & McLean, 1990
    subfamily: Tricoliinae Woodring, 1928
    subfamily: Turbininae Rafinesque, 1815
Superfamily: Seguenzioidea Verrill, 1884
  Family: Seguenziidae Verrill, 1884
Superorder: Neritaemorphi Koken, 1896
Order: Neritopsina Cox & Knight, 1960
Superfamily: Neritoidea Lamarck, 1809
  Family: Neritidae Lamarck, 1809
    subfamily: Neritinae Lamarck, 1809
    subfamily: Septariinae Golokov & Staroboga-tov, 1975
    subfamily: Theodoxinae Bandel, 2001
    subfamily: Smaragdiinae H.B. Baker, 1923
  Family: Neritiliidae Baker, 1923
  Family: Neritopsidae J.E. Gray, 1847
  Family: Phenacolepadidae Pilsbry, 1895
  Family: Hydrocenidae: Troschel, 1856
  Family: Helicinidae Férussac, 1822
    subfamily: Helicininae Latreille, 1825
    subfamily: Hendersoniinae Baker, 1926

subfamily: Ceratodiscinae Pilsbry, 1927
subfamily: Vianinae Baker, 1922
  Family: Proserpinidae Gray, 1857
  Family: Ceresidae Thompson, 1980
  Family: Titiscaniidae Bergh, 1890
Superorder: Caenogastropoda Cox, 1960
Order: Architaenioglossa Haller, 1890
Superfamily: Cyclophoroidea J.E. Gray, 1847
  Family: Cyclophoridae J.E. Gray, 1847
  Family: Craspedopomatidae Kobelt & Möllendorf, 1898
  Family: Pupinidae H. & A. Adams, 1855
  Family: Diplommatinidae Pfeiffer, 1856
  Family: Cochlostomatidae Kobelt, 1902
  Family: Neocyclotidae Kobelt & Möllendorf, 1897
  Family: Neopupinidae Kobelt, 1902
  Family: Aciculidae J.E. Gray, 1850
Superfamily: Ampullarioidea J.E. Gray, 1824
  Family: Ampullariidae J.E. Gray, 1824
  Family: Viviparidae J.E. Gray, 1847
    subfamily: Viviparinae J.E. Gray, 1847
    subfamily: Bellamyinae Rourbach, 1937
Order: Sorbeoconcha Ponder & Lindberg, 1997
Suborder: Discopoda P. Fischer, 1884
Superfamily: Cerithioidea Férussac, 1822
  Family: Batillariidae Thiele, 1929
  Family: Cerithiidae Férussac, 1822
    subfamily: Bittiinae Cossmann, 1906
    subfamily: Cerithiinae Férussac, 1822
  Family: Dialidae Ludbrook, 1941
  Family: Diastomatidae Cossmann, 1894
  Family: Litiopidae J.E. Gray, 1847
  Family: Melanopsidae H. & A. Adams, 1854
  Family: Modulidae P. Fischer, 1884
  Family: Pachychilidae Troschel, 1857
  Family: Planaxidae J.E. Gray, 1850
    subfamily: Fossarinae Troschel, 1861
    subfamily: Planaxinae J.E. Gray, 1850
  Family: Potamididae H. & A. Adams, 1854
  Family: Scaliolidae Jousseaume, 1912
  Family: Siliquariidae Anton, 1838
  Family: Thiaridae Troschel, 1857
  Family: Turritellidae Lovén, 1847
    subfamily: Turritellinae Lovén, 1847
    subfamily: Vermiculariinae Faustino, 1928
Superfamily: Campaniloidea Douvillé, 1904
  Family: Campanilidae Douvillé, 1904
  Family: Plesiotrochidae Houbrick, 1990
Suborder: Murchisoniina Cox & Knight, 1960
Superfamily: Loxonematoidea Koken, 1889
  Family: Abyssochrysidae Tomlin, 1927
  Family: Provannidae Warén & Ponder, 1991
Suborder: Hypsogastropoda Ponder & Lindberg, 1997
Infraorder: Littorinimorpha Golikov & Staroboga-tov, 1975
Superfamily: Littorinoidea [Children], 1834
  Family: Littorinidae [Children], 1834
    subfamily: Lacuninae J.E. Gray, 1857
    subfamily: Laevilitorininae Reid, 1989
    subfamily: Littorininae [Children], 1834
  Family: Pickworthiidae Iredale, 1917
  Family: Skeneopsidae Iredale, 1915
  Family: Zerotulidae Warén & Hain, 1996
  Family: Pomatiasidae J.E. Gray, 1852
  Family: Annulariidae Henderson & Bartsch,

1920
Superfamily: Cingulopsoidea Fretter & Patil, 1958
  Family: Cingulopsidae Fretter & Patil, 1958
  Family: Eatoniellidae Ponder, 1965
  Family: Rastodentidae Ponder, 1966
Superfamily: Rissooidea J.E. Gray, 1947
  Family Anabathridae Coan, 1964
  Family Assimineidae H. & A. Adams, 1856
   subfamily: Assimineinae H. & A. Adams, 1856
   subfamily: Omphalotropidinae Thiele, 1927
  Family: Barleeidae J.E. Gray, 1857
  Family: Bythiniidae Troschel, 1857
  Family: Caecidae M.E. Gray, 1850
   subfamily: Caecinae M.E. Gray, 1850
   subfamily: Ctiloceratinae Iredale & Laseron, 1957
  Family: Calopiidae Ponder, 1999
  Family: Elachisinidae Ponder, 1985
  Family: Emblandidae Ponder, 1985
  Family: Emmericiidae Brusina, 1870
  Family: Epigridae Ponder, 1985
  Family: Falsicingulidae Slavoshevskaya, 1975
  Family: Hydrobiidae Troschel, 1857
   subfamily: Hydrobiinae Troschel, 1857
   subfamily: Littoridininae J.E. Gray, 1857
   subfamily: Potamopyrginae Boeters 1984
  Family: Hydrococcidae Thiele, 1928
  Family: Iravadiidae Thiele, 1928
  Family: Moitessieriidae Bourguignat, 1863
  Family: Pomatiopsidae Stimpson, 1865
  Family: Rissoidae J.E. Gray 1847
   subfamily: Rissoinae J.E. Gray, 1847
   subfamily: Rissoininae Stimpson, 1865
  Family: Stenothyridae P. Fisher, 1885
  Family: Tornidae Sacco, 1896
  Family: Truncatellidae J.E. Gray, 1840
  Family: Vitrinellidae Bush, 1897
Superfamily: Stromboidea Rafinesque, 1815
  Family: Aporrhaiidae J.E. Gray, 1850
  Family: Rostellariidae Gabb, 1868
  Family: Seraphidae Gray, 1853
  Family: Strombidae Rafinesque, 1815
  Family: Struthiolariidae P. Fischer, 1884
Superfamily: Vanikoroidea J.E. Gray, 1840
  Family: Caledoniellidae Rosewater, 1969
  Family: Haloceratidae Warén & Bouchet, 1991
  Family: Hipponicidae Troschel, 1861
  Family: Vanikoridae J.E. Gray, 1840
Superfamily: Calyptraeoidea Lamarck, 1809
  Family: Calyptraeidae Lamarck, 1809
Superfamily: Capuloidea J. Fleming, 1822
  Family: Capulidae J. Fleming, 1822
Superfamily: Xenophoroidea Troschel, 1852
  Family: Xenophoridae Troschel, 1852
Superfamily: Vermetoidea Rafinesque, 1815
  Family: Vermetidae Rafinesque, 1815
Superfamily: Cypraeoidea Rafinesque, 1815
  Family: Cypraeidae Rafinesque, 1815
   subfamily: Bernayinae Schilder, 1927
   subfamily: Cypraeinae Rafinesque, 1815
   subfamily: Cypraeovulinae Schilder, 1927
   subfamily: Erosariinae Schilder, 1924
  Family: Ovulidae J. Fleming, 1822
   subfamily: Ovulinae J. Fleming, 1822
   subfamily: Simniinae Schilder, 1927
  Family: Pediculariidae J.E. Gray, 1853
Superfamily: Trivioidea Troschel, 1863

  Family: Triviidae Troschel, 1863
   subfamily: Triviinae Troschel, 1863
   subfamily: Eratoinae Gill, 1871
   subfamily: Triviinae Troschel, 1863
Superfamily: Velutinoidea J.E. Gray, 1840
  Family: Velutinidae J.E. Gray, 1840
   subfamily: Lamellariinae D'Orbigny, 1842
   subfamily: Velutininae J.E. Gray, 1840
Superfamily: Naticoidea Forbes, 1838
  Family: Naticidae Forbes, 1838
   subfamily: Ampullospirinae Cox, 1930
   subfamily: Naticinae Forbes, 1838
   subfamily: Polinicinae J.E. Gray, 1847
   subfamily: Sininae Woodring, 1928
Superfamily: Tonnoidea Suter, 1913
  Family: Bursidae Thiele, 1925
  Family: Cassidae Latreille, 1825
   subfamily: Cassinae Latreille, 1825
   subfamily: Oocorythinae P. Fischer, 1885
   subfamily: Phaliinae Beu, 1981
  Family: Personidae J.E. Gray, 1854
  Family: Ranellidae J.E. Gray, 1854
   subfamily: Cymatiinae Iredale, 1913
   subfamily: Ranellinae J.E. Gray, 1854
  Family: Tonnidae Suter, 1913
Superfamily: Ficoidea Meek, 1864
  Family: Ficidae Meek, 1864
  Family: Thalassocyonidae F. Riedel, 1994
Superfamily: Laubierinoidea Warén & Bouchet, 1990
  Family: Laubierinidae Warén & Bouchet, 1990
  Family: Pisanianuridae Warén & Bouchet, 1990
Superfamily: Carinarioidea Blainville, 1818
  Family: Atlantidae Rang, 1829
  Family: Carinariidae Blainville, 1818
  Family: Firolidae Rang, 1829
Infraorder: Ptenoglossa J.E. Gray, 1853
Superfamily: Triphoroidea J.E. Gray, 1847
  Family: Cerithiopsidae H. & A. Adams, 1853
   subfamily: Aliptinae Marshall, 1978
   subfamily: Cerithiopsinae H. & A. Adams, 1853
   subfamily: Eumetulinae Golikov & Starobogatov, 1975
  Family: Triphoridae J.E. Gray, 1847
   subfamily: Adelacerithinae Marshall, 1984
   subfamily: Laiocochlinae Golikov & Starobogatov, 1987
   subfamily: Metaxiinae Marshall, 1977
   subfamily: Triphorinae J.E. Gray, 1847
  Family: Triforidae Jousseaume, 1884
Superfamily: Janthinoidea Lamarck, 1812
  Family: Aclididae G.O. Sars, 1878
  Family: Epitoniidae Berry, 1910
   subfamily: Epitoniinae Berry, 1910
   subfamily: Nystiellinae Clench & Turner, 1952
   subfamily: Pseudonininae Bertolaso & Palazzi, 1994
  Family: Janthinidae Lamarck, 1812
Superfamily: Eulimoidea Philippi, 1853
  Family: Eulimidae Philippi, 1853
Infraorder: Neogastropoda Thiele, 1929
Superfamily: Muricoidea Rafinesque, 1815
  Family: Coralliophilidae Chenu, 1859
  Family: Muricidae Rafinesque, 1815
   subfamily: Ergalataxinae Kuroda & Habe, 1971

subfamily: Muricinae Rafinesque, 1815
subfamily: Muricopsinae Radwin & D'Attilio, 1971
subfamily: Ocenebrinae Cossmann, 1903
subfamily: Rapaninae J.E. Gray, 1853
subfamily: Trophoninae Cossmann, 1903
subfamily: Tripterotyphinae d'Attilio & Hertz, 1988
subfamily: Typhinae Cossmann, 1903
Family: Buccinidae Rafinesque, 1815
subfamily: Buccininae Rafinesque, 1815
subfamily: Photinae J.E. Gray, 1857
subfamily: Pisaniinae Tryon, 1881
subfamily: Volutopsiinae Habe & Sato, 1972
Family: Columbellidae Swainson, 1840
subfamily: Columbellinae Swainson, 1840
subfamily: Pyreninae Suter, 1909
Family: Fasciolariidae J.E. Gray, 1853
subfamily: Fasciolariinae J.E. Gray, 1853
subfamily: Fusininae Wringley, 1927
subfamily: Peristerniinae Tryon, 1880
Family: Melongenidae Gill, 1871
subfamily: Busyconinae Wade, 1917
subfamily: Melongeninae Gill, 1871
Family: Nassariidae Iredale, 1916
subfamily: Bulliinae Allmon, 1990
subfamily: Cylleninae Bellardi, 1882
subfamily: Dorsaninae Cossmann, 1901
subfamily: Nassariinae Iredale, 1916
Family: Costellariidae McDonald, 1860
Family: Cystiscidae Stimpson, 1865
subfamily: Cystiscinae Stimpson, 1865
subfamily: Granulininae G.A. & H.K. Coovert, 1995
subfamily: Persiculinae G.A. & H.K. Coovert, 1995
subfamily: Plesiocystiscinae G.A. & H.K. Coovert, 1995
Family: Harpidae Bronn, 1840
subfamily: Harpinae Bronn, 1840
subfamily: Moruminae Hughes & Emerson, 1987
Family: Marginellidae J. Fleming, 1828
subfamily: Marginellinae J. Fleming, 1828
subfamily: Marginelloninae Coan, 1965
Family: Mitridae Swainson, 1831
subfamily: Cylindromitrinae Cossmann, 1899
subfamily: Imbricariinae Troschel, 1868
subfamily: Mitrinae Swainson, 1831
Family: Olividae Latreille, 1825
subfamily: Agaroniinae Olsson, 1956
subfamily: Ancillinae Swainson, 1835
subfamily: Olivellinae Troschel, 1869
subfamily: Olivinae Latreille, 1825
Family: Pleioptygmatidae Quinn, 1989
Family: Pseudolividae P. Fischer, 1884
Family: Strepsiduridae Cossmann, 1901
Family: Turbinellidae Swainson, 1840
subfamily: Columbariinae Tomlin, 1928
subfamily: Ptychatractinae Stimpson, 1865
subfamily: Tudiclinae Cossmann, 1901
subfamily: Turbinellinae Swainson, 1840
subfamily: Vasinae H. & A. Adams, 1853
Family: Volutidae Rafinesque, 1815
subfamily: Athletinae Pilsbry & Olsson, 1954
subfamily: Calliotectinae Pilsbry & Olsson, 1954

subfamily: Cymbiolinae Bondarev, 1995
subfamily: Fulgorariinae Pilsbry & Olsson, 1954
subfamily: Plicolivinae Bouchet, 1989
subfamily: Scaphellinae H. & A. Adams, 1858
subfamily: Volutinae Rafinesque, 1815
subfamily: Zidoninae H. & A. Adams, 1853
Family: Volutomitridae J.E. Gray, 1854
Superfamily: Cancellarioidea Forbes & Hanley, 1851
Family: Cancellariidae Forbes & Hanley, 1851
subfamily: Admetinae Troschel, 1866
subfamily: Cancellariinae Forbes & Hanley, 1851
subfamily: Plesiotritoninae Beu & Maxwell, 1987
Superfamily: Conoidea Rafinesque, 1815
Family: Conidae Rafinesque, 1815
Family: Terebridae Mörch, 1852
Family: Turridae Swainson, 1840
subfamily: Borsoniinae Bellardi, 1888
subfamily: Clathurellinae H. & A. Adams, 1858
subfamily: Clavatulinae J.E. Gray, 1853
subfamily: Conorbinae De Gregorio, 1890
subfamily: Crassispirinae Morrison, 1966
subfamily: Daphnellinae Deshayes, 1863
subfamily: Drilliinae Olsson, 1964
subfamily: Mangeliinae P. Fischer, 1884
subfamily: Mitromorphinae Casey, 1904
subfamily: Pseudomelatominae Morrison, 1966
subfamily: Strictispirinae McLean, 1971
subfamily: Thatcheriinae Powell, 1942
subfamily: Turriculinae Blainville, 1824
subfamily: Turrinae Swainson, 1840
subfamily: Zonulispirinae McLean, 1971
Superorder: Heterobranchia J.E. Gray, 1840
Order: Heterostropha P. Fischer, 1885
Superfamily: Architectonicoidea J.E. Gray, 1840
Family: Architectonicidae J.E. Gray, 1840
Family: Mathildidae Dall, 1889
Superfamily: Omalogyroidea G.O. Sars 1878
Family: Omalogyridae G.O. Sars, 1878
Superfamily: Pyramidelloidea J.E. Gray 1840
Family: Amathinidae Ponder, 1987
Family: Anisocyclidae Van Aartsen, 1995
Family: Cimidae Warén, 1993
Family: Odostomiidae Pelseneer, 1928
subfamily: Chrysallidinae Saurin, 1958
subfamily: Cyclostremellinae Moore, 1966
subfamily: Odostomellinae Saurin, 1959
subfamily: Odostomiinae Pelseneer, 1928
Family: Pyramidellidae J.E. Gray, 1840
subfamily: Pyramidellinae J.E. Gray, 1840
subfamily: Sayellinae Wise, 1996
Family: Syrnolidae Saurin, 1958
subfamily: Syrnolinae Saurin, 1958
subfamily: Tiberiinae Saurin, 1958
Family: Tjaernoeidae Warén, 1991
Family: Turbonillidae Bronn, 1849
subfamily: Eulimellinae Saurin, 1958
subfamily: Cingulininae Saurin, 1959
subfamily: Turbonillinae Bronn, 1849
Superfamily: Rissoelloidea M.E. Gray, 1850
Family: Rissoellidae M.E. Gray, 1850
Superfamily: Valvatoidea J.E. Gray, 1840

Family: Cornirostridae Ponder, 1990
Family: Hyalogyrinidae Warén & Bouchet, 1993
Family: Orbitestellidae Iredale, 1917
Family: Valvatidae J.E. Gray, 1840
Family: Xylodisculidae Warén, 1992
Order: Opisthobranchia Milne-Edwards, 1848
Suborder: Cephalaspidea P. Fischer, 1883
Superfamily: Acteonoidea D'Orbigny, 1835
Family: Acteonidae D'Orbigny, 1835
Family: Bullinidae Lamarck, 1801
Family: Hydatinidae Pilsbry, 1893
Superfamilies: Bulloidea Lamarck, 1801
Family: Bullidae Lamarck, 1801
Superfamily: Cylindrobulloidea Thiele, 1931
Family: Cylindrobullidae Thiele, 1931
Superfamily: Diaphanoidea Odhner, 1914
Family: Diaphanidae Odhner, 1914
subfamily: Diaphaninae Odhner, 1914
subfamily: Toledoniinae Warén, 1989
Family: Notodiaphanidae Thiele, 1931
Superfamily: Haminoeoidea Pilsbry, 1895
Family: Bullactidae Thiele, 1926
Family: Haminoeidae Pilsbry, 1895
Family: Smaragdinellidae Thiele, 1925
Superfamily: Philinoidea J.E. Gray, 1850
Family: Aglajidae Pilsbry, 1895
Family: Cylichnidae H. & A. Adams, 1854
Family: Gastropteridae Swainson, 1840
Family: Philinidae J.E. Gray, 1850
Family: Philinoglossidae Hertling, 1932
Family: Retusidae Thiele, 1926
Superfamily: Ringiculoidea Philippi, 1853
Family: Ringiculidae Philippi, 1853
Suborder: Sacoglossa Von Ihering, 1876
Superfamily: Oxynooidea H. & A. Adams, 1854
Family: Oxynoidae H. & A. Adams, 1854
Family: Juliidae E.A. Smith, 1885
subfamily: Bertheliniinae Beets, 1949
subfamily: Juliinae E.A. Smith, 1885
Family: Volvatellidae Pilsbry, 1893
Suborder: Anaspidea P. Fischer, 1883
Superfamily: Akeroidea Pilsbry 1893
Family: Akeridae Pilsbry, 1893
Superfamily: Aplysioidea Lamarck, 1809
Family: Aplysiidae Lamarck, 1809
subfamily: Aplysiinae Lamarck, 1809
subfamily: Dolabellinae MacFarland, 1918
subfamily: Dolabriferinae Pilsbry, 1895
subfamily: Notarchinae Eales & Engel, 1935
Suborder: Notaspidea P. Fischer, 1883
Superfamily: Tylodinoidea J.E. Gray 1847
Family: Tylodinidae J.E. Gray, 1847
Family: Umbraculidae Dall, 1889
Superfamily: Pleurobranchoidea Férussac, 1822
Family: Pleurobranchidae Férussac, 1822
Suborder: Thecosomata Blainville, 1824
Family: Cavoliniidae D'Orbigny, 1842
subfamily: Cavoliniinae D'Orbigny, 1842
subfamily: Clioniinae Van der Spoel, 1967
subfamily: Cuvierininae Gray, 1840
Family: Cymbuliidae Gray, 1840
subfamily: Cymbuliinae Cantraine, 1841
subfamily: Glebinae Van der Spoel, 1967
Family: Desmopteridae Chun, 1889
Family: Limacinidae Blainville, 1823
Family: Peraclididae Tesch, 1913
Suborder: Nudibranchia Blainville, 1814

many families of sea slugs
Order: Pulmonata Cuvier in Blainville, 1814
Suborder: Systellommatophora Pilsbry, 1948
Superfamily: Onchidioidea Rafinesque, 1815
Family: Onchidiidae Rafinesque, 1815
Superfamily: Otinoidea H. & A. Adams 1855
Family: Otinidae H. & A. Adams, 1855
Family: Smeagolidae Climo, 1980
Superfamily: Rathouisioidea Sarasin, 1899
Family: Rathouisiidae Sarasin, 1889
Family: Veronicellidae J.E. Gray, 1840
Suborder: Basommatophora Keferstein in Bronn, 1864
Superfamily: Acroloxoidea Thiele, 1931
Family: Acroloxidae Thiele, 1931
Superfamily: Amphiboloidea J.E. Gray, 1840
Family: Amphibolidae J.E. Gray, 1840
Superfamily: Chilinoidea H. & A. Adams, 1855
Family: Chilinidae H. & A. Adams, 1855
Family: Latiidae Hannibal, 1914
Superfamily: Glacidorboidea Ponder, 1986
Family: Glacidorbidae Ponder, 1986
Superfamily: Lymnaeoidea Rafinisque, 1815
Family: Lymnaeidae Rafinesque, 1815
Superfamily: Planorboidea Rafinesque, 1815
Family: Physidae Fitzinger, 1833
Family: Planorbidae Rafinesque, 1815
Superfamily: Siphonarioidea J.E. Gray, 1840
Family: Siphonariidae J.E. Gray, 1840
Suborder: Eupulmonata Haszprunar & Huber, 1990
Infraorder: Acteophila Dall, 1885
Superfamily: Ellobioidea L. Pfeiffer, 1854
Family: Carychiidae Jeffreys, 1830
Family: Ellobiidae L. Pfeiffer, 1854
subfamily: Ellobiinae L. Pfeiffer, 1854
subfamily: Melampinae Stimpson, 1851
subfamily: Pedipedinae P. Fischer & Crosse, 1880
subfamily: Pythiinae Odhner, 1925
Infraorder: Trimusculiformes Minichev & Starobogatov, 1975
Superfamily: Trimusculoidea Zilch, 1959
Family: Trimusculidae Zilch, 1959
Infraorder: Stylommatophora A. Schmidt, 1855
many families of land snails
Class: Bivalvia Linnaeus, 1758
Subclass: Protobranchia Pelseneer, 1889
Order: Nuculoida Dall, 1889
Superfamily: Nuculoidea J.E. Gray, 1824
Family: Nuculidae J.E. Gray, 1824
subfamily: Nuculinae J.E. Gray, 1824
subfamily: Nuculominae Maxwell, 1988
Family: Pristiglomidae Sanders & Allen, 1973
Superfamily: Nuculanoidea H. & A. Adams, 1858
Family: Lametilidae Allen & Sanders, 1973
Family: Malletiidae H. & A. Adams, 1858
Family: Neilonellidae Schileyko, 1978
Family: Nuculanidae H. & A. Adams, 1858
subfamily: Ledellinae Allen & Sanders, 1982
subfamily: Nuculaninae H. & A. Adams, 1858
subfamily: Bathyspinulinae Coan & Scott, 1997
Family: Phaseolidae Scarlato & Starobogatov, 1971
Family: Sareptidae A. Adams, 1860
subfamily: Sareptinae A. Adams, 1860

subfamily: Yoldiellinae Allen & Hannah, 1986
subfamily: Yoldiinae Habi, 1977
Family: Siliculidae Allen & Sanders, 1973
Family: Tindariidae Verrill & Bush, 1897
Order: Solemyoida Dall, 1889
Suborder: Solemyina Dall, 1889
Superfamily: Solemyoidea J.E. Gray, 1840
Family: Solemyidae J.E. Gray, 1840
Suborder: Nucinellina Scarlato & Starobogatov, 1971
Superfamily: Manzanelloidea Chronic, 1952
Family: Nucinellidae H.E. Vokes, 1956
Subclass: Pteriomorphia Beurlen, 1944
Order: Arcioida Stoliczka, 1871
Superfamily: Arcoidea Lamarck, 1809
Family: Arcidae Lamarck, 1809
subfamily: Anadarinae Reinhart, 1935
subfamily: Arcinae Lamarck, 1809
Family: Cucullaeidae Stewart, 1930
Family: Noetiidae Stewart, 1930
subfamily: Noetiinae Stewart, 1930
subfamily: Striarcinae MacNeil, 1938
Family: Parallelodontidae Dall, 1898
Superfamily: Limopsoidea Dall, 1895
Family: Glycymerididae Newton, 1916
Family: Limopsidae Dall, 1895
Family: Philobryidae F. Bernard, 1897
Order: Mytilida Férussac, 1822
Superfamily: Mytiloidea Rafinesque, 1815
Family: Mytilidae Rafinesque, 1815
subfamily: Bathymodiolinae Kenk & Wilson, 1985
subfamily: Crenellinae J.E. Gray, 1840
subfamily: Lithophaginae H. & A. Adams, 1857
subfamily: Modiolinae Keen, 1958
subfamily: Mytilinae Rafinesque, 1815
Order: Pterioida Newell 1965
Suborder: Pteriina Newell, 1965
Superfamily: Pterioida J.E. Gray, 1847
Family: Isognomonidae Woodring, 1925
Family: Malleidae Lamarck, 1819
Family: Pteriidae J.E. Gray, 1847
Family: Pulvinitidae Stephenson, 1941
Suborder: Pinnina Waller, 1978
Superfamily: Pinnoidea Leach, 1819
Family: Pinnidae Leach, 1819
Order: Limida Waller, 1978
Superfamily: Limoida Rafinesque, 1815
Family: Limidae Rafinesque, 1815
Order: Ostreoida Férussac, 1822
Suborder: Ostreina Férussac, 1822
Superfamily: Ostreoidea Rafinesque, 1815
Family: Gryphaeidae Vyalov, 1936
subfamily: Pycnodonteinae Stenzel, 1959
Family: Ostreidae Rafinesque, 1815
subfamily: Crassostreinae Scarlato & Starobogatov, 1979
subfamily: Lophinae Vyalov, 1936
subfamily: Ostreinae Rafinesque, 1815
Superfamily: Dimyoidea P. Fischer, 1886
Family: Dimyidae P. Fischer, 1886
Superfamily: Plicatuloidea Watson, 1930
Family: Plicatulidae Watson, 1930
Suborder: Pectinina Waller, 1978
Superfamily: Pectinoidea Wilkes, 1810
Family: Entoliidae Korobkov, 1960

Family: Pectinidae Wilkes, 1810
subfamily: Camptonectinae Habe, 1977
subfamily: Chlamydinae Von Teppner, 1922
subfamily: Pectininae Wilkes, 1810
Family: Propeamussiidae Abbott, 1954
Family: Spondylidae J.E. Gray, 1826
Superfamily: Anomioidea Rafinesque, 1815
Family: Anomiidae Rafinesque, 1815
subfamily: Anomiinae Rafinesque, 1815
subfamily: Placunanomiinae Beu, 1967
Family: Placunidae J.E. Gray, 1842
Subclass: Palaeoheterodonta Newell, 1965
Order: Trigoniida Dall, 1889
Superfamily: Trigonioidea Lamarck, 1819
Family: Trigoniidae Lamarck, 1819
Order: Unionida Stoliczka, 1871
Superfamily: Unionoidea Rafinesque, 1820
Family: Hyriidae Swainson, 1840
subfamily: Hyridellinae McMichael, 1956
subfamily: Hyriinae Swainson, 1840
Family: Margaritiferidae F. Haas, 1940
subfamily: Cumberlandiinae Heard & Guckert, 1971
subfamily: Margaritiferinae F. Haas, 1940
Family: Unionidae Rafinesque, 1820
subfamily: Anodontinae Rafinesque, 1820
subfamily: Unioninae Rafinesque, 1820
Superfamily: Muteloidea Gray, 1847
Family: Etheriidae Deshayes, 1830
subfamily: Etheriinae Deshayes, 1830
subfamily: Acostaeinae Morrison, 1973
Family: Iridinidae Swainson, 1840
Family: Mycetopodidae Gray, 1840
subfamily: Anodontitinae Modell, 1942
subfamily: Leilinae Morretes, 1949
subfamily: Monocondylaeinae Modell, 1942
subfamily: Mycetopodinae Gray, 1840
Subclass: Heterodonta Neumayr, 1884
Order: Veneroida H. & A. Adams, 1856
Superfamily: Chamoidea Lamarck, 1809
Family: Chamidae Lamarck, 1809
Superfamily: Lucinoidea J. Fleming, 1828
Family: Cyrenididae H. & A. Adams, 1857
Family: Fimbriidae Nicol, 1950
Family: Lucinidae J. Fleming, 1828
subfamily: Lucininae J. Fleming, 1828
subfamily: Milthinae Chavan in Moore, 1969
subfamily: Myrteinae Chavan in Moore, 1969
Family: Mactromyidae Cox, 1929
Family: Thyasiridae Dall, 1901
subfamily: Axinopsidinae F.R. Bernard, 1983
subfamily: Thyasirinae Dall, 1901
Family: Ungulinidae H. & A. Adams, 1857
Superfamily: Galeommatoidea J.E. Gray, 1840
Family: Galeommatidae J.E. Gray, 1840
Family: Lasaeidae J.E. Gray, 1842
Superfamily: Cyamioidea G.O. Sars, 1878
Family: Cyamiidae G.O. Sars, 1878
subfamily: Cyamiinae G.O. Sars, 1878
subfamily: Gaimardiinae Hedley, 1916
Family: Galatheavalvidae Knudsen, 1970
Family: Neoleptonidae Thiele, 1934
Superfamily: Carditoidea J. Fleming, 1828
Family: Carditidae J. Fleming, 1828
subfamily: Carditamerinae Chavan in Moore, 1969
subfamily: Carditellinae Iredale & McMichael,

1962
subfamily: Carditesinae Chavan in Moore, 1969
subfamily: Carditinae J. Fleming, 1828
subfamily: Miodomeridinae Chavan in Moore, 1969
subfamily: Thecaliinae Dall, 1903
subfamily: Venericardiinae Chavan in Moore, 1969
Family: Condylocardiidae F. Bernard, 1897
subfamily: Condylocardiinae F. Bernard, 1897
subfamily: Cuninae Chavan in Moore, 1969
Superfamily: Crassatelloidea Férussac, 1822
Family: Crassatellidae Férussac, 1822
subfamily: Crassatellinae Férussac, 1822
subfamily: Scambulinae Chavan, 1952
Superfamily: Astartoidea D'Orbigny, 1844
Family: Astartidae D'Orbigny, 1844
Family: Cardiniidae Zittel, 1881
Superfamily: Cardioidea Lamarck, 1809
Family: Cardiidae Lamarck, 1809
subfamily: Cardiinae Lamarck, 1809
subfamily: Clinocardiinae Kafanov, 1975
subfamily: Fraginae Stewart, 1930
subfamily: Laevicardiinae Keen, 1936
subfamily: Lymnocardiinae Stoliczka, 1870
subfamily: Protocardiinae Keen, 1951
subfamily: Trachycardiinae Stewart, 1930
subfamily: Tridacninae Lamarck, 1819
Family: Hemidonacidae Iredale & McMichael, 1962
Superfamily: Mactroidea Lamarck, 1809
Family: Anatinellidae J.E. Gray, 1853
Family: Cardiliidae P. Fischer, 1887
Family: Mactridae Lamarck, 1809
subfamily: Lutrariinae J.E. Gray, 1853
subfamily: Mactrinae Lamarck, 1809
subfamily: Pteropsellinae Keen in Moore, 1969
subfamily: Zenatiinae Dall, 1895
Family: Mesodesmatidae J.E. Gray, 1839
subfamily: Davilinae Dall, 1895
subfamily: Mesodesmatinae J.E. Gray, 1839
Superfamily: Solenoidea Lamarck, 1809
Family: Pharidae H. & A. Adams, 1858
subfamily: Pharellinae Tryon, 1884
subfamily: Pharinae H. & A. Adams, 1858
Family: Solenidae Lamarck, 1809
Superfamily: Tellinoidea Blainville, 1814
Family: Donacidae J. Fleming, 1828
Family: Psammobiidae J. Fleming, 1828
subfamily: Psammobiinae J. Fleming, 1828
subfamily: Sanguinolariinae Grant & Gale, 1931
Family: Semelidae Stoliczka, 1870
subfamily: Scrobiculariinae H. & A. Adams, 1856
subfamily: Semelinae Stoliczka, 1870
Family: Solecurtidae D'Orbigny, 1846
subfamily: Novaculininae Ghosh, 1920
subfamily: Solecurtinae D'Orbigny, 1846
Family: Tellinidae Blainville, 1814
subfamily: Macominae Olsson, 1961
subfamily: Tellininae Blainville, 1814
Superfamily: Dreissenoidea Gray in Turton, 1840
Family Dreissenidae Gray in Turton, 1840
Superfamily: Arcticoidea Newton, 1891
Family: Arcticidae Newton, 1891

Family: Bernardinidae Keen, 1963
Family: Trapeziidae Lamy, 1920
Superfamily: Glossoidea J.E. Gray, 1847
Family: Glossidae J.E. Gray, 1847
Family: Kelliellidae P. Fischer, 1887
Family: Vesicomyidae Dall, 1908
Superfamily: Corbiculoidea J.E. Gray, 1847
Family: Corbiculidae J.E. Gray, 1847
Family: Sphaeriidae Jeffreys, 1862
Superfamily: Veneroidea Rafinesque, 1815
Family: Cooperellidae Dall, 1900
Family: Glauconomidae J.E. Gray, 1853
Family: Sportellidae Dall, 1899
Family: Petricolidae D'Orbigny, 1837
Family: Turtoniidae Clark, 1855
Family: Veneridae Rafinesque, 1815
subfamily: Circinae Dall, 1896
subfamily: Clementiinae Frizzell, 1936
subfamily: Cyclininae Frizzell, 1936
subfamily: Dosiniinae Deshayes, 1853
subfamily: Gemminae Dall, 1895
subfamily: Meretricinae J.E. Gray, 1847
subfamily: Pitarinae Stewart, 1930
subfamily: Samarangiinae Keen in Moore, 1969
subfamily: Sunettinae Stoliczka, 1870
subfamily: Tapetinae H. & A. Adams, 1857
subfamily: Venerinae Rafinesque, 1815
Order: Myoida Goldfuss, 1820
Suborder: Myina Goldfuss, 1820
Superfamilies: Myoidea Lamarck, 1809
Family: Corbulidae Lamarck, 1818
subfamily: Corbulinae Lamarck, 1818
subfamily: Lentidiinae H.E. Vokes, 1945
Family: Erodonidae Winckworth, 1932
Family: Myidae Lamarck, 1809
Family: Spheniopsidae Gardner, 1928
Superfamily: Gastrochenoidea J.E. Gray, 1840
Family: Gastrochaenidae J.E. Gray, 1840
Superfamily: Hiatelloidea J.E. Gray, 1824
Family: Hiatellidae J.E. Gray, 1824
Suborder: Pholadina H. & A. Adams, 1858
Superfamily: Pholadoidea Lamarck, 1809
Family: Pholadidae Lamarck, 1809
subfamily: Jouannetiinae Tryon, 1862
subfamily: Martesiinae Grant & Gale, 1931
subfamily: Pholadinae Lamarck, 1809
subfamily: Xylophagainae Purchon, 1941
Family: Teredinidae Rafinesque, 1815
subfamily: Bankiinae Turner, 1966
subfamily: Kuphinae Tryon, 1862
subfamily: Teredininae Rafinesque, 1815
Subclass: Anomalodesmata Dall, 1889
Order: Pholadomyoida Newell, 1965
Superfamily: Pholadomyoidea Newell, 1965
Family: Parilimyidae Morton, 1982
Family: Pholadomyidae J.E. Gray, 1847
Superfamily: Clavagelloidea D'Orbigny, 1844
Family: Clavagellidae D'Orbigny, 1844
Superfamily: Pandoroidea Rafinesque, 1815
Family: Cleidothaeridae Hedley, 1918
Family: Lyonsiidae P. Fischer, 1887
Family: Myochamidae Bronn, 1862
Family: Pandoridae Rafinesque, 1815
Superfamily: Thracioidea Stoliczka, 1870
Family: Laternulidae Hedley, 1918
Family: Periplomatidae Dall, 1895

Family: Thraciidae Stoliczka, 1870
Order: Septibranchia Pelseneer, 1888
Superfamily: Poromyoidea Dall, 1886
   Family: Poromyidae Dall, 1886
     subfamily: : Cetomyinae Krylova, 1997
     subfamily: : Poromyinae Dall, 1886
Superfamily: Cuspidarioidea Dall, 1886
   Family: Cuspidariidae Dall, 1886
Superfamily: Verticordioida Stoliczka, 1871
   Family: Verticordiidae Stoliczka, 1871
Class: Scaphopoda Keferstein in Bronn, 1862
Order: Dentaliida Da Costa, 1776
   Family: Gadilinidae Chistikov, 1975
     subfamily: Gadilininae Chistikov, 1975
     subfamily: Episiphoninae Chistikov, 1975
   Family: Fustiariidae Steiner, 1991
   Family: Omniglyptidae Chistikov, 1975
   Family: Dentaliidae [Children], 1834
   Family: Calliodentaliidae Chistikov, 1975
   Family: Laevidentaliidae Palmer, 1974
   Family: Rhabdidae Chistikov, 1975
   Family: Anulidentaliidae Chistikov, 1975
Order: Gadilida Starobogatov, 1974
Suborder: Entalimorpha Steiner, 1992
   Family: Entalinidae Chistikov, 1979
     subfamily: Bathoxiphinae Chistikov, 1983
     subfamily: Entaliniinae Chistikov, 1979
     subfamily: Heteroschismoidinae Chistikov, 1982
Suborder: Gadilimorpha Steiner, 1992
   Family: Pulsellidae Boss, 1982
   Family: Wemersoniellidae Scarabino, 1986
   Family: Gadilidae Stoliczka, 1868
     subfamily: Gadilinae Stoliczka, 1868
     subfamily: Siphonodentaliinae Tryon, 1884
Class: Cephalopoda Cuvier, 1797
Subclass: Nautiloidea Agassiz, 1847
Order: Nautilida Agassiz, 1847
   Family: Nautilidae Blainville, 1825
Subclass: Coleoidea Bather, 1888
Superorder: Decapodiformes Young et al., 1998
Order: Spirulida Stolley, 1919
   Family: Spirulidae Owen 1836
Order: Sepiida Zittel, 1895
   Family: Sepiadariidae Fischer, 1882
   Family: Sepiidae Leach, 1817
Order: Sepiolida Fioroni, 1981
   Family: Idiosepiidae Appellöf, 1898
   Family: Sepiolidae Leach, 1817
     subfamily: Sepiolinae Leach, 1817
     subfamily: Rossiinae Appellöf, 1898
     subfamily: Heteroteuthinae Appellöf, 1898
Order: Teuthida Naef, 1916
Suborder: Myopsida D'Orbigny, 1841
   Family: Loliginidae Lesuer, 1821
Suborder: Oegopsida D'Orbigny, 1845
   Over 25 families, including:
   Family: Architeuthidae Pfeffer, 1900
   Family: Ommastrephidae Steenstrup, 1857
Superorder: Octopodiformes Young et al., 1998
Order: Octopoda Leach, 1818
Suborder: Cirrina Grimpe, 1916
   Family: Cirroteuthidae Keferstein, 1866
   Family: Opisthoteuthidae Verrill, 1896
   Family: Grimpoteuthidae O'Shea, 1999
   Family: Lutheuthididae O'Shea, 1999
   Family: Stauroteuthidae Grimpe, 1916

Suborder: Incirrina Grimpe, 1916
   Family: Alloposidae Verill, 1881
   Family: Amphitretidae Hoyle, 1886
   Family: Argonautidae Tryon, 1879
   Family: Bolitaenidae Chun, 1911
   Family: Idioctopodidae Taki, 1962
   Family: Octopodidae D'Orbigny, 1840
     subfamily: Octopodinae D'Orbigny, 1840
     subfamily: Eledoninae Grimpe, 1921
     subfamily: Graneledoninae Voss, 1988
     subfamily: Megaleledoninae Taki, 1961
     subfamily: Bathypolypodinae Robson, 1928
   Family: Ocythoidae Gray, 1849
   Family: Tremoctopidae Tryon, 1879
   Family: Vitreleledonellidae Robson, 1932
Order: Vampyromorpha Pickford, 1939
   Family: Vampyroteuthidae Thiele in Chun, 1915

Bibliography

A great array of scientific and popular literature has become available over the last few decades. The list supplied below is only a selection from this. It includes material quoted in and used in the compilation of this encyclopedia.

Abbott, R.T. & S.P. Dance, 1983. Compendium of Seashells. New York. 410 pp.
Apte, D., 1998. The book of Indian shells. Calcutta, Chennai, Delhi & Mumbai. 115 pp.
Ardovini, R. & T. Cossignani, 1999. Atlante delle conchiglie di profondita del Mediterraneo. Ancona. 111 pp.
Aubry, U., 1999. Nuove Terebre e antichi versi New Terebras and ancient verses. Ancona. 47 pp.
Beesley, P.L., G.J.B. Ross & A. Wells (eds), 1998. Mollusca: The Southern Synthesis. Fauna of Australia. Vol. 5. Melbourne. Part A: I–XVI, 1–563, Part B: I–VIII, 565–1234.
Beu, A.G., 1998. Indo-West Pacific Ranellidae, Bursidae and Personidae (Mollusca: Gastropoda). A monograph of the New Caledonian fauna and revisions of related taxa. Mém.Mus.natn.Hist.nat., 178: 1-255.
Beu, A.G. & W.F. Ponder, 1979. A revision of the species of Bolma Risso, 1826 (Gastropoda: Turbinidae). Records of the Australian Museum. 68 pp.
Bieler, R., 1992. Tenagodus or Siliquaria? Unraveling Taxonomic Confusion in Marine 'Worm Snails' (Cerithioidea: Siliquariidae). The Nautilus, 106(1): 15–20.
Bieler, R., 1993. Architectonicidae of the Indo-Pacific (Mollusca, Gastropoda). Abhandlungen des Naturwissenschaftlichen Vereins in Hamburg, (NF) 30: 1–376.
Bondarev, I., 1997. Based on evolution and biogeography: Systematics of the Volutidae. La Conchiglia, 282: 32–44.
Bosch, D.T., S.P. Dance, R.G. Moolenbeek & P.G. Oliver, 1995. Seashells of Eastern Arabia. Dubai & London. 296 pp.
Bouchet, P, 1990. Turrid genera and mode of development: The use and abuse of protoconch

morphology. Malacologia, 32(1): 69–77.

Bouchet, P. & A. Warén, 1986. Mollusca Gastropoda: Taxonomical notes on tropical deep water Buccinidae with descriptions of new taxa. Mém.Mus.natn.Hist.nat., sér A, Zool., 133: 457–518.

Bratcher, T. & W.O. Cernohorsky, 1987. Living terebras of the world A Monograph of the Recent Terebridae of the World. Melbourne & Burlington. 240 pp.

Brulet, T., S.P. Dance & G.T. Poppe, 1999. The family Harpidae. pp. 1–69. In: G.T. Poppe & K. Groh. A Conchological Iconography. Hackenheim.

Bruyne, R.H. de, R.A. Bank, J.P.H.M. Adema & F.A. Perk, 1994. Nederlandse naamlijst van de weekdieren (Mollusca) van Nederland en België. Feestuitgave ter gelegenheid van het zestigjarig jubileum van de Nederlandse Malacologische Vereniging. Leiden. 149 pp.

Bruyne, R.H. de & C.M. Neckheim, 2001. Van Nonnetje tot Tonnetje, de recente en fossiele weekdieren (slakken en schelpen) van Amsterdam. Haarlem. 207 pp.

Cate, C.N., 1973. A Systematic Revision of the Recent Cypraeid Family Ovulidae (Mollusca: Gastropoda). The Veliger, 15 (supplement): I–IV, 1–116, pl. 1–51.

Cate, C.N., 1979. A review of the Triviidae (Mollusca: Gastropoda). San Diego Society of Natural History Memoir 10: 1–126.

Cernohorsky, W.O., 1970. Systematics of the families Mitridae & Volutomitridae (Mollusca: Gastropoda). Bulletin of the Auckland Institute and Museum No. 8.

Cernohorsky, W.O., 1976. The Mitridae of the world Part I. The Subfamily Mitrinae. Indo-Pacific Mollusca, 3(17).

Cernohorsky, W.O., 1984. Systematics of the familiy Nassariidae (Mollusca: Gastropoda). Bulletin of the Auckland Institute and Museum No. 14.

Cernohorsky, W.O., 1991. The Mitridae of the World. Part 2. The Subfamily Mitrinae Concluded and Subfamilies Imbricariinae and Cylindromitrinae. Monographs of marine Mollusca No. 4.

CLEMAM. Checklist of European Marine Mollusca. Internet-database. www.mnhn.fr/cgi-bin/mamlist.

Coan, E.V., P.V. Scott & F.R. Bernard, 2000. Bivalve seashells of western North America – Marine Bivalve Mollusks from Arctic Alaska to Baja California. Santa Barbara Museum of Natural History Monographs Number 2/Studies in Biodiversity Number 2: I–VIII, 1–764.

Coovert, G.A. & Coovert, H.K., 1995. Revision of the supraspecific classification of Marginelliform Gastropods. The Nautilus, 109(2/3): 43–110.

Coulombel, A., 1994. Coquillages de Djibouti. Aix-en-Provence. 143 pp.

Dolin, L., 2001. Les Triviidae (Mollusca: Caenogastropoda) de l'Indo-Pacifique: Révision des genres Trivia, Dolichupis et Trivellona. Mém.Mus.natn.Hist.nat., 185: 201–241.

Dong, Z., 2002. Fauna Sinica Invertebrata Vol. 29 Phylum Mollusca Class Gastropoda Order Archaeogastropoda Superfamily Trochacea. Beijing. VIII + 210 pp., 2 pl.

Drivas, J. & M. Jay, 1988. Coquillages de la Réunion et de l'île Maurice. Neuchâtel & Paris. 160 pp.

Geiger, D.L. & G.T. Poppe, 2000. The family Haliotidae. pp. 1–135, pl. 1–83. In: G.T. Poppe & K. Groh. A Conchological Iconography. Hackenheim.

Habe, T., 1977. Systematics of Mollusca in Japan, Bivalvia and Scaphopoda. XIII + 372 pp.

Haszprunar, G., 1985. The Heterobranchia – a new concept of the phylogeny of the higher Gastropoda. Zeitschrift für zoologische Systematik und Evolutionsforschung, 23(1): 15–37.

Houart, R., 1986. Mollusca Gastropoda: Noteworthy Muricidae from the Pacific Ocean, with description of seven new species. Mém.Mus.natn.Hist.nat., sér. A, Zool., 133: 427-455.

Houart, R., 1995. The Ergalataxinae (Gastropoda, Muricidae) from the New Caledonia region with some comments on the subfamily and the description of thirteen new species from the Indo-West Pacific. Bull.Mus.natl.Hist.nat., 4e sér., 16, section A, n° 2–4: 245–297.

Houart, R., 2001. A review of the Recent Mediterranean and northeastern Atlantic species of Muricidae. Rome. 227 pp.

Houbrick, R.S., 1978. The family Cerithiidae in the Indo-Pacific Part 1: The Genera Rhinoclavis, Pseudovertagus And Clavocerithium. Monographs of Marine Mollusca, No. 1: 1–130.

Houbrick, R.S., 1979. Classification and Systematic Relationships of the Abyssochrysidae, a Relict Family of Bathyal Snails (Prosobranchia: Gastropoda). Smithsonian Contributions to Zoology, number 290: I–IV, 1–21.

Houbrick, R.S., 1992. Monograph of the Genus Cerithium Bruguière in the Indo-Pacific (Cerithiidae: Prosobranchia). Smithsonian Contributions to Zoology, number 510: I–IV, 1–211.

Jansen, P., 2000. Seashells of South-East Australia. Lindfield. 118 pp.

Jarrett, A.G., 2000. Marine shells of the Seychelles. Swavesey. XIV + 149 pp.

Jong, K.M. de & H.E. Coomans, 1988. Marine gastropods from Curaçao, Aruba and Bonaire. Leiden, New York, København & Köln. 261 pp.

Kabat, A.R., 1991. The Classification of the Naticidae (Mollusca: Gastropoda): Review and Analysis of the supraspecific taxa. Bulletin Museum of Comparative Zoology, 52(7): 417–449.

Kantor, Y.I., 1996. Phylogeny and relationships of Neogastropoda. pp. 221–230. In: J. Taylor (ed.). Origin and evolutionary radiation of the Mollusca. Oxford.

Kilburn, R.N. & E. Rippey, 1982. Sea shells of southern Africa. Johannesburg. 249 pp.

Kilias, R. (ed.), 1997. Lexicon Marine Muscheln und Schnecken. Stuttgart. 340 pp.

Kirtisinghe, P., 1978. Sea shells of Sri Lanka, including forms scattered throughout the Indian and Pacific Oceans. Rutland & Tokyo. 202 pp.

Kool, S.P., 1993. Phylogenetic analysis of the Rapaninae (Neogastropoda: Muricidae). Malacologia, 35(2): 155–259.

Kosuge, S. & M. Suzuki, 1985. Illustrated catalogue of Latiaxis and its related groups Family Coralliophilidae. Institute of Malacology of Tokyo Special Publication No. 1.

Lamprell, K.L. & J.M. Healy, 1998. A Revision of the Scaphopoda from Australian Waters (Mollusca). Records of the Australian Museum, Supplement 24: 1–189.

Lindner, G., 2001. Tirion Schelpengids. Schelpen uit de wereldzeeën. 320 pp.

Lorenz, F. & A. Hubert, 1993. A guide to worldwide Cowries. Wiesbaden. 571 pp.

Marquet, R., 1998. De Pliocene gastropodenfauna van Kallo (Oost-Vlaanderen, België). Publicatie van de Belgische Vereniging voor Paleontologie v.z.w. 17: 1–246.

Marshall, B.A., 1992. A Revision of the Recent Species of Eudolium Dall, 1889 (Gastropoda: Tonnoidea). The Nautilus, 106(1): 24–38.

Mayr, E., 1967. Artbegriff und Evolution. Hamburg & Berlin. 617 pp.

McLean, J.H., 1971. A revised classification of the family Turridae, with the proposal of new subfamilies, genera and subgenera from the Eastern Pacific. The Veliger, 14(1): 114–130.

McLean, J.H., 1990. Neolepetopsidae, a new docoglossate limpet family from hydrothermal vents and its relevance to patellogastropod evolution. Journal of Zoology, 222: 485–528.

Okutani, T., 2000. Marine molluscs in Japan. Tokyo. xlviii + 1173 pp.

Oliver, P.G., 1992. Bivalved seashells of the Red Sea. Wiesbaden & Cardiff. 330 pp.

Parkinson, B., 2000. Common seashells of New Zealand. Auckland. 96 pp.

Ponder, W.F, 1973. The origin and evolution of the Neogastropoda. Malacologia, 12(2): 295–338.

Ponder, W.F., 1983. Xenophoridae of the World. The Australian Museum Memoir 17: 1–126.

Ponder, W.F. & E.H. Vokes, 1988. A Revision of the Indo-West Pacific Fossil and Recent Species of Murex s.s. and Haustellum (Mollusca: Gastropoda: Muricidae). Records of the Australian Museum, Supplement 8: 1–160.

Ponder, W.F. & A. Warén, 1988. Appendix, Classification of the Caenogastropoda and Heterostropha – a list of the family-group names and higher taxa. Malacological Review, Supplement 4: 288-326.

Poppe, G.T. & Y. Goto, 1991. European Seashells Volume I (Polyplacophora, Caudofoveata, Solenogastra, Gastropoda). Wiesbaden. 352 pp.

Poppe, G.T. & Y. Goto, 1993. European Seashells Volume II (Scaphopoda, Bivalvia, Cephalopoda). Wiesbaden. 221 pp.

Poppe, G.T. & M. Verhaeghe, 2000. The family Ficidae. pp. 1–31, pl. 1–27. In: G.T. Poppe & K. Groh. A Conchological Iconography. Hackenheim.

Powell, A.W.B., 1962. Shells of New Zealand, an illustrated handbook. Christchurch, etc. 203 pp.

Powell, A.W.B., 1966. The molluscan families Speightiidae and Turridae. Bulletin of the Auckland Institute and Museum No. 5.

Radwin, G.E. & A. d'Attilio, 1976. Murex Shells of the World An Illustrated Guide to the Muricidae. Stanford. 284 pp., 32 pl.

Röckel, D., W. Korn & A.J. Kohn, 1995. Manual of the Living Conidae Volume 1: Indo-Pacific Region. Wiesbaden. 517 pp.

Satyamurti, S.T., 1952. The Mollusca of Krusadai Island (in the Gulf of Manaar) I. – Amphineura and Gastropoda. Bulletin of the Madras Government Museum (New Series), Natural History Section, 1(2[6]): 1–267, pl. 1–34.

Schilder, F.A., 1941. Verwandschaft und Verbreitung der Cypraeacea. Archiv für Molluskenkunde, 73(2/3): 57–120.

Severns, M., 2000. Hawaiian seashells. Honolulu. 278pp.

Sharabati, D., 1984. Red Sea shells. London, Boston, Melbourne & Henley. 128 pp.

Steyn, D.G. & M. Lussi, 1998. Marine Shells of South Africa An illustrated collector's guide to beached shells. Hartebeespoort. II + 264 pp.

Swennen, C., R.G. Moolenbeek, N. Ruttanadakul, H. Hobbelink, H. Dekker & S. Hajisamae, 2001. The molluscs of the southern Gulf of Thailand. Thai studies in biodiversity no. 4: i–ix, 1–210.

Turck, K. de, K. Kreipl, L. Man in 't Veld & G.T. Poppe, 1999. The family Strombidae. pp. 1-60, pls. 1–130. In: G.T. Poppe & K. Groh. A Conchological Iconography. Hackenheim.

Turner, H., 2001. Katalog der Familie Costellariidae Macdonald 1860 (Gastropoda: Prosobranchia: Muricoidea) Katalog supraspezifischer Taxa Katalog infragenerischer Taxa Bibliographie. Hackenheim. 100 pp.

Tursch, B. & D. Greifeneder, 2001. Oliva Shells The genus Oliva and the Species problem. Ancona. X + 570 pp.

Vaught, K.C., 1989. A classification of the living Mollusca. Melbourne. XII + 195 pp.

Wagner, R.J.L. & R.T. Abbott, 1978. Wagner and Abbott's standard catalog of shells third edition (with supplements). Greenville.

Walls, J. G., 1980. Conchs, Tibias, and Harps. Hong Kong. 191 pp.

Weil, A., L. Brown & B. Neville, 1999. The Wentletrap Book Guide to the Recent Epitoniidae of the world. Rome. 245 pp.

Wilson, B., 1993. Australian marine shells 1 prosobranch gastropods part one. Kallaroo. 408 pp.

Wilson, B., 1994. Australian marine shells 2 prosobranch gastropods part two (neogastropods). Kallaroo. 370 pp.

Wye, K.R., 1991. The encyclopedia of Shells. London. 288 pp.

Zhuang, Q., 2001. Fauna Sinica. Phyllum Mollusca, class Bivalvia, family Veneridae. Beijing. viii + 278 pp.

Glossary of terms

aberration	a distortion or deviation from the normal shape
abyssal	the deep sea: depths of 500–6000 meters
accessory shell plate	one or more additional pieces of shell found between the upper (dorsal) margins of both valves in some bivalves (e.g., piddocks)
acrembolic proboscis	a proboscis that folds completely inside the animal when retracted
adductor muscle scar	place of attachment of the adductor muscles (used for opening and closing), visible as marks on the inside of a bivalve shell
Amphineura	the group of mollusks known as chitons
anal canal	a canal, normally open, at the posterior (upper) end of a gastropod aperture through which solid waste is expelled (same as posterior canal)
anal siphon	the respiratory tube of a mollusk through which water containing waste material is expelled from the body
anterior	at or towards the front or head end of the shell. Opposite: posterior
anterior canal	an open or closed tubular shell extension at the anterior (lower) end of a gastropod aperture through which the siphon is extended (same as siphonal canal)
apertural margin/edge	the outer edge of the aperture
aperture	the opening in the final whorl of a gastropod shell, which in many instances may be sealed by an operculum
apex	the uppermost, earliest formed part of a gastropod shell
apical whorls	those whorls near the apex
auricle(s)	ear-shaped projections to the anterior and/or posterior of the hinge line in bivalves (as in Pectinidae)
axial	following or parallel to the shell axis (also radial ribs; transverse ribs)
axis	an imaginary line through the apex of a gastropod shell around which the whorls coil (see columella)
basal	pertaining to the base of a (gastropod) shell (the part most recently formed)
bead	a small hemispherical protuberance like a bead that is smaller than a nodule
benthic	living on the seabed
bilateral symmetry	the left side being an exact counterpart of the right: where the animal or subject can be divided into two equal halves
biotope	the habitat (territory) of a particular species of animal or plant
Bivalvia	the group of mollusks known as bivalves
body whorl	the final whorl of a gastropod shell; the section in which the body rests
byssal orifice/notch	an opening at the margin of some bivalves through which the foot protrudes (e.g., Pectinidae)
byssate	indicates a mollusk that attaches to a substrate by byssus threads
byssus	chitinous threads with which some bivalves attach themselves to a substrate (rocks, shells, etc.)
calcareous	(mostly) made of calcium carbonate
callus	a thick or thin calcareous layer (often transparent or glossy) around the inner lip of a gastropod shell and/or extending over its parietal wall
cardinal teeth	the chief projections (teeth) found centrally on the heterodont hinge plate of a bivalve: usually located directly below the umbo.
Cephalopoda	the group of mollusks including squids, octopuses, cuttlefishes, and nautiluses
chitons	mollusks bearing seven or eight shell plates, overlaying each other like roof tiles and held in place by an underlying girdle (also known as coat-of-mail shells)
chomata	short, tube-like locking nodules in the hinges of some bivalves (e.g., Gryphaeidae)
chondrophore	a spoon-like projection in the hinge of some bivalve shells below the umbo, serving as the attachment for an internal ligament (e.g., soft-shell clams)
columella	the central pillar or axis (visible in the aperture) around which a gastropod shell twists in a spiral
columellar folds/teeth	callused or thickened structures on the columella or in a gastropod shell's inner lip. Folds and teeth also occur on and within the outer lip.
concentric	indicates ribs or grooves following the direction of growth lines on a bivalve, parallel to the lower (ventral) margin of the valve
conchiolin	an organic material from which part of the shell is made (see also periostracum)
conchology	the study of mollusk shells (see malacology)

corneous	made of horny material (chitin)
coronate	with tubercules or nodules around whorl shoulders
crenulated	serrated, notched. Some bivalves have a crenulated lower (ventral) margin
denticles	small tooth-shaped projections
desomdont hinge	a common bivalve hinge in which the teeth are very reduced or absent
dextral	coiled to the right: clockwise
dorsal	the back of an animal or object (in bivalves, the hinge side)
doublet	both (duplicate) valves of a bivalve when still connected by a hinge and ligament
dysodont hinge	rudimentary teeth found near the edge of the valve
endoskeleton	an internal skeleton. Some Cephalopoda species have internal shells that act as endoskeletons
epidermis	the outer skin (in a shell, more properly periostracum)
equilateral	where the posterior of a bivalve shell (to the rear of the umbones) is the same size and shape as its anterior (to the front of the umbones) with the umbones central. Opposite: inequilateral
equivalved	where the individual valves in a bivalve shell are mirror images of each other. Opposite: inequivalved
escutcheon	a depression, usually flattened, found to the rear of the umbones of a bivalve shell. Ornament usually differs from the rest of the shell (e.g., Veneridae)
exoskeleton	an external skeleton. The shells of virtually all mollusks serve as an exoskeleton
fasciole	a groove or raised spiral band formed by successive growth stages and found at the base of certain gastropods on the lowest columellar part of the inner lip (e.g., Buccinidae)
flaring	opening or spreading outward (e.g., the outer lip of the aperture in gastropod shells)
fold	a major constriction or gathering on the shell surface
foliaceous	leaf-shaped or lamellate features or with thin, leaf-like lamellae
fusiform	spindle-shaped; swollen at the center, tapering almost equally toward the ends
gaping	used to describe the valves of some bivalves that do not make a close fit when shut and continue to "gape open"
Gastropoda	the group of mollusks containing all snails and slugs
genus	a group of related species
girdle	the muscular mantle surrounding and binding a chiton's shell plates
granulose	grainy, covered in granules
growth lines	more or less regularly interspaced lines on the surface of a shell that show its continued growth. Not to be confused with surface ornament ribs or grooves
height	in gastropods: distance from the apex to the basal (anterior) tip of the shell—also called length; in bivalves: the greatest distance from the umbones to the lower (ventral) margin
hermaphroditic	animals that have both male and female reproductive organs
heterodont hinge	describes a type of hinge in bivalves characterized by two or three (vertical) cardinal teeth below the umbo as well as elongated (sub-horizontal) lateral teeth anterior and posterior to these
heterostrophic	the protoconch coils in a different direction than the rest of the shell
hinge	the bivalve's hinge is composed of an elastic ligament and a number of hinge teeth (and sockets). This keeps both shell valves in position
hinge line	the area along the upper (dorsal) margin of a bivalve shell where the two valves are hinged
hinge plate	the infolded dorsal margin of a valve bearing hinge teeth
hinge teeth	opposing sockets and grooves along or under the upper (dorsal) margin of bivalve shells that lock together to prevent lateral slippage
infaunal	(bivalves) living buried deep within sediment
inner lip	the inner side of a gastropod aperture on the side of the axis or columella. The part of the body whorl extending behind the columella is referred to as the parietal wall (sometimes covered by callus). The inner lip sometimes has teeth, folds, or nodules
intertidal	between high and low tide levels
isodont hinge	symmetrical arrangement of large teeth and sockets in a bivalve hinge, located on either side of a central ligament pit
keel	a defined and prominent ridge on the exterior of a shell
labial palps	paired flaps (with cilia—small tentacles) on either side of the mouth in bivalves
lamella (plural: lamellae)	a thin plate or scale, more or less erect
Lamellibranchia	the group of mollusks to which bivalves belong

lateral teeth	in the heterodont hinge of a bivalve, these teeth are located (sub-horizontally) on either side of the umbo. They are usually far more elongated than the other (cardinal) teeth
lateral	relates to the side of an object or animal
lattice ornament/sculpture	both horizontal and vertical ribs that cross each other to form a net-like pattern (not necessarily at right angles)
ligament	an elastic material that joins together the two halves of a bivalve shell. It can be internal or external
left valve	the left valve of the shell where the bivalve's hinge is facing up and the anterior (front) end is pointing away
lira (plural: lirae)	a ridge on the shell surface within the aperture of a gastropod shell
lithodesma	a narrow calcareous plate that strengthens the internal ligament in some bivalves
littoral	the coastal zone between the highest high-water mark and the lowest low-water mark: the maximum area ever to be left exposed at low water
Loricata	the group of mollusks known as chitons
lunule	a crescent shape. In bivalves, a heart-shaped, flattened area to the front of the umbones. Its ornament differs from the rest of the shell.
malacology	the study of mollusks. Unlike conchologists, malacologists are interested not only in mollusks' shells but also in their anatomy, behavior, and habitat
mantle	a skin-like organ covering the body mass that lines the inside of the shell wall and secretes the mollusk's shell
mantle cavity	a cavity between the mantle and the rest of the body of a mollusk containing, for example, the respiratory organs
Mesozoic	a geological era covering the period between approximately 240 and 65 million years ago
micro-mollusks	species that attain dimensions of only a few millimeters when adult (in practice: any species measuring under 6–8 mm)
Mollusca	mollusks
mucro	the raised central section of a chiton's shell plate
muscle scar	see adductor muscle scars
nacreous	a layer of nacre, or mother-of-pearl
nodulose	bearing rounded protuberances (nodules: larger than beads)
operculum	trapdoor or lid that seals the aperture of some snails
Opisthobranchia	snails (Gastropoda) in which the gills are located behind the heart
opisthogyrate	the umbones pointing backward (to the posterior) in bivalves
ornament	structures visible on the exterior, or within the interior, of a shell (same as sculpture)
orthogyrate	the umbones pointing toward each other in bivalves
outer lip	the part of the aperture of a gastropod shell furthest away from the axis. The outer lip may curl over or be thickened (callused) and may display folds, teeth, or nodules
pallets	small, calcareous plates (shell plates). Shipworms have two positioned at the end of their bore tunnels surrounding the siphons
pallial line	a line that marks the position of the mantle edge in bivalves. In empty shells, this shows as a thin line that links together both adductor muscle scars.
pallial sinus	in bivalves, the area of attachment for the siphons. This can be seen in an empty bivalve shell as an embayment in the pallial line (mantle line)
pallium	another word for the mollusk's mantle
parietal shield	a callused area in some gastropod shells covering the parietal wall
parietal wall or area	the part of a gastropod shell that extends from the columella away from the inner lip, and around the top of the aperture up to the outer lip
pelagic	living in the open sea or deep sea
Pelecypoda	the group of mollusks containing the bivalves
pen	the cartilaginous "shell" found in squids
periostracum	a thin, membranous layer composed of conchiolin attached to the exterior of most species of shell-bearing mollusks
periphery	the greatest extent, or width, of a whorl in a gastropod shell (often marked by a keel or shoulder), farthest from the axis of coiling
phylum	a major subdivision of the animal kingdom. Mollusks belong to the phylum Mollusca
planospiral	coiled in a single plane
pleurothetic	of bivalves, having one valve less convex than the other
Polyplacophora	the group of mollusks containing chitons
porcelaneous	surface and texture like porcelain
posterior canal	see anal canal

proboscis	an extendible "snout" in some snails, usually with a mouth at the end (not to be confused with the siphons)
prodissoconch	the larval, first stage of a bivalve shell
Prosobranchia	snails (Gastropoda) in which the gills are in front of the heart
prosogyrate	umbones that project forward (toward the anterior)
protandrously hermaphroditic	describes species whose immature specimens are male but become female at a later stage
protoconch	the initial, larval whorls of a gastropod shell. When magnified, these usually appear different from the rest of the shell in terms of form and ornament
Pulmonata	pulmonate snails (Gastropoda) having no true gills but primitive lungs instead. Pulmonate snails live chiefly on land
pustulose	pimple-like or blister-like swellings
radial	radiating—usually used to describe a shell's ornament (e.g., radial, or axial, ribs)
radula	the rasping mouth parts of some mollusks, chiefly used to grind and crush food particles
recurved	with the end bent away from the shell axis
reflected	turned outward and backward
reticulate	lines, riblets, threads, or grooves crossing over each other like a net
ribs	interspaced ridges on the exterior of a shell that can run horizontally as well as vertically. Smaller ones: riblets (see ornament)
right valve	the right valve of the shell where the bivalve's hinge is facing up and the anterior (front) end is pointing away
rugose	rough. May be wrinkled, folded, or creased.
scabrous	covered in scales
Scaphopoda	the group of mollusks containing tusk shells
sculpture	see ornament
septum	a partition
sessile	attached or tied to a fixed spot
shoulder	a flattened or downward sloping area at the top of a whorl that may be demarcated by an angle or keel
sinistral	coiled to the left: counterclockwise
siphon	a type of respiratory tube in many mollusks with which food particles are sucked in, together with water, and expelled again along with waste material
siphonal canal	a channel at the base of the aperture of some gastropod shells through which the living animal's siphon protrudes (see anterior canal)
slit	an incision at the top of the apertural edge or margin of the shell
spicule	a small, slender, needle-like spine
spiral lines	lines or grooves on a shell that run across whorls in a spiral fashion
spirals	grooves or ribs running parallel to the suture located between whorls
spire	the coiled part of a gastropod shell apart from the body whorl
splash zone	see supralittoral
spring tide	describes when tides are at their highest and lowest (usually a few days after a full moon)
stromboid notch	in some gastropods an embayment in the lower part of the outer lip through which the eye of the living animal protrudes
sublittoral	the part of the coast immediately below the low water mark which is never exposed
substrate	the surface on which, or below which, a species of animal or plant occurs
supralittoral	the uppermost area of the coast referred to as the "splash zone," which is subject only to sea spray and the very highest tides
surface ornament	see ornament
suture	the boundary line between two whorls
taxodont hinge	numerous similarly shaped teeth, usually arranged in a row in a bivalve hinge
trapdoor	see operculum
truncated	cut off abruptly: description of a bivalve shell with a blunt or square end and for a gastropod shell with an abruptly terminated spire
umbilicus	the axis around which a gastropod shell turns is sometimes hollow and a small hole may then be visible next to the inner lip: this is the umbilicus
umbo (plural: umbones)	the uppermost, earliest formed part of a bivalve valve immediately above the hinge. It is also known as the beak
valve	indicates one half of a bivalve shell's two halves
varix (plural: varices)	a resting point in the growth process, usually the former, callused apertural edge, and visible on some shells as very wide ribs
ventral	the front side of an animal or object. In bivalves the side of the shell opposite the hinge
whorl	when, in the course of its growth, a gastropod shell makes one complete revolution around the axis, this constitutes one whorl

Index